Contents

Momentum and Impulse

These pages are for** AQA A Unit 4, **Edexcel Unit 4,** OCR A Unit 4 **and OCR B Unit 4.

These pages are about linear momentum — that's momentum in a straight line (not a circle).

Understanding **Momentum** helps you do **Calculations** on **Collisions**

The **momentum** of an object depends on two things — its **mass** and **velocity**.
The **product** of these two values is the momentum of the object.

momentum = mass × velocity or in symbols: $\boldsymbol{p}$ (in kg ms^{-1}) = $\boldsymbol{m}$ (in kg) × $\boldsymbol{v}$ (in ms^{-1})

Remember, velocity is a vector quantity, so it has size and direction.

Momentum is always **Conserved**

1) Assuming **no external forces** act, momentum is always **conserved**.
2) This means the **total momentum** of two objects **before** they collide **equals** the total momentum **after** the collision.
3) This is really handy for working out the **velocity** of objects after a collision (as you do...):

Example A skater of mass 75 kg and velocity 4 ms^{-1} collides with a stationary skater of mass 50 kg. The two skaters join together and move off in the same direction. Calculate their velocity after impact.

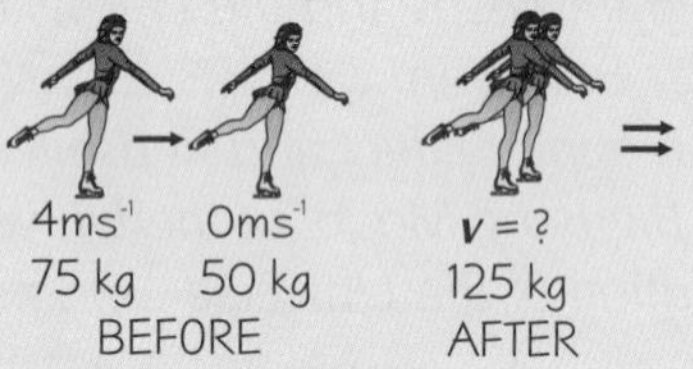

Before you start a momentum calculation, always draw a quick sketch.

Momentum of skaters before = Momentum of skaters after

$(75 \times 4) + (50 \times 0) = 125\boldsymbol{v}$

$300 = 125\boldsymbol{v}$

So $\boldsymbol{v} = 2.4$ ms^{-1}

4) The same principle can be applied in **explosions**. E.g. if you fire an **air rifle**, the **forward momentum** gained by the pellet **equals** the **backward momentum** of the rifle, and you feel the rifle recoiling into your shoulder.

Example A bullet of mass 0.005 kg is shot from a rifle at a speed of 200 ms^{-1}. The rifle has a mass of 4 kg. Calculate the velocity at which the rifle recoils.

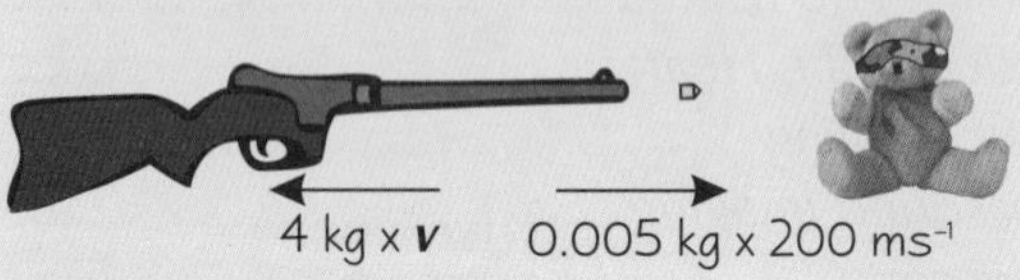

Momentum before explosion = Momentum after explosion

$0 = (0.005 \times 200) + (4 \times \boldsymbol{v})$

$0 = 1 + 4\boldsymbol{v}$

$\boldsymbol{v} = -0.25$ ms^{-1}

5) In reality, collisions usually happen in **more than one** dimension. Momentum is still conserved — the only difference is that you have to **resolve** the velocity vectors of the colliding objects to find the components that affect the collision.

Example ***This example is for Edexcel only.***

A neutron travelling to the right at 5 ms^{-1} collides with a stationary helium nucleus as shown in the diagram. After the collision, the neutron moves in a direction perpendicular to the line of the collision. Draw and label a diagram to show how the particles will move after the impact.

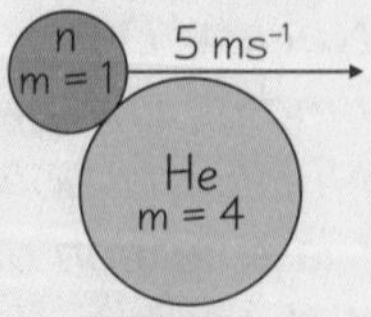

1) Resolve the velocity vector into the components parallel and perpendicular to the line of the collision.

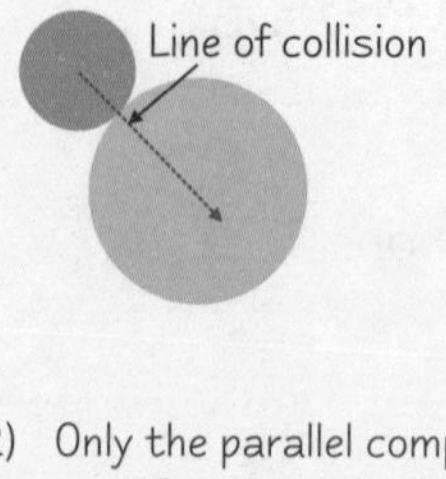

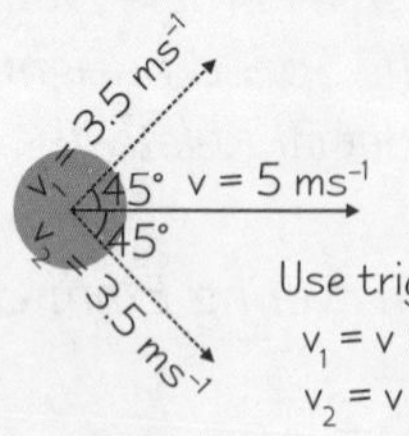

Use trig to resolve:
$v_1 = v \times \cos(45°)$
$v_2 = v \times \sin(45°)$

2) Only the parallel components interact during the collision. The perpendicular components don't change.

3) Then you can ignore v_1 and use v_2 to work out the new velocity of the helium nucleus just like you normally would.

Momentum before = Momentum after

$(1 \times 3.5) + (4 \times 0) = (1 \times 0) + (4 \times \boldsymbol{v})$

$3.5 = 4\boldsymbol{v}$

$\boldsymbol{v} = 0.9$ ms^{-1}

4) And finally, draw a diagram — remembering to include v_1 and the new velocity vector.

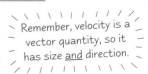

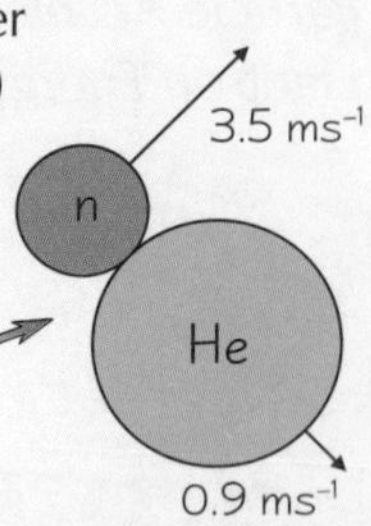

A2-Level Physics

A2 Physics is seriously tricky — no question about that.
To do well, you're going to need to revise properly and practise hard.

This book has thorough notes on all the theory you need,
and it's got practice questions... lots of them.
For every topic there are warm-up and exam-style questions.

And of course, we've done our best to make the whole thing vaguely entertaining for you.

Complete Revision and Practice

Editors:
Amy Boutal, Sarah Hilton, Alan Rix, Julie Wakeling, Sarah Williams

Contributors
Stuart Barker, Jane Cartwright, Peter Cecil, Mark A. Edwards, D. Kamya, Barbara Mascetti,
John Myers, Zoe Nye, Moira Steven, Andy Williams, Tony Winzor.

Proofreaders:
Ian Francis, Glenn Rogers

Published by CGP

This book covers:

AQA A (with Option A: Astrophysics
Option B: Medical Physics
Option D: Turning Points in Physics

Edexcel

OCR A

OCR B (Advancing Physics)

There are notes on the pages to tell you which bits you need for your syllabus.

Many thanks to Professor Peter Watkins at the University of Birmingham for his kind permission to reproduce the photographs used on page 66.

ISBN: 978 1 84762 269 3

Groovy website: www.cgpbooks.co.uk
Jolly bits of clipart from CorelDRAW®
Printed by Elanders Ltd, Newcastle upon Tyne.

Based on the classic CGP style created by Richard Parsons.

Momentum and Impulse

Collisions can be *Elastic* or *Inelastic*

AQA A, Edexcel and OCR A.

An **elastic collision** is one where **momentum** is **conserved** and **kinetic energy** is **conserved** — i.e. no energy is dissipated as heat, sound, etc. If a collision is **inelastic** it means that some of the kinetic energy is converted into other forms during the collision. But **momentum is always conserved.**

Example A toy lorry (mass 2 kg) travelling at 3 ms^{-1} crashes into a smaller toy car (mass 800 g), travelling in the same direction at 2 ms^{-1}. The velocity of the lorry after the collision is 2.6 ms^{-1} in the same direction. Calculate the new velocity of the car and the total kinetic energy before and after the collision.

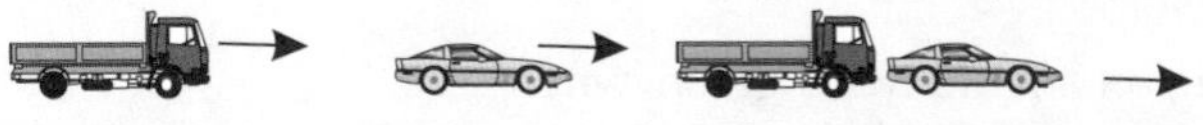

2 kg 3 ms^{-1} — 800 g 2 ms^{-1} — BEFORE

v = 2.6 ms^{-1} v = ? — AFTER

Momentum before collision = Momentum after collision

$(2 \times 3) + (0.8 \times 2) = (2 \times 2.6) + (0.8v)$

$7.6 = 5.2 + 0.8v$

$2.4 = 0.8v$

$v = 3$ ms^{-1}

Kinetic Energy before = KE of lorry + KE of car

$= \frac{1}{2}mv^2$ (lorry) + $\frac{1}{2}mv^2$ (car)

$= \frac{1}{2}(2 \times 3^2) + \frac{1}{2}(0.8 \times 2^2)$

$= 9 + 1.6$

$= 10.6$ J

Kinetic Energy after $= \frac{1}{2}(2 \times 2.6^2) + \frac{1}{2}(0.8 \times 3^2)$

$= 6.76 + 3.6$

$= 10.36$ J

The difference in the two values is the amount of kinetic energy dissipated as heat or sound, or in damaging the vehicles — so this is an inelastic collision.

Impulse = *Change* in *Momentum*

AQA A and OCR A

1) Newton's second law says **force = rate of change of momentum** (see page 4), or $F = (mv - mu) \div t$

2) **Rearranging** Newton's 2nd law gives:
Impulse is defined as **average force × time**, Ft.
The units of impulse are **newton seconds**, Ns.

$Ft = mv - mu$
(where v is the final velocity and u is the initial velocity)
so ***impulse = change of momentum***

Impulse is the area under a force-time graph.

3) So, the **force** of an impact can be **reduced** by **increasing the time** of the impact.

For example, a toy car with a mass of 1 kg, travelling at 5 ms^{-1}, hits a wall and stops in a time of 0.5 seconds.

The average force on the car is: $F = \frac{mv - mu}{t} = \frac{(1\times5)-(1\times0)}{0.5} = 10$ N

But if the time of impact is doubled to 1 second, the force on the car is halved.

This is the idea behind car crumple zones which increase the time of an impact to reduce the force on the passengers.

Practice Questions

Q1 Give two examples of conservation of momentum in practice.

Q2 Describe what happens when a tiny object makes an elastic collision with a massive object, and why.

Exam Questions

Q1 A ball of mass 0.6 kg moving at 5 ms^{-1} collides with a larger stationary ball of mass 2 kg.
The smaller ball rebounds in the opposite direction at 2.4 ms^{-1}.

(a) What is the velocity of the larger ball immediately after the collision? [3 marks]

(b) Is this an elastic or inelastic collision? Explain your answer. [3 marks]

Q2 A toy train of mass 0.7 kg, travelling at 0.3 ms^{-1}, collides with a stationary toy carriage of mass 0.4 kg.
The two toys couple together. What is their new velocity? [3 marks]

Momentum will never be an endangered species — it's always conserved...

It seems a bit of a contradiction to say that momentum's always conserved then tell you that impulse is the change in momentum. The difference is that impulse is only talking about the change of momentum of one of the objects, whereas conservation of momentum is talking about the ***whole*** *system.*

Newton's Laws of Motion

These pages are for AQA A Unit 4, Edexcel Unit 4, OCR A Unit 4 and OCR B Unit 4.

You did most of this at GCSE, but that doesn't mean you can just skip over it now. You'll be kicking yourself if you forget this stuff in the exam — easy marks...

Newton's **1st Law** says that a **Force** is Needed to Change Velocity

1) **Newton's 1st law of motion** states the **velocity** of an object will **not change** unless a **resultant force** acts on it.
2) In plain English this means a body will remain at rest or moving in a **straight line** at a **constant speed**, unless acted on by a **resultant force**.

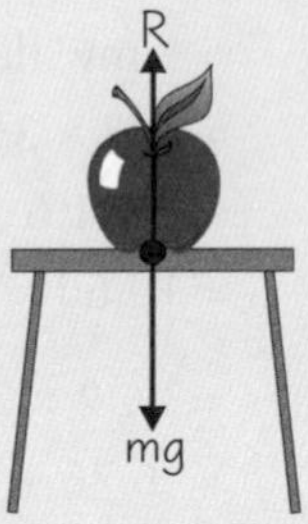

An apple sitting on a table won't go anywhere because the **forces** on it are **balanced**.

reaction (***R***) = **weight** (mg)

(force of table pushing apple up) (force of gravity pulling apple down)

3) If the forces **aren't balanced**, the **overall resultant force** will cause the body to **accelerate** — if you gave the apple above a shove, there'd be a resultant force acting on it and it would roll off the table. Acceleration can mean a change in **direction**, or **speed**, or both. (See Newton's 2nd law, below.)

Newton's 2nd Law says that Force is the **Rate of Change in Momentum...**

*"The **rate of change of momentum** of an object is **directly proportional** to the **resultant force** which acts on the object."* so $F = \frac{\Delta mv}{\Delta t}$

If mass is constant, this can be written as the well-known equation:

resultant force (F) = mass (m) × acceleration (a)

Learn this — it crops up all over the place in A2 Physics.
And learn what it means too:

1) It says that the **more force** you have acting on a certain mass, the **more acceleration** you get.
2) It says that for a given force the **more mass** you have, the **less acceleration** you get.

REMEMBER:
1) The **resultant force** is the **vector sum** of all the forces.
2) The force is **always** measured in **newtons**. Always.
3) The **mass** is always measured in **kilograms**.
4) **a** is the **acceleration** of the object as a result of F. It's **always** measured in **metres per second per second** (ms^{-2}).
5) The **acceleration** is always in the **same direction** as the **resultant force**.

F = ma is a ***Special Case*** of ***Newton's 2nd Law***

Newton's 2nd law says that if the **mass** of an object is **constant**, then the **bigger** the **force** acting on it, the **greater** its **acceleration** — i.e. ***F = ma***. But, if the **mass** of the object is **changing** — e.g. if it is accelerating at close to the **speed of light** — then you **can't** use ***F = ma***.

Don't worry though — **Newton's 2nd law still applies**, it's just that the 'rate of **change of momentum**' bit refers to a **change in mass** and velocity.

Daisy was always being told that she was a special case.

Newton's Laws of Motion

This section is for OCR A and OCR B — those doing AQA and Edexcel can skip straight to the questions.

*Newton's **3rd Law** says each Force has an **Equal, Opposite Reaction Force***

There are a few different ways of stating Newton's 3rd law, but the clearest way is:

> **If an object A EXERTS a FORCE on object B, then object B exerts AN EQUAL BUT OPPOSITE FORCE on object A.**

You'll also hear the law as "every action has an equal and opposite reaction". But this confuses people who wrongly think the forces are both applied to the same object. (If that were the case, you'd get a resultant force of zero and nothing would ever move anywhere...)

The two forces actually represent the **same interaction**, just seen from two **different perspectives**:

1) If you **push against a wall**, the wall will **push back** against you, **just as hard**. As soon as you stop pushing, so does the wall. Amazing...
2) If you **pull a cart**, whatever force **you exert** on the rope, the rope exerts the **exact opposite** pull on you.
3) When you go **swimming**, you push **back** against the water with your arms and legs, and the water pushes you **forwards** with an equal-sized force.

This looks like Newton's 3rd law...

But it's NOT.

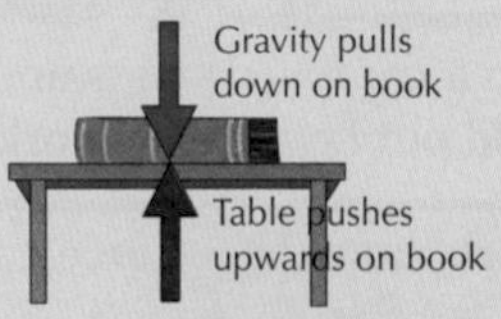

...because both forces are acting on the book, and they're not of the same type. This is two separate interactions. The forces are equal and opposite, resulting in zero acceleration, so this is showing Newton's 1st law.

Newton's 3rd law applies in **all situations** and to all **types of force**. But the pairs of forces are always the **same type**, e.g. both gravitational or both electrical.

Newton's 3rd law is a consequence of the **conservation of momentum** (page 2). A **resultant force** acting means a change in **mass** or **acceleration** (F = ma) — which means a **change in momentum**. Momentum is always **conserved**, so whenever one object exerts a force on another (and changes its momentum) the second object must exert an equal-sized force back onto the first object so that the overall change in momentum is zero.

Practice Questions

Q1 State Newton's 1st, 2nd and 3rd laws of motion, and explain what they mean.

Q2 Give an example of a situation where you couldn't use F = ma. Why wouldn't the equation apply?

Q3 Sketch a force diagram of a book resting on a table to illustrate Newton's 3rd law.

Exam Questions

Q1 A parachutist with a mass of 78 kg jumps out of a plane. As she falls, the resultant force acting on her changes.
(a) Use Newton's 2nd law to explain why she initially accelerates. [2 marks]
(b) What is the initial vertical force on the parachutist? Use $g = 9.81$ ms^{-2}. [1 mark]
(c) After a time, the parachutist reaches terminal velocity and stops accelerating.
Use Newton's 1st law to explain why the resultant force on the parachutist is zero at this point. [2 marks]

Q2 A boat is moving across a river. The engines provide a force of 500 N at right angles to the flow of the river, and the boat experiences a drag of 100 N in the opposite direction. The force on the boat due to the flow of the river is 300 N. The mass of the boat is 250 kg. Calculate the magnitude of the acceleration of the boat. [4 marks]

Newton's three incredibly important laws of motion...

These equations may not really fill you with a huge amount of excitement (and I hardly blame you if they don't)... but it was pretty fantastic at the time — suddenly people actually understood how forces work, and how they affect motion. I mean arguably it was one of the most important scientific discoveries ever...

Work and Energy

This page is for OCR B Unit 4 only.

As everyone knows, work in Physics isn't like normal work. It's harder. Work also has a specific meaning that's to do with movement and forces. You'll have seen this at GCSE — it just comes up in more detail for A2.

Work is done whenever Energy is Transferred

This table gives you some examples of **work being done** and the **energy changes** that happen.

1) Usually you need a force to move something because you're having to **overcome another force**.
2) The thing being moved has **kinetic energy** while it's **moving**.
3) The kinetic energy is transferred to **another form of energy** when the movement stops.

ACTIVITY	WORK DONE AGAINST	FINAL ENERGY FORM
Lifting up a box.	gravity	gravitational potential energy
Pushing a chair across a level floor.	friction	heat (thermal)
Pushing two magnetic north poles together.	magnetic force	magnetic energy
Stretching a spring.	stiffness of spring	elastic potential energy

The word **'work'** in Physics means the **amount of energy transferred** from one form to another when a force causes a movement of some sort.

Work = Force × Distance

When a car tows a caravan, it applies a force to the caravan to move it.
To **find out** how much **work** is **done**, you need to use the **equation**:

> **work done** (*W*) = **force causing motion** (*F*) × **distance moved** (*s*)
> ...where ***W*** is measured in joules (J), ***F*** is measured in newtons (N) and ***s*** is measured in metres (m).

Points to remember:

1) **Work** is the **energy** that's been **changed** from one form to another — it's not necessarily the **total** energy. E.g. moving a book from a low shelf to a higher one will increase its gravitational potential energy, but it had some potential energy to start with. Here, the **work done** would be the **increase** in potential energy, **not the total** potential energy.
2) Remember, the distance needs to be measured in metres — if you have **distance in centimetres or kilometres**, you need to **convert** to metres first.
3) The force ***F*** will be a **fixed** value in any calculations, either because it's **constant** or because it's the **average** force.
4) The equation assumes that the **direction of the force** is the **same** as the **direction of movement**.
5) The equation gives you the **definition** of the joule (symbol J):
'one joule is the work done when a force of 1 newton moves an object through a distance of 1 metre'
6) If you plotted a graph of force (*F*) against distance moved (*s*), the **area under the graph** would equal the work done.

The Force isn't always in the Same Direction as the Movement

Sometimes the **direction of movement** is **different** from the **direction of the force**.

Example

1) To **calculate the work done** in a situation like the one in the diagram, you need to consider the **horizontal** and **vertical components** of the **force**.
2) The only **movement** is in the **horizontal** direction. This means the **vertical force** is not causing any motion (and hence not doing any work) — it's just **balancing** out some of the **weight**, meaning there's a **smaller reaction force**.

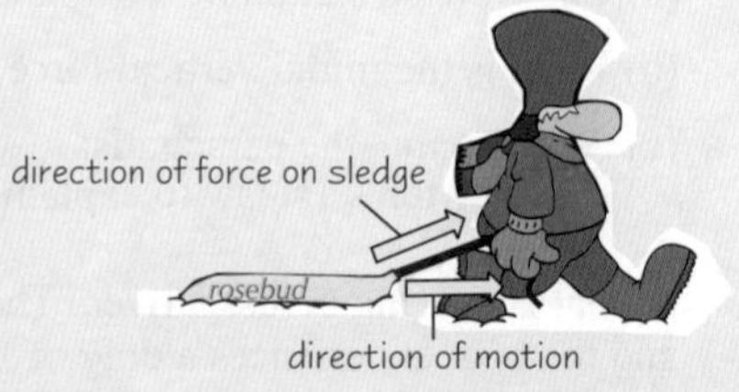

3) The horizontal force is causing the motion — so to **calculate** the **work done**, this is the **only force** you need to consider. Which means we get: $W = Fs\cos\theta$

Where θ is the **angle** between the **direction of the force** and the **direction of motion**.

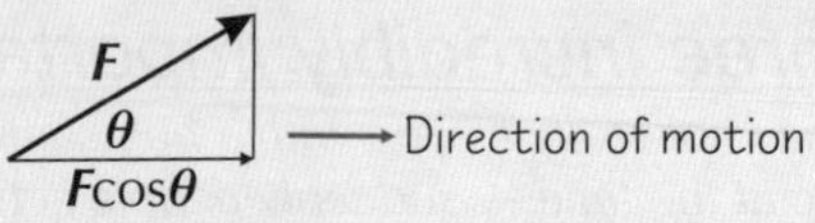

Work and Energy

This page is for Edexcel Unit 4 and OCR B Unit 4.

Learn the Principle of Conservation of Energy

The **principle of conservation of energy** says that:

Energy **cannot be created** or **destroyed**. Energy **can be transferred** from one form to another but the total amount of energy in a closed system will not change.

Example

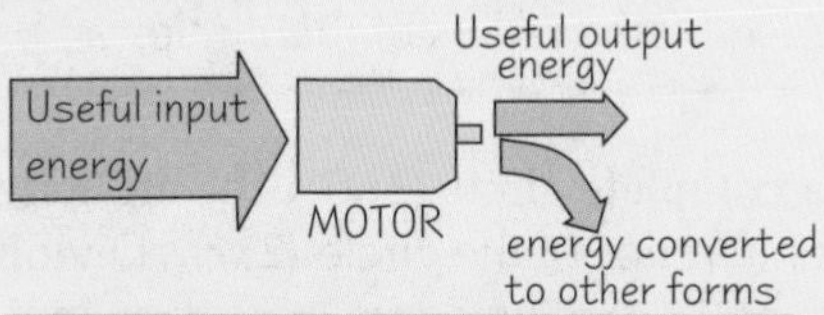

Total energy in = Total energy out

You can talk about how well energy is transferred in terms of **efficiency**.

$$\text{Efficiency} = \frac{\text{useful power output}}{\text{power input}}$$

You need it for Questions about Kinetic and Potential Energy

The principle of conservation of energy nearly always comes up when you're doing questions about changes between kinetic and potential energy. Why — because energy is only ever exchanged from one form to another, not destroyed.

A quick reminder:

1) **Kinetic energy** is energy of anything **moving**. You work it out from $E_k = \frac{1}{2}mv^2$, where v is the velocity it's travelling at and m is its mass. A different way of writing this is $E_k = \frac{p^2}{2m}$ where p is the momentum of the object — if you're doing ***Edexcel*** you need to be able to **derive** this formula, see right.

2) There are **different types of potential energy** — e.g. gravitational and elastic.

3) **Gravitational potential energy** is the energy something gains if you lift it up. You work it out using: $\Delta E_p = mg\Delta h$, where m is the mass of the object, Δh is the height it is lifted and **g** is the gravitational field strength (9.81 Nkg^{-1} on Earth).

4) **Elastic potential energy** (elastic stored energy) is the energy you get in, say, a stretched rubber band or spring. You can find it by plotting a **force-extension graph** — the area under the graph is the elastic potential energy.
Or, you can work it out using $E = \frac{1}{2}kx^2$, where x is the extension of the spring and k is the stiffness constant.

Deriving $E_k = \frac{p^2}{2m}$

$E_k = \frac{1}{2}mv^2$ and $p = mv$.

Substituting, $E_k = \frac{pv}{2}$.

But $v = \frac{p}{m}$, so $E_k = \frac{p^2}{2m}$.

Practice Questions

Q1 Write down the equation used to calculate work if the force and motion are in the same direction.

Q2 Write down the equation for work if the force is at an angle to the direction of motion.

Exam Questions

Q1 A traditional narrowboat is drawn by a horse walking along a towpath. The horse pulls the boat at a constant speed between two locks which are 1500 m apart. The tension in the rope is 100 N at 40° to the direction of motion. How much work is done on the boat? [2 marks]

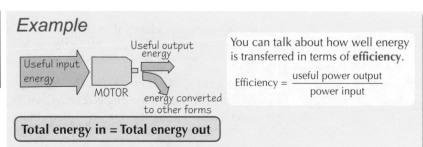

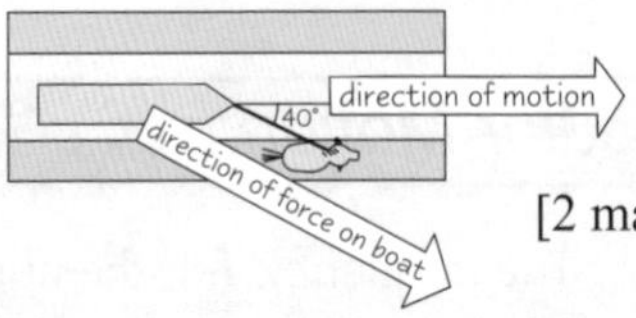

Q2 A motor is used to lift a 20 kg load a height of 3 m. (Take g = 9.81 Nkg^{-1}.)

(a) Calculate the work done in lifting the load. [2 marks]

(b) The speed of the load during the lift is 0.25 ms^{-1}. Calculate the power delivered by the motor. [2 marks]

Work, work, work — when will it all end..*

So work is the amount of energy needed for a force to move something a certain distance — easy. Now all you need to do is learn the equations and what to do when the force and movement are in different directions, and you'll be fine...

*Answer: page 139

Circular Motion

These pages are for AQA A Unit 4, Edexcel Unit 4, OCR A Unit 4 and OCR B Unit 4.

*It's probably worth putting a bookmark in here — this stuff is needed **all over** the place.*

Angles can be Expressed in ***Radians***

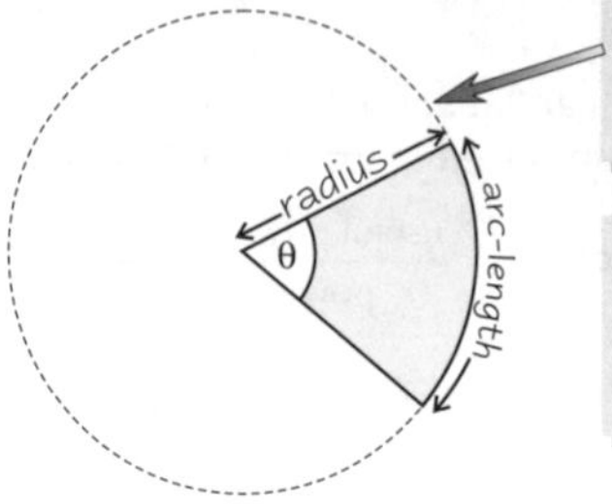

The angle in **radians**, θ, is defined as the **arc-length** divided by the radius of the circle.

For a **complete circle** (360°), the arc-length is just the circumference of the circle ($2\pi r$). Dividing this by the radius (r) gives 2π. So there are 2π radians in a complete circle.

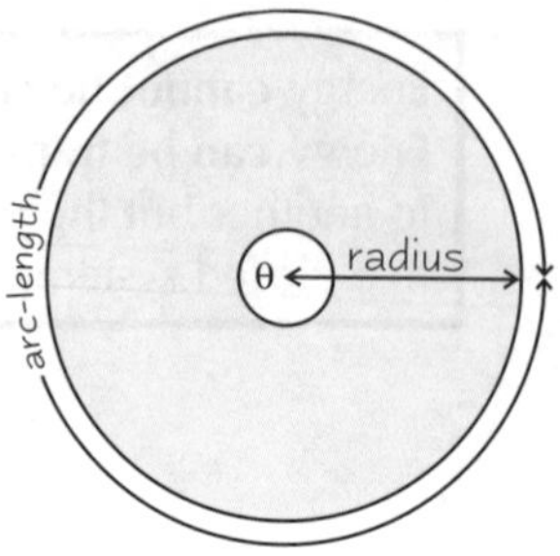

Some common angles:

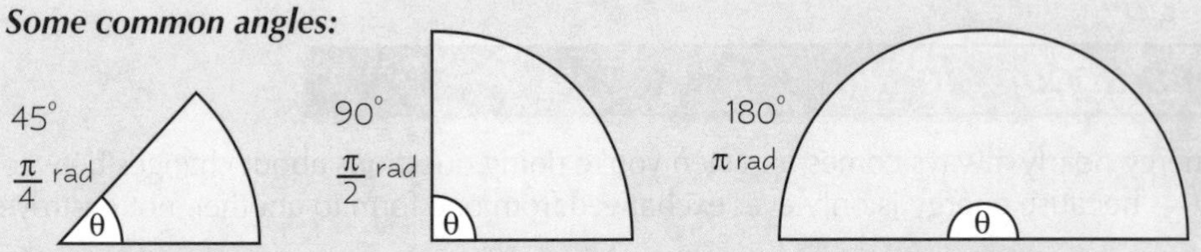

$$\text{angle in radians} = \frac{2\pi}{360} \times \text{angle in degrees}$$

1 radian is about 57°

The ***Angular Speed*** is the ***Angle*** an Object Rotates Through ***per Second***

1) Just as **linear speed**, v, is defined as distance ÷ time, the **angular speed**, ω, is defined as **angle ÷ time**. The unit is rad s⁻¹ — radians per second.

$$\omega = \frac{\theta}{t}$$

ω = angular speed (rad s^{-1}) — the symbol for angular speed is the little Greek 'omega', not a w.
θ = angle (radians) turned through in a time, t (seconds)

2) The **linear speed**, v, and **angular speed**, ω, of a rotating object are linked by the equation:

$$v = r\omega$$

v = linear speed (ms^{-1}), r = radius of the circle (m), ω = angular speed (rad s^{-1})

Example — *Beam of Particles in a Cyclotron*

(See page 68)

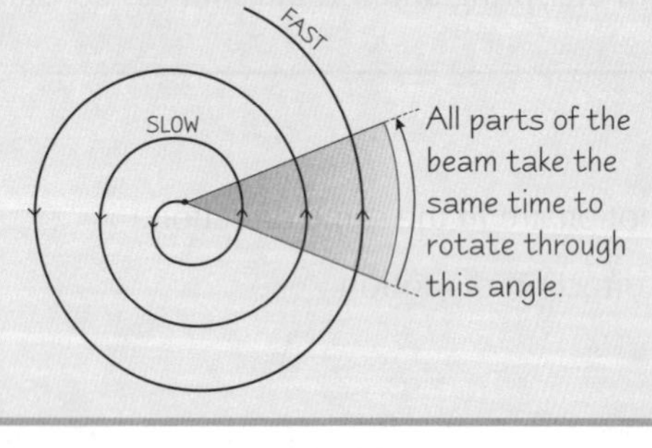

1) Different parts of the particle beam are rotating at **different linear speeds**, v. (The linear speed is sometimes called **tangential velocity**.)
2) But all the parts **rotate** through the **same angle** in the **same time** — so they have the **same angular speed**.

Circular Motion has a ***Frequency*** and ***Period***

1) The frequency, f, is the number of complete **revolutions per second** (rev s^{-1} or hertz, Hz).
2) The period, T, is the **time taken** for a complete revolution (in seconds).
3) Frequency and period are **linked** by the equation: $f = \dfrac{1}{T}$ — f = frequency in rev s^{-1}, T = period in s
4) For a complete circle, an object turns through 2π radians in a time T, so frequency and period are related to ω by:

$$\omega = 2\pi f \quad \text{and} \quad \omega = \frac{2\pi}{T}$$

f = frequency in rev s^{-1}, T = period in s, ω = angular speed in rad s^{-1}

Circular Motion

Objects Travelling in Circles are **Accelerating** since their **Velocity is Changing**

1) Even if the car shown is going at a **constant speed**, its **velocity** is changing since its **direction** is changing.
2) Since acceleration is defined as the **rate of change of velocity**, the car is accelerating even though it isn't going any faster.
3) This acceleration is called the **centripetal acceleration** and is always directed towards the **centre of the circle**.

There are two formulas for centripetal acceleration:

$$a = \frac{v^2}{r} \quad \text{and} \quad a = \omega^2 r$$

a = centripetal acceleration in ms^{-2}
v = linear speed in ms^{-1}
ω = angular speed in $rad\,s^{-1}$
r = radius in m

The **Centripetal Acceleration** is produced by a **Centripetal Force**

From Newton's laws, if there's a **centripetal acceleration**, there must be a **centripetal force** acting towards the **centre of the circle**.

Since $F = ma$, the centripetal force must be:

$$F = \frac{mv^2}{r} \quad \text{and} \quad F = m\omega^2 r$$

The centripetal force is what keeps the object moving in a circle — remove the force and the object would fly off at a tangent.

Men cowered from the force of the centripede.

Practice Questions

Q1 How many radians are there in a complete circle?
Q2 How is angular speed defined and what is the relationship between angular speed and linear speed?
Q3 Define the period and frequency of circular motion. What is the relationship between period and angular speed?
Q4 In which direction does the centripetal force act, and what happens when this force is removed?

Exam Questions

Q1 (a) At what angular speed does the Earth orbit the Sun? (1 year = 3.2×10^7 s) [2 marks]

(b) Calculate the Earth's linear speed. (Assume radius of orbit = 1.5×10^{11} m) [2 marks]

(c) Calculate the centripetal force needed to keep the Earth in its orbit. (Mass of Earth = 6.0×10^{24} kg) [2 marks]

(d) What is providing this force? [1 mark]

Q2 A bucket full of water, tied to a rope, is being swung around in a vertical circle (so it is upside down at the top of the swing). The radius of the circle is 1 m.

(a) By considering the acceleration due to gravity at the top of the swing, what is the minimum frequency with which the bucket can be swung without any water falling out? [3 marks]

(b) The bucket is now swung with a constant angular speed of 5 $rad\,s^{-1}$. What will be the tension in the rope when the bucket is at the top of the swing if the total mass of the bucket and water is 10 kg? [2 marks]

I'm spinnin' around, move out of my way...

*"Centripetal" just means "centre-seeking". The centripetal force is what actually causes circular motion. What you **feel** when you're spinning, though, is the reaction (centrifugal) force. Don't get the two mixed up.*

Simple Harmonic Motion

These pages are for AQA A Unit 4, Edexcel Unit 5, OCR A Unit 4 and OCR B Unit 4.

*SHM is Defined in terms of **Acceleration** and **Displacement***

1) An object moving with **simple harmonic motion** (SHM) **oscillates** to and fro, either side of a **midpoint**.
2) The distance of the object from the midpoint is called its **displacement**.
3) There is always a **restoring force** pulling or pushing the object back **towards** the **midpoint**.
4) The **size** of the **restoring force** depends on the **displacement**, and the force makes the object **accelerate** towards the midpoint:

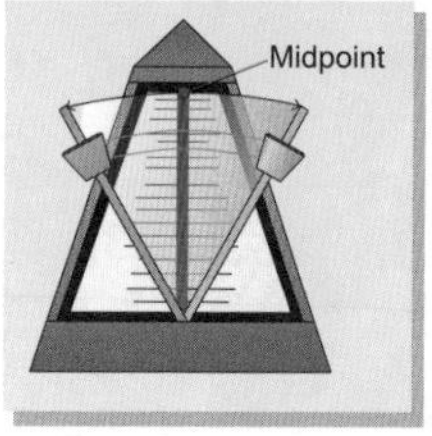

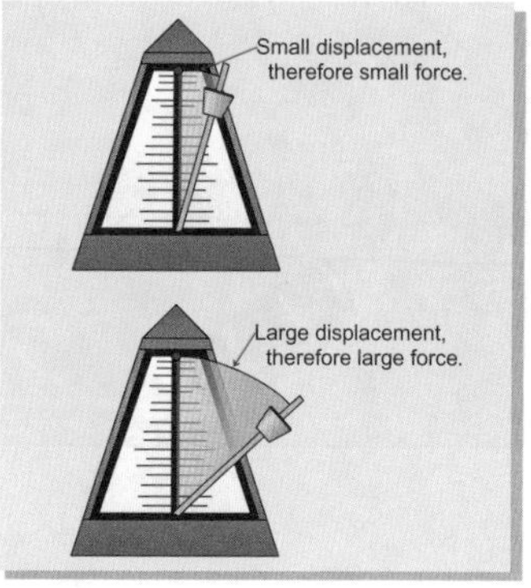

> **SHM**: an oscillation in which the **acceleration** of an object is **directly proportional** to its **displacement** from the **midpoint**, and is directed **towards the midpoint**.

*The **Restoring Force** makes the Object Exchange **PE** and **KE***

1) The **type** of **potential energy** (PE) depends on **what it is** that's providing the **restoring force**. This will be **gravitational PE** for pendulums and **elastic PE** (elastic stored energy) for masses on springs.
2) As the object moves **towards the midpoint**, the restoring force **does work** on the object and so **transfers** some **PE** to **KE**. When the object is moving **away from the midpoint**, all that KE is transferred **back to PE** again.
3) At the **midpoint**, the object's **PE** is **zero** and its **KE** is **maximum**.
4) At the **maximum displacement** (the **amplitude**) on both sides of the midpoint, the object's **KE** is **zero** and its **PE** is **maximum**.

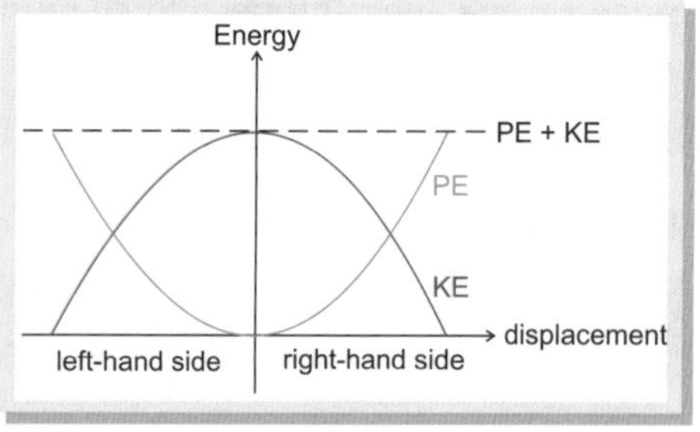

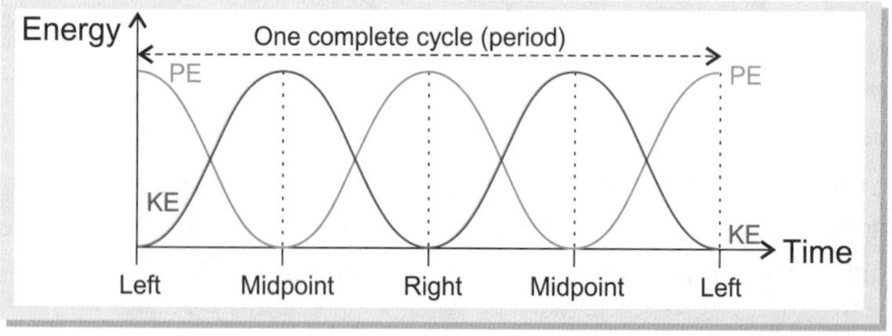

5) The **sum** of the **potential** and **kinetic** energy is called the **mechanical energy** and **stays constant** (as long as the motion isn't damped — see p. 14-15).
6) The **energy transfer** for one complete cycle of oscillation (see graph) is: PE to KE to PE to KE to PE … and then the process repeats…

*You can Draw **Graphs** to Show **Displacement**, **Velocity** and **Acceleration***

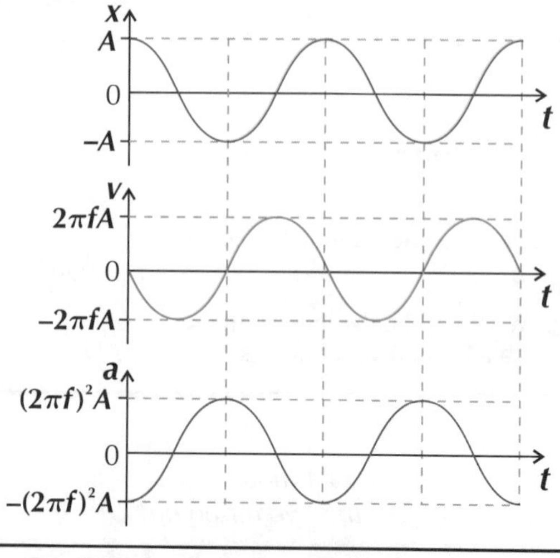

Displacement, x, varies as a cosine or sine wave with a maximum value, A (the amplitude) or x_0 if you're doing Edexcel.

Velocity, v, is the gradient of the displacement-time graph (dx/dt). It has a maximum value of $(2\pi f)A$ (where f is the frequency of the oscillation) and is a quarter of a cycle in front of the displacement.

Acceleration, a, is the gradient of the velocity-time graph (d^2x/dt^2). It has a maximum value of $(2\pi f)^2 A$, and is in antiphase with the displacement.

Simple Harmonic Motion

The **Frequency** and **Period** don't depend on the **Amplitude**

1) From **maximum positive displacement** (e.g. maximum displacement to the right) to **maximum negative displacement** (e.g. maximum displacement to the left) and **back again** is called a **cycle** of oscillation.
2) The **frequency**, f, of the SHM is the number of cycles per second (measured in Hz).
3) The **period**, T, is the **time** taken for a complete cycle (in seconds).

> In SHM, the **frequency** and **period** are independent of the **amplitude** (i.e. constant for a given oscillation). So a pendulum clock will keep ticking in regular time intervals even if its swing becomes very small.

Learn the SHM Equations

Which equations you need depend on your exam board.

1) According to the definition of SHM, the **acceleration**, a (or d^2x/dt^2 — **OCR B**), is directly proportional to the **displacement**, x. The **constant of proportionality** depends on the **frequency**, and the acceleration is always in the **opposite direction** from the displacement (so there's a minus sign in the equation).
2) The **velocity** is **positive** if the object's moving **away** from the **midpoint**, and **negative** if it's moving **towards** the midpoint. Hence the ± sign in the *AQA A* velocity equation.

AQA A acceleration and velocity equations

$a = -(2\pi f)^2 x$

Max acceleration: $a_{max} = (2\pi f)^2 A$

$v = \pm 2\pi f \sqrt{A^2 - x^2}$

Max velocity: $v_{max} = 2\pi f A$

Edexcel

$a = -\omega^2 x$

$a = -A\omega^2 \cos(\omega t)$

$v = -A\omega \sin(\omega t)$

OCR A

$a = -(2\pi f)^2 x$

Max velocity: $v_{max} = 2\pi f A$

OCR B

$$\frac{d^2x}{d^2t} = -(2\pi f)^2 x$$

3) The **displacement** varies with time according to two equations depending on **where** the object was when the timing was started — again the equation(s) you need to learn depend on which board you're doing.

For someone starting a stopwatch with a pendulum at **maximum displacement**:

$x = A\cos(2\pi f t)$ — ***AQA A, OCR A and OCR B***

$x = A\cos(\omega t)$ — ***Edexcel***

For someone releasing a pendulum but starting a stopwatch as the pendulum swings through **the midpoint**:

$x = A\sin(2\pi f t)$

This one's for OCR A and OCR B.

Practice Questions

Q1 Sketch a graph of how the velocity of an object oscillating with SHM varies with time.

Q2 What is the special relationship between the acceleration and the displacement in SHM?

Q3 Given the amplitude and the frequency, how would you work out the maximum acceleration?

Exam Questions

Q1 (a) Define *simple harmonic motion*. [2 marks]

(b) Explain why the motion of a ball bouncing off the ground is not SHM. [1 mark]

Q2 A pendulum is pulled a distance 0.05 m from its midpoint and released.
It oscillates with simple harmonic motion with a frequency of 1.5 Hz. Calculate:

(a) its maximum velocity [1 mark]

(b) its displacement 0.1 s after it is released [2 marks]

(c) the time it takes to fall to 0.01 m from the midpoint after it is released [2 marks]

"Simple" harmonic motion — hmmm, I'm not convinced...

The basic concept of SHM is simple enough (no pun intended). Make sure you can remember the shapes of all the graphs on page 10 and the equations from this page, then just get as much practice at using the equations as you can.

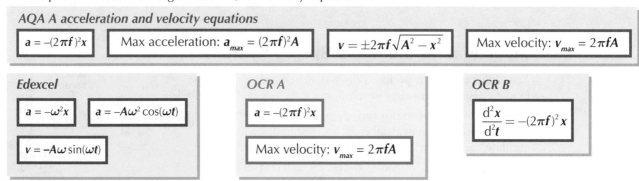

Simple Harmonic Oscillators

These pages are for AQA A Unit 4, Edexcel Unit 5 and OCR B Unit 4.

A **Mass** on a **Spring** is a **Simple Harmonic Oscillator (SHO)**

1) When the mass is **pushed to the left** or **pulled to the right** of the **equilibrium position**, there's a **force** exerted on it.
2) The size of this force is:

$F = -kx$ where k is the **spring constant** (stiffness) of the spring in Nm^{-1} and x is the displacement in m.

3) After a bit of jiggery-pokery involving Newton's second law and some of the ideas on the previous page, you get the **formula for the period of a mass oscillating on a spring**:

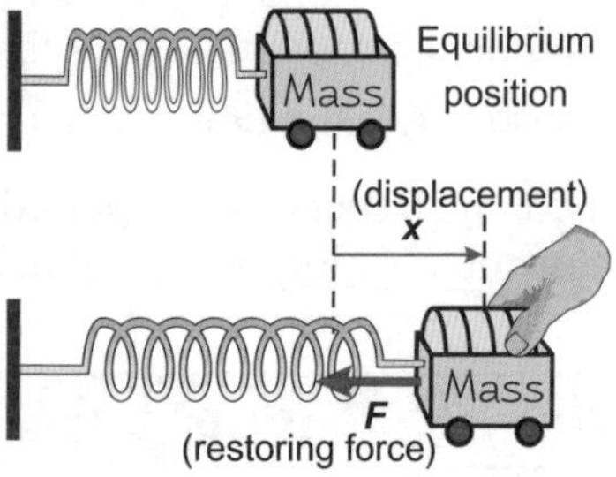

$$T = 2\pi\sqrt{\frac{m}{k}}$$

where T = period of oscillation in seconds
m = mass in kg
k = spring constant in Nm^{-1}

A simple theory of how atoms in a lattice (i.e. a solid) behave can be worked out by considering them as masses oscillating on springs. So there you go.

You can check this result **EXPERIMENTALLY** by changing **one variable at a time** and seeing what happens.

Investigating the Mass-Spring System

1) You could measure the **period**, T, by getting a computer to plot a **displacement-time graph** from a **data logger**.
2) Attach a **trolley** between two **springs**, pull it to one side by a certain amount and then let go. The trolley will **oscillate** back and forth as the springs pull it in each direction.

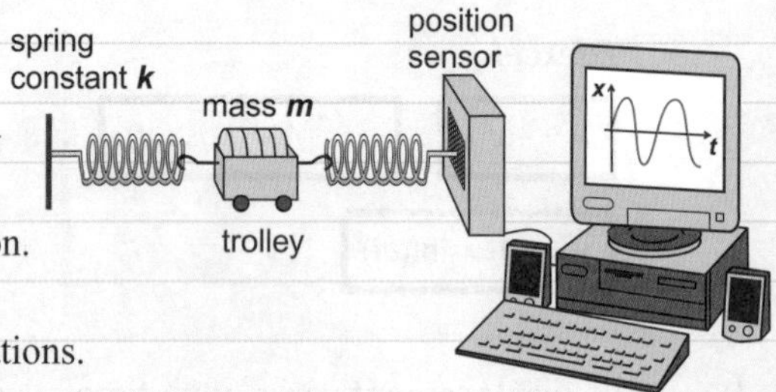

3) Change the **mass**, m, by loading the trolley with **masses** — don't forget to include the mass of the trolley in your calculations.
4) Change the **spring stiffness**, k, by using different combinations of springs.
5) Change the **amplitude**, A, by pulling the trolley across by different amounts.
6) You'll get the following **results**: *($\propto$ means "is proportional to")*

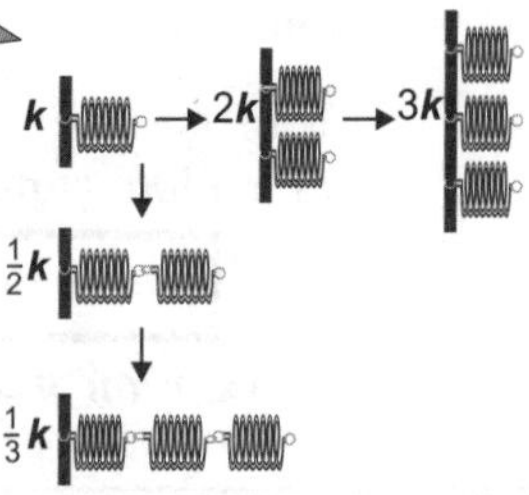

a) $T \propto \sqrt{m}$ so $T^2 \propto m$

b) $T \propto \sqrt{\frac{1}{k}}$ so $T^2 \propto \frac{1}{k}$

c) T doesn't depend on amplitude, A.

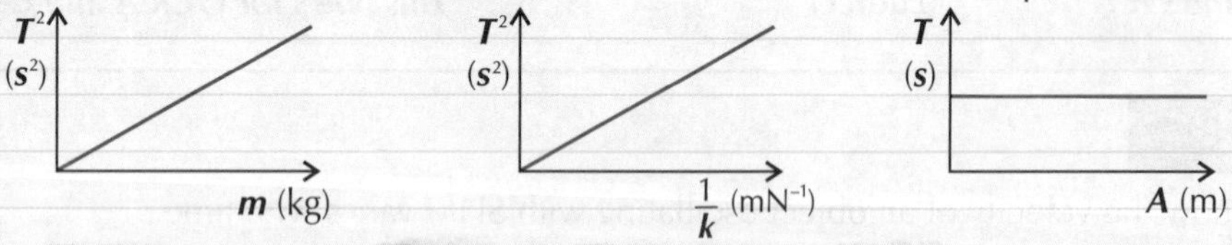

The Force on an SHO is **Proportional** to its **Displacement**

OCR B only

If you draw a **displacement-time graph** for a **simple harmonic oscillator**, you'll get a **sine** or **cosine** curve. If you **differentiate** that graph you'll get the **velocity-time graph** for the oscillator. **Differentiate** again and you'll see that the **acceleration-time graph** is the **inverse** of the **displacement-time graph** (it's the same, but upside down).

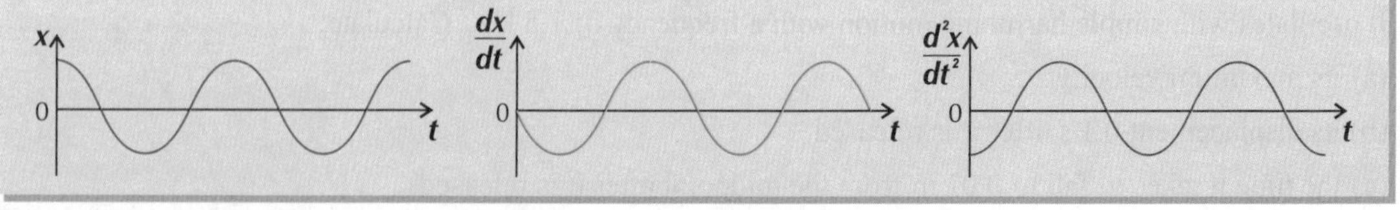

This shows that the **acceleration** of an SHO is **proportional** to its **displacement**. And, because **acceleration** is **proportional** to **force** ($F = ma$ remember), the **force** on an SHO must also be **proportional** to its **displacement**.

Put all this together and you get: $F = ma = m\frac{d^2x}{dt^2}$ and $F = -kx$ (see above), which means that $\frac{d^2x}{dt^2} = \frac{-k}{m}x$.

Simple Harmonic Oscillators

The Simple Pendulum is the Classic Example of an SHO

If you set up a simple pendulum attached to an angle sensor and computer like this — then change the length, l, the mass of the bob, m, and the amplitude, A, you get the following results:

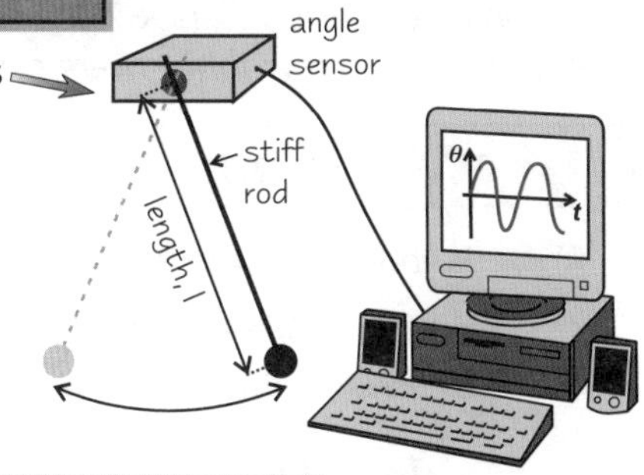

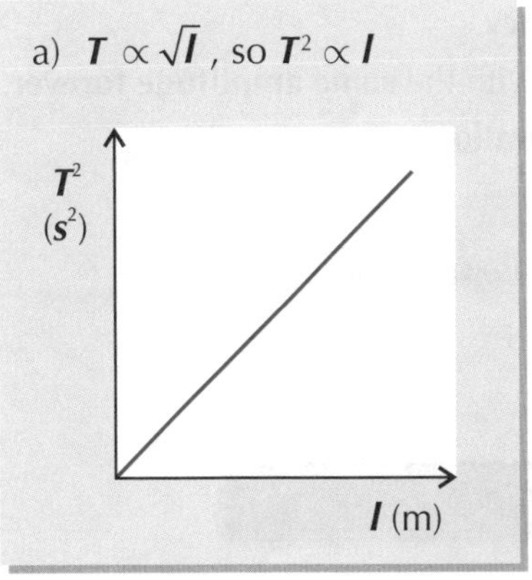

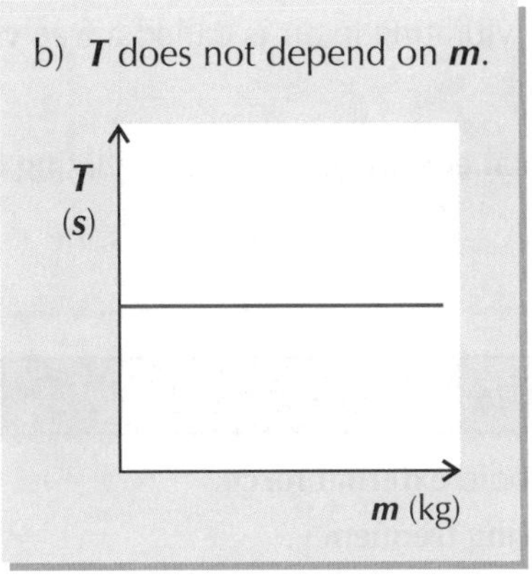

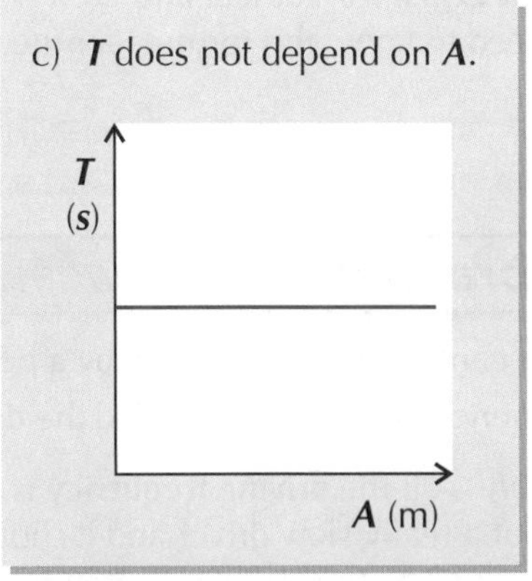

Bob hung around waiting for the experiment to start.

The **formula for the period of a pendulum** is:
(The derivation's quite hard, so you don't need to know it.)
This formula only works for small angles of oscillation — up to about 10° from the equilibrium point.

$$T = 2\pi\sqrt{\frac{l}{g}}$$

where T = period of oscillation in seconds
l = length of pendulum (between pivot and centre of mass of bob) in m
g = gravitational field strength in Nkg^{-1}

Practice Questions

Q1 Write down the formulae for the period of a mass on a spring and the period of a pendulum.

Q2 Describe a method you could use to measure the period of an oscillator.

Q3 For a mass-spring system, what graphs could you plot to find out how the period depends on: a) the mass, b) the spring constant, and c) the amplitude? What would they look like?

Exam Questions

Q1 A spring of original length 0.10 m is suspended from a stand and clamp.
A mass of 0.10 kg is attached to the bottom and the spring extends to a total length of 0.20 m.

(a) Calculate the spring constant of the spring in Nm^{-1}. ($g = 9.81\ Nkg^{-1}$) [2 marks]

The spring isn't moving at this point, so the forces on it must be balanced.

(b) The mass is pulled down a further 2 cm and then released. Assuming the spring oscillates with simple harmonic motion, calculate the period of the subsequent oscillations. [1 mark]

(c) What mass would be needed to make the period of oscillation twice as long? [2 marks]

Q2 Two pendulums of different lengths were released from rest at the top of their swing.
It took exactly the same time for the shorter pendulum to make five complete oscillations as it took the longer pendulum to make three complete oscillations.
The shorter pendulum had a length of 0.20 m. Show that the length of the longer one was 0.56 m. [3 marks]

Go on — SHO the examiners what you're made of...

The most important things to remember on these pages are those two period equations. You'll be given them in your exam, but you need to know what they mean and be happy using them.

Free and Forced Vibrations

These pages are for AQA A Unit 4, Edexcel Unit 5, OCR A Unit 4 and OCR B Unit 4.

Resonance... hmm... tricky little beast. Remember the Millennium Bridge, that standard-bearer of British engineering? The wibbles and wobbles were caused by resonance. How was it sorted out? By damping, which is coming up too.

Free Vibrations — No Transfer of Energy To or From the Surroundings

1) If you stretch and release a mass on a spring, it oscillates at its **natural frequency**.
2) If **no energy's transferred** to or from the surroundings, it will **keep** oscillating with the **same amplitude forever**.
3) In practice this **never happens**, but a spring vibrating in air is called a **free vibration** anyway.

This bit is just for Edexcel and OCR B.
You need to know this formula for the **total energy** of a freely oscillating mass on a spring:

$$E_{total} = \frac{1}{2}mv^2 + \frac{1}{2}kx^2 \text{ (in other words, KE + PE)}$$

Forced Vibrations happen when there's an External Driving Force

1) A system can be **forced** to vibrate by a periodic **external force**.
2) The frequency of this force is called the **driving frequency**.

AQA A only — If the **driving frequency** is much **less than** the **natural frequency** then the two are **in phase** — think about a really slow driver and it should make sense. But, if the **driving frequency** is much **greater than** the **natural frequency**, the oscillator won't be able to keep up — you end up with the driver completely **out of phase** with the oscillator. At **resonance** (see below) the **phase difference** between the driver and oscillator is **90°**.

Resonance happens when Driving Frequency = Natural Frequency

When the **driving frequency** approaches the **natural frequency**, the system gains more and more energy from the driving force and so vibrates with a **rapidly increasing amplitude**. When this happens the system is **resonating**.

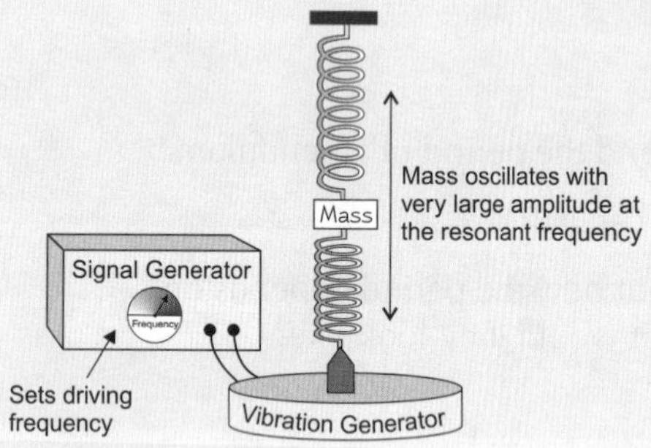

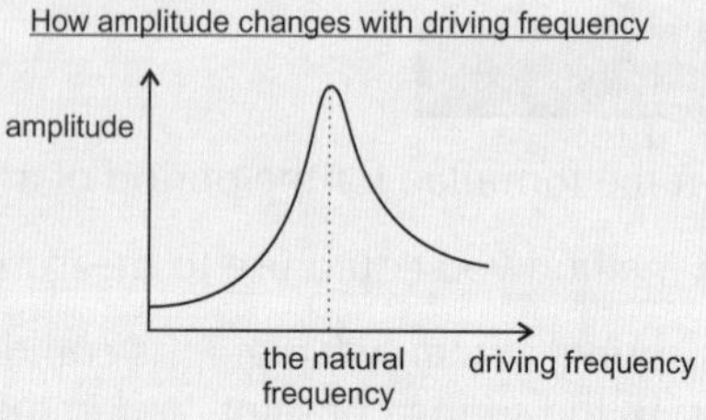

Armies deliberately march 'out of step' when they cross a bridge. This reduces the risk of the bridge resonating and breaking apart.

Examples of resonance:

a) organ pipe

The column of air resonates, driven by the motion of air at the base.

b) swing

A swing resonates if it's driven by someone pushing it at its natural frequency.

c) glass smashing

A glass resonates when driven by a sound wave at the right frequency.

d) radio

A radio is tuned so the electric circuit resonates at the same frequency as the radio station you want to listen to.

Damping happens when Energy is Lost to the Surroundings

1) In practice, **any** oscillating system **loses energy** to its surroundings.
2) This is usually down to **frictional forces** like air resistance.
3) These are called **damping forces**.
4) Systems are often **deliberately damped** to **stop** them oscillating or to **minimise** the effect of **resonance**.

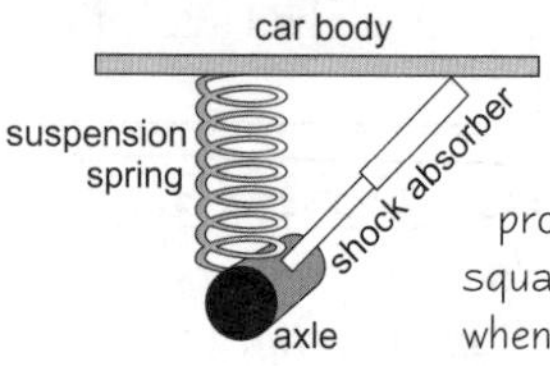

Shock absorbers in a car suspension provide a damping force by squashing oil through a hole when compressed.

Free and Forced Vibrations

Different Amounts of Damping have Different Effects

1) The **degree** of damping can vary from **light** damping (where the damping force is small) to **overdamping**.
2) Damping **reduces** the **amplitude** of the oscillation over time. The **heavier** the damping, the **quicker** the amplitude is reduced to zero.
3) **Critical damping** reduces the amplitude (i.e. stops the system oscillating) in the **shortest possible time**.
4) Car **suspension systems** and moving coil **meters** are critically damped so that they **don't oscillate** but return to equilibrium as quickly as possible.
5) Systems with **even heavier damping** are **overdamped**. They take **longer** to return to equilibrium than a critically damped system.

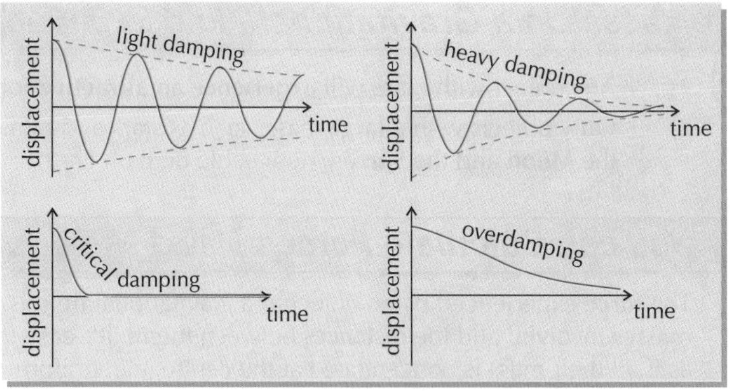

6) **Plastic deformation** of ductile materials **reduces** the **amplitude** of oscillations in the same way as damping. As the material changes shape, it **absorbs energy**, so the oscillation will become smaller.

Damping Affects Resonance too

1) **Lightly damped** systems have a **very sharp** resonance peak. Their amplitude only increases dramatically when the **driving frequency** is **very close** to the **natural frequency**.
2) **Heavily damped** systems have a **flatter response**. Their amplitude doesn't increase very much near the natural frequency and they aren't as **sensitive** to the driving frequency.

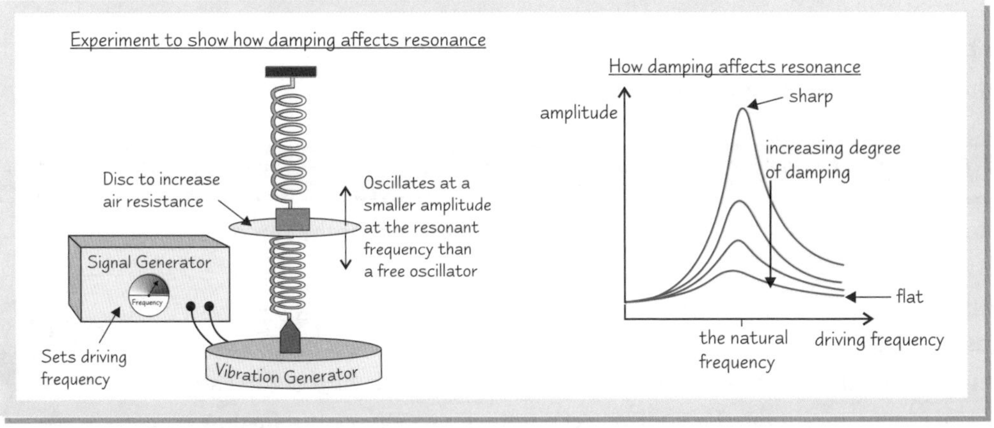

Structures are damped to avoid being damaged by resonance. Loudspeakers are also made to have as flat a response as possible so that they don't 'colour' the sound.

Practice Questions

Q1 What is a free vibration? What is a forced vibration?

Q2 Draw diagrams to show how a damped system oscillates with time when the system is lightly damped and when the system is critically damped.

Exam Questions

Q1 (a) What is resonance? [2 marks]

(b) Draw a diagram to show how the amplitude of a lightly damped system varies with driving frequency. [2 marks]

(c) On the same diagram, show how the amplitude of the system varies with driving frequency when it is heavily damped. [1 mark]

Q2 (a) What is critical damping? [1 mark]

(b) Describe a situation where critical damping is used. [1 mark]

A2 Physics — it can really put a damper on your social life...

Resonance can be really useful (radios, oboes, swings — yay) or very, very bad...

Gravitational Fields

These pages are for AQA A Unit 4, Edexcel Unit 5, OCR A Unit 4 and OCR B Unit 4.

*Gravity's all about masses **attracting** each other. If the Earth didn't have a **gravitational field,** apples wouldn't fall to the ground and you'd probably be floating off into space instead of sitting here reading this page...*

Masses in a Gravitational Field Experience a Force Of Attraction

1) Any object with mass will **experience an attractive force** if you put it in the **gravitational field** of another object.
2) Only objects with a **large** mass, such as stars and planets, have a significant effect. E.g. the gravitational fields of the **Moon** and the **Sun** are noticeable here on Earth — they're the main cause of our **tides**.

You can Calculate Forces Using Newton's Law of Gravitation

The **force** experienced by an object in a gravitational field is always **attractive**. It's a **vector** which depends on the **masses** involved and the **distances** between them. It's easy to work this out for **point masses** — or objects which behave as if all their mass is concentrated at the centre, e.g. uniform spheres. You just put the numbers into this equation...

NEWTON'S LAW OF GRAVITATION:

$$F = (-)\frac{GMm}{r^2}$$

There's sometimes a negative sign, to show that the vector ***F*** is in the opposite direction to ***r*** (displacement of ***m*** from ***M***).

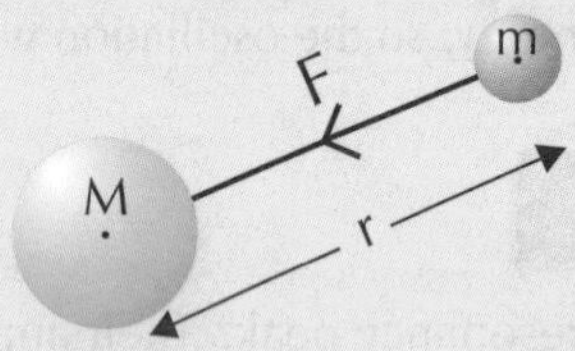

The diagram shows the force acting on ***m*** due to ***M***. (The force on ***M*** due to ***m*** is equal but in the opposite direction.)

M and ***m*** behave as point masses.

G is the **gravitational constant** — 6.67 × 10^{-11} Nm^2kg^{-2}.

r is the distance (in metres) between the centres of the two masses.

It doesn't matter what you call the masses: M and m, m_1 and m_2, Paul and Larry...

The law of gravitation is an **inverse square law** $\left(F \propto \frac{1}{r^2}\right)$ so:

1) if the distance **r** between the masses **increases** then the force **F** will **decrease**.
2) if the **distance doubles** then the **force** will be one **quarter** the strength of the original force.

You can Draw Lines of Force to Show the Field Around an Object

AQA A, OCR A and OCR B.

Gravitational lines of force (or "**field lines**") are **arrows** showing the **direction of the force** that masses would feel in a gravitational field.

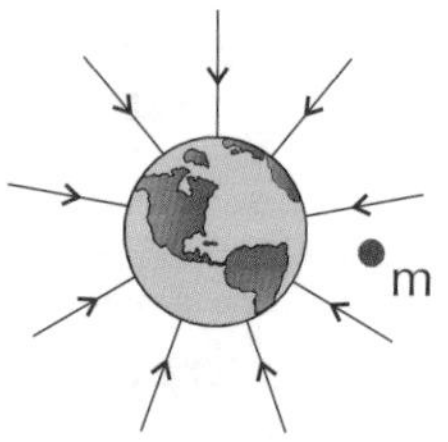

1) If you put a small mass, ***m***, anywhere in the Earth's gravitational field, it will always be attracted **towards** the Earth.
2) The Earth's gravitational field is **radial** — the lines of force meet at the centre of the Earth.
3) If you move mass ***m*** further away from the Earth — where the **lines** of force are **further apart** — the **force** it experiences **decreases**.
4) The small mass, ***m***, has a gravitational field of its own. This doesn't have a noticeable effect on the Earth though, because the Earth is so much **more massive**.
5) Close to the Earth's surface, the field is (almost) uniform — the **field lines** are (almost) **parallel**.

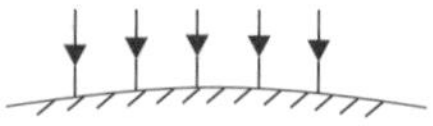

The Field Strength is the Force per Unit Mass

Gravitational field strength, ***g***, is the **force per unit mass**. Its value depends on **where you are** in the field. There's a really simple equation for working it out:

$$g = \frac{F}{m}$$

g has units of newtons per kilogram (Nkg^{-1})

1) ***F*** is the force experienced by a mass ***m*** when it's placed in the gravitational field. Divide ***F*** by ***m*** and you get the **force per unit mass**.
2) **g** is a **vector** quantity, always pointing towards the centre of the mass whose field you're describing.
3) Since the gravitational field is almost uniform at the Earth's surface, you can assume **g** is a constant.
4) **g** is just the **acceleration** of a mass in a gravitational field. It's often called the **acceleration due to gravity**.

The **value** of **g** at the **Earth's surface** is approximately **9.81** ms^{-2} (or 9.81 Nkg^{-1}).

Gravitational Fields

In a *Radial Field*, g is *Inversely Proportional* to r^2

Point masses have **radial** gravitational fields. The value of g depends on the distance r from the point mass M...

$$g = (-)\frac{GM}{r^2}$$

And here's a quick derivation — for Edexcel only
The force on a point mass m in the gravitational field of a point mass M is $F = (-)\frac{GMm}{r^2}$. So, $g = \frac{F}{m} = (-)\frac{GM\not{m}}{\not{m}r^2} = (-)\frac{GM}{r^2}$

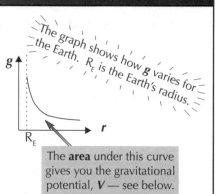

And it's an **inverse square law** again — as r **increases,** g **decreases**.

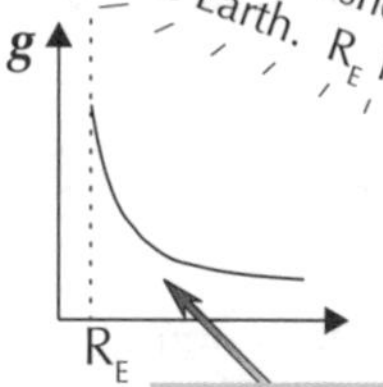
The graph shows how g varies for the Earth. R_E is the Earth's radius.
g
r
R_E

The **area** under this curve gives you the gravitational potential, V — see below.

You gain Gravitational Potential Energy if you Move Away from the Earth

OCR B only

The **gravitational potential energy** of a mass m is E_{grav}. This is the **work** that would need to be done to move m to a distance r from a large point mass M...

$$E_{grav} = -\frac{GMm}{r}$$

1) A mass on the Earth's surface has **negative** gravitational potential energy.
2) As you move a mass away from the Earth, it **gains potential energy**.
3) Potential energy is **zero** at an **infinite** distance from the Earth.

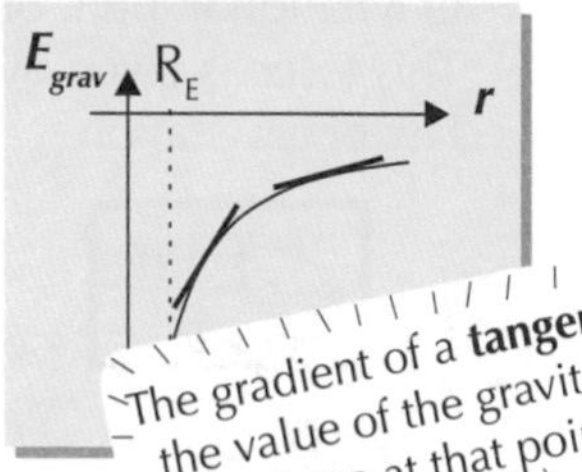
E_{grav}
R_E
r
The gradient of a **tangent** gives the value of the gravitational **force** at that point.

Gravitational Potential is Potential Energy per Unit Mass

AQA A and OCR B.

The **gravitational potential** at a point, V, is the **potential energy per unit mass**, $V = \frac{E_{grav}}{m}$.

If you're doing AQA A, you need to know this equation the other way round too to find the work done, ΔW, moving a mass m from one potential to another: $\Delta E_{grav} = \Delta W = m\Delta V$

In a **radial field**, the equation is...

$$V = (-)\frac{GM}{r}$$

As with potential energy, gravitational potential, V, increases with distance from the mass, and $V = 0$ **at infinity**.

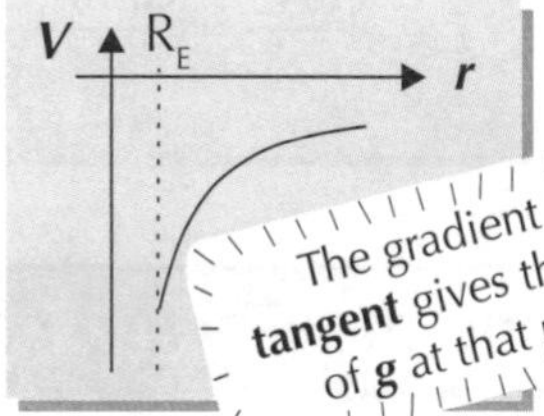
V
R_E
r
The gradient of a **tangent** gives the value of **g** at that point.

OCR B only **Equipotentials** show **all the points** in a field which have the **same potential**.

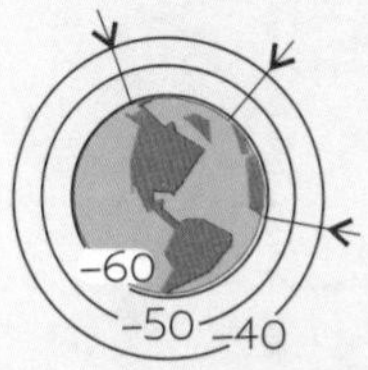
-60
-50
-40

Equipotentials of –60, –50 and –40 $MJkg^{-1}$ around Earth.

1) If you travel along a line of equipotential you **don't lose or gain energy**.
2) For a uniform spherical mass (you can usually assume the Earth's one) the equipotentials are spherical surfaces.
3) **Equipotentials** and **field lines** are **perpendicular**.
4) At the Earth's surface, V = 63 $MJkg^{-1}$.

Practice Questions

Q1 Write down Newton's law of gravitation.

Q2 Draw a diagram showing the Earth's gravitational field and sketch equipotentials of –60, –40 and –20 $MJkg^{-1}$.

Exam Questions

Q1 The Earth's radius is approximately 6400 km. Estimate its mass (use g = 9.81 Nkg^{-1} at the Earth's surface). [2 marks]

Q2 The Moon has a mass of 7.35×10^{22} kg and a radius of 1740 km.

(a) Calculate the value of g at the Moon's surface. [1 mark]

(b) Calculate the gravitational potential energy of a 25 kg mass at a height of 10 km above the Moon's surface. [2 marks]

If you're really stuck, put 'Inverse Square Law'...

Clever chap, Newton, but famously tetchy. He got into fights with other physicists, mainly over planetary motion and calculus... the usual playground squabbles. Then he spent the rest of his life trying to turn scrap metal into gold. Weird.

Motion of Masses in Gravitational Fields

This page is for AQA A Unit 4, Edexcel Unit 5, OCR A Unit 4 and OCR B Unit 4.

*Planets just go round and round in circles. Well, **ellipses** really, but I won't tell if you don't...*

Planets** are **Satellites** which **Orbit** the **Sun

1) A **satellite** is just any **smaller mass** which **orbits** a **much larger mass** — the **Moon** is a satellite of the Earth.
2) In our Solar System, the planets have **nearly circular orbits**... **so** you can use the **equations of circular motion**.

*The **Speed** of an Orbit depends on its **Radius** and the Mass of the **Larger Body**...*

1) Earth feels a force due to the gravitational 'pull' of the **Sun**. This force is given by Newton's law of gravitation...

$$F = \frac{GMm}{r^2}$$

(see p. 16)

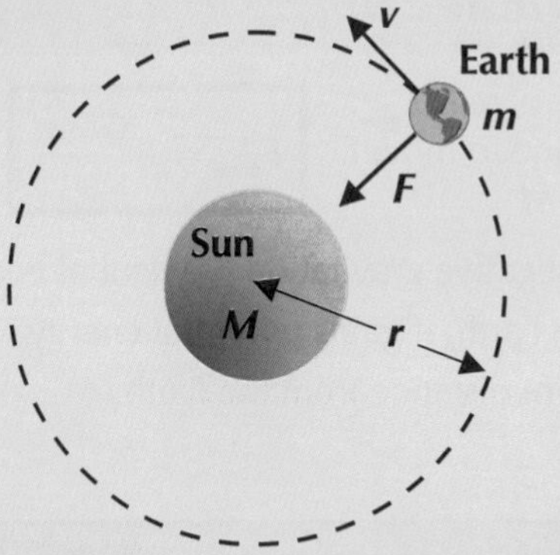

2) The Earth has velocity v. Its linear speed is constant (if you assume the motion is circular) but its **direction** is not — so it's accelerating.
The **centripetal force** causing this acceleration is:

$$F = \frac{mv^2}{r}$$

2) The **centripetal force** on the Earth must be a result of the **gravitational force** due to the Sun, and so these forces must be **equal**...

$$\frac{mv^2}{r} = \frac{GMm}{r^2}$$ and rearranging... $$v = \sqrt{\frac{GM}{r}}$$

*... and the **Period** does too*

AQA A and OCR A

The **time** taken **for one orbit** is called the **period**, T. For circular motion, $T = \frac{2\pi r}{v}$.

Substitute for v and rearrange... $$T = \sqrt{\frac{4\pi^2 r^3}{GM}}$$

Example

The Moon takes 27.3 days to orbit the Earth. Calculate its distance from the Earth.
Take the mass of the Earth to be 5.975 × 10²⁴ kg.

You're trying to find the radius of the orbit, r. Use the formula for period, T:

$$T = \sqrt{\frac{4\pi^2 r^3}{GM}}$$

You've been given the values of T (27.3 days) and M, and you'll be able to look up the value of G on the exam data sheet — $G = 6.67 \times 10^{-11}\ \text{Nm}^2\text{kg}^{-2}$.

and rearrange it for r^3:

$$r^3 = \frac{T^2 GM}{4\pi^2}$$

$T = 27.3$ days $= 2.36 \times 10^6$ s
$G = 6.67 \times 10^{-11}\ \text{Nm}^2\text{kg}^{-2}$
$M = 5.975 \times 10^{24}$ kg

and put the numbers in (convert to SI units first):

$$r^3 = \frac{(2.36\times10^6)^2 \times (6.67\times10^{-11}) \times (5.975\times10^{24})}{4\pi^2} = 5.62\times10^{25}$$

$r = 3.83 \times 10^8$ m
$= \underline{\mathbf{3.83 \times 10^5\ km}}$ (this is the distance between the centre of the Earth and the centre of the Moon)

Motion of Masses in Gravitational Fields

Geosynchronous Satellites Orbit the Earth once in **24 hours**

AQA A **and** *OCR A*

1) Geosynchronous (**geostationary**) satellites orbit over the **equator** and are **always above the same point** on Earth.
2) A geosynchronous satellite travels at the **same angular speed as the Earth** turns below it.
3) These satellites are really useful for sending TV and telephone signals — the satellite is **stationary** relative to a certain point on the **Earth**, so you don't have to alter the angle of your receiver (or transmitter) to keep up.
4) Their orbit takes exactly **one day**.

Kepler's Laws are about the **Motion of Planets** in the **Solar System**

OCR A ***only***

Kepler came up with these three laws around 1600, about 80 years before Newton developed his law of gravitation:

1) Each planet moves in an **ellipse** around the Sun (a circle is just a special kind of ellipse).
2) A line joining the Sun to a planet will sweep out **equal areas in equal times**.
(Don't worry, you don't need to know about that one.)
3) The **period** of the orbit and the **mean distance** between the Sun and the planet are related by **Kepler's third law**:

$$T^2 \propto r^3$$

For circular motion, where r = radius of the orbit, $\frac{r^3}{T^2} = \text{constant} = \frac{GM}{4\pi^2}$.

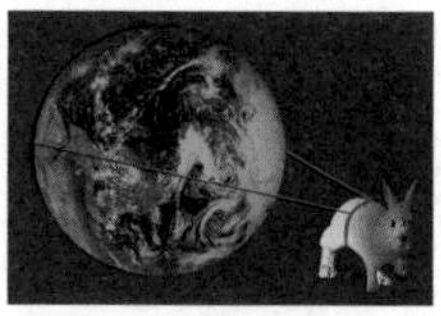

It's either gravity or a giant white rabbit that makes the Earth orbit the Sun. I know which one I believe...

Example The diagram shows the orbits of two of Jupiter's moons, Io and Europa. The moon Io completes one orbit of Jupiter in 42.5 hours. Estimate the orbital period of Europa to the nearest hour, assuming both orbits are circular.

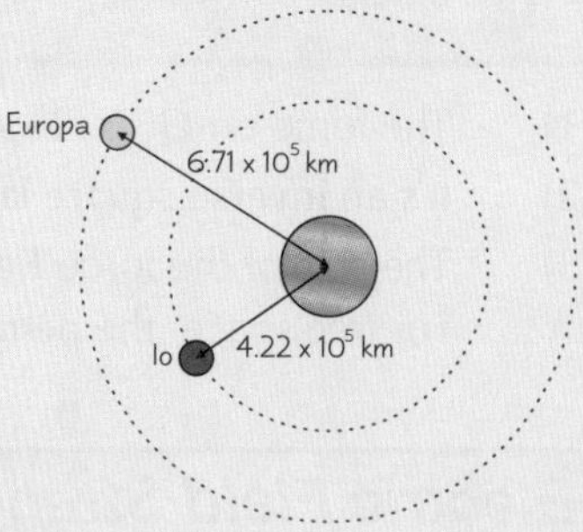

Using Kepler's third law: $\frac{T_{Io}^2}{r_{Io}^3} = \frac{T_{Europa}^2}{r_{Europa}^3}$,

so $T_{Europa} = \sqrt{\frac{T_{Io}^2 r_{Europa}^3}{r_{Io}^3}} = \sqrt{\frac{(42.5)^2 \times (6.71\times10^5)^3}{(4.22\times10^5)^3}}$ = 85 hours to the nearest hour.

Practice Questions

Q1 Derive an expression for the radius of the orbit of a planet around the Sun, in terms of the period of its orbit.

Q2 The International Space Station orbits the Earth with velocity *v*. If another vehicle docks with it, increasing its mass, what difference, if any, does this make to the speed or radius of the orbit?

Q3 Would a geosynchronous satellite be useful for making observations for weather forecasts? Give reasons.

Exam Questions

(Use $G = 6.67 \times 10^{-11}$ Nm^2kg^{-2}, mass of Earth = 5.98×10^{24} kg, radius of Earth = 6400 km)

Q1 (a) A satellite orbits 200 km above the Earth's surface. Calculate the period of the satellite's orbit. [2 marks]

(b) Calculate the linear speed of the satellite. [1 mark]

Q2 At what height above the Earth's surface would a geosynchronous satellite orbit? [3 marks]

Q3 The Sun has a mass of 2.0×10^{30} kg, but loses mass at a rate of around 6×10^9 kgs^{-1}.
Discuss whether this will have had any significant effect on the Earth's orbit over the past 50 000 years. [2 marks]

No fluffy bunnies were harmed in the making of these pages...

Kepler is sometimes proclaimed as the first science fiction writer. He wrote a tale about a fantastic trip to the Moon, where the book narrator's mum asks a demon the secret of space travel, to boldly go where — oh wait, different story. Unfortunately Kepler's book might have sparked the actual witchhunt on Kepler's mum, whoops-a-daisy...

Electric Fields

These pages are for AQA A Unit 4, Edexcel Unit 4, OCR A Unit 5 and OCR B Unit 5.

*Electric fields can be attractive or repulsive, so they're different from gravitational ones. It's all to do with **charge**.*

There is an Electric Field around a Charged Object

Any object with **charge** has an **electric field** around it — the region where it can attract or repel other charges.

1) Electric charge, Q, is measured in **coulombs** (C) and can be either positive or negative.
2) **Oppositely** charged particles **attract** each other. **Like** charges **repel**.
3) If a **charged object** is placed in an electric field, then it will experience a **force**.

You can Calculate Forces using Coulomb's Law

You'll need **Coulomb's law** to work out F — the force of attraction or repulsion between two point charges...

COULOMB'S LAW:

$$F = \frac{kQ_1Q_2}{r^2} \quad \text{where} \quad k = \frac{1}{4\pi\varepsilon}$$

ε ("epsilon") = permittivity of material between charges
Q_1 and Q_2 are the charges
r is the distance between Q_1 and Q_2

If the charges are **opposite** then the force is **attractive**. F will be **negative**.

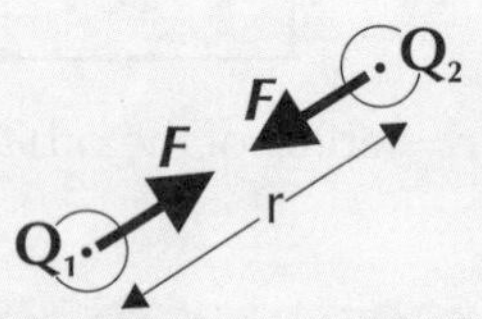

If Q_1 and Q_2 are **like** charges then the force is **repulsive**, and F will be **positive**.

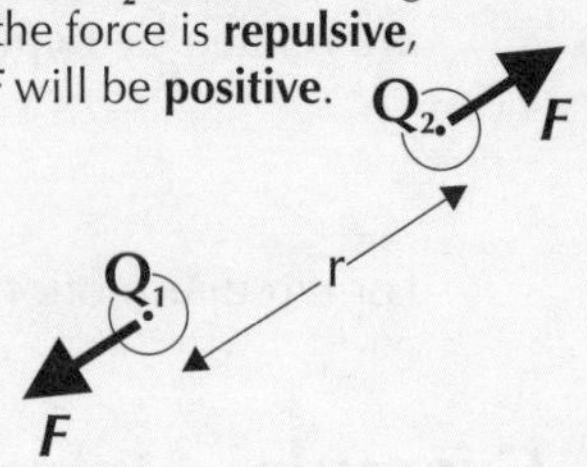

1) The force on Q_1 is always **equal** and **opposite** to the force on Q_2.
2) It's an **inverse square law**. Again. The further apart the charges are, the weaker the force between them.
3) The size of the force F also depends on the **permittivity**, ε, of the material between the two charges.
For free space, the permittivity is $\varepsilon_0 = 8.85 \times 10^{-12}\ C^2N^{-1}m^{-2}$ (this unit can also be written as Fm^{-1} — farads per metre).

Electric Field Strength is Force per Unit Charge

Electric field strength, E, is defined as the **force per unit positive charge** — the force that a charge of +1 C would experience if it was placed in the electric field.

$$E = \frac{F}{q}$$

F is the force on a 'test' charge q.

1) E is a **vector** pointing in the **direction** that a **positive charge** would **move**.
2) The units of E are **newtons per coulomb** (NC^{-1}).
3) Field strength depends on **where you are** in the field.
4) A **point charge** — or any body that behaves as if all its charge is concentrated at the centre — has a **radial** field.

In a Radial Field, E is Inversely Proportional to r^2

1) E is the force per unit charge that a small, positive 'test' charge, q, would feel at different points in the field. In a **radial field**, E depends on the distance r from the point charge Q...

$$E = \frac{kQ}{r^2} \quad \left(k = \frac{1}{4\pi\varepsilon}\right)$$

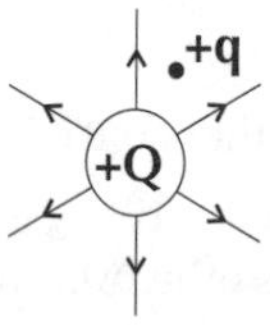

For a **positive** Q, the small positive 'test' charge q would be **repelled**, so the field lines point **away** from Q.

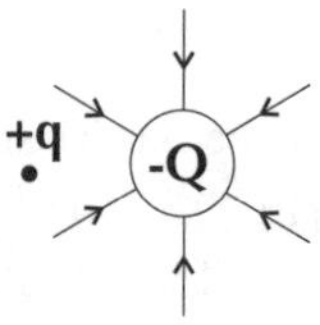

For a **negative** Q, the small positive charge q would be **attracted**, so the field lines point **towards** Q.

2) It's another **inverse square law** — $E \propto \frac{1}{r^2}$

3) Field strength **decreases** as you go **further away** from Q — on a diagram, the **field lines** get **further apart**.

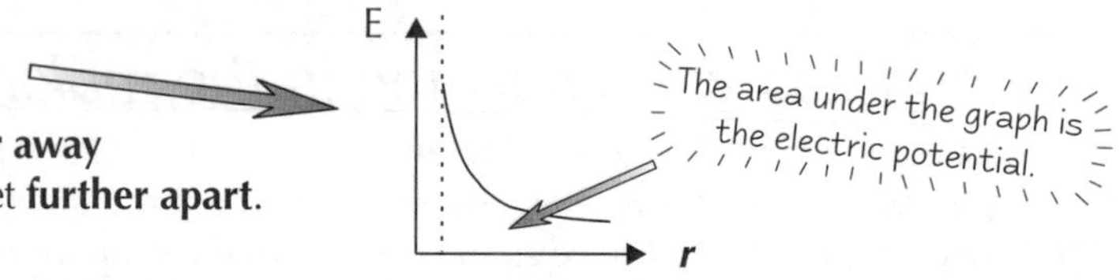

Electric Fields

A Charge in an Electric Field has Electric Potential Energy

OCR B only

The electric potential energy, $E_{electric}$, is the **work** that would need to be done to move a small charge, q, from infinity to a distance r away from a point charge, Q...

$$E_{electric} = \frac{kQq}{r} \quad \left(k = \frac{1}{4\pi\varepsilon}\right)$$

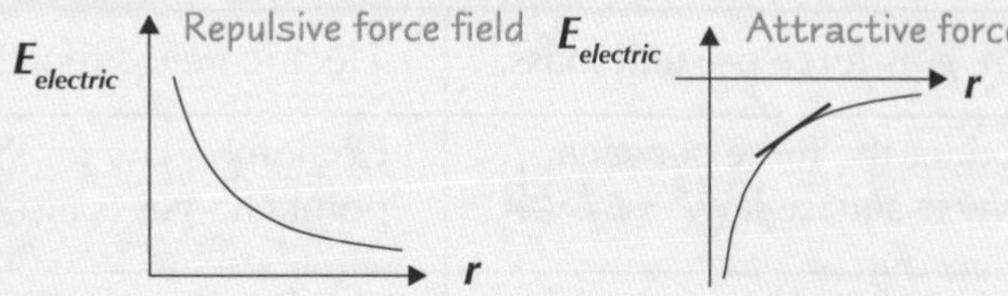

The **gradient** of a **tangent** gives the electric **force** at that point.

1) At an **infinite** distance from Q, a charged particle q would have **zero potential energy.**
2) In a **repulsive** force field (e.g. Q and q are both positive) you have to **do work** against the repulsion to bring q closer to Q. The charge q **gains** potential energy as r **decreases**.
3) In an **attractive** field (e.g. Q negative and q positive) the charge q **gains** potential energy as r **increases**.

Electric Potential is Potential Energy per Unit Charge

AQA A and OCR B

Electric potential, V, is electric **potential energy** per **unit positive charge**...

V has a value of zero at infinity — see above.

$V = \frac{E_{electric}}{q}$ and substituting for $E_{electric}$ gives

$$V = \frac{kQ}{r} \quad \left(k = \frac{1}{4\pi\varepsilon}\right)$$

If you're doing AQA A, ΔW is the work done moving a charge q from one potential to another: $\Delta E_{electric} = \Delta W = q\Delta V$

1) V is measured in **volts**.
2) As with E, V is **positive** when the force is **repulsive**, and **negative** when the force is **attractive**...

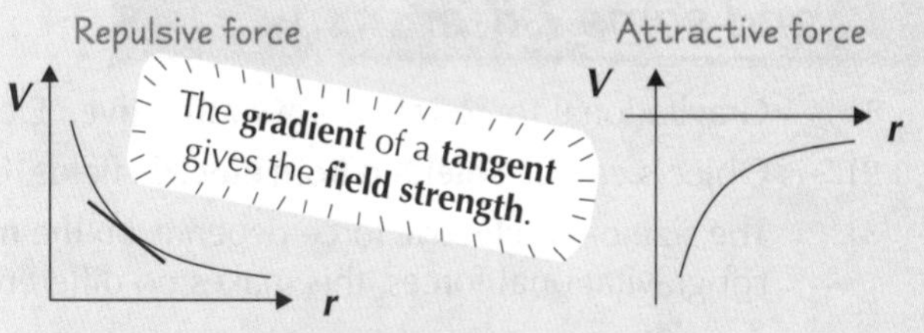

Field Strength is the Same Everywhere in a Uniform Field

A **uniform field** can be produced by connecting two **parallel plates** to the opposite poles of a battery.

1) Field strength E is the **same** at **all points** between the two plates and is...

$$E = \frac{V}{d}$$

V is the **potential difference** between the plates
d is the distance between them

2) E can be measured in volts per metre (Vm^{-1}).

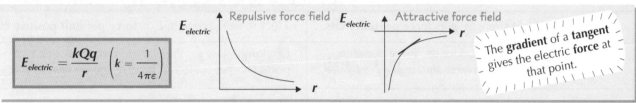

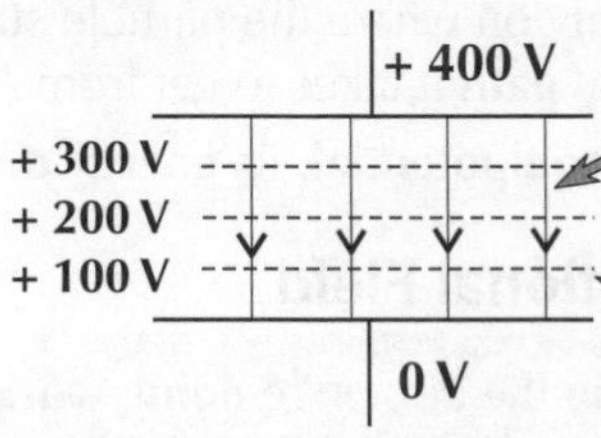

Practice Questions

Q1 Draw the electric field lines due to a positive charge, and due to a negative charge.

Q2 Write down Coulomb's law.

Exam Questions

Q1 The diagram shows two electric charges with equal but opposite charge, Q
Draw electric field lines to show the electric field in the area surrounding the charges. [3 marks]

+Q   -Q

Q2 Find the electric field strength at a distance of 1.75×10^{-10} m from a 1.6×10^{-19} C point charge. [2 marks]

Q3 (a) Two parallel plates are separated by an air gap of 4.5 mm. The plates are connected to a 1500 V dc supply. What is the electric field strength between the plates? Give a suitable unit and state the direction of the field. [3 marks]

(b) The plates are now pulled further apart so that the distance between them is doubled. The electric field strength remains the same. What is the new voltage between the plates? [2 marks]

Electric fields — one way to roast beef...

At least you get a choice here — uniform or radial, positive or negative, attractive or repulsive, chocolate or strawberry...

Gravitational and Electric Fields

These pages are for AQA A Unit 4, Edexcel Unit 5 and OCR A Unit 5.

Gravitational and electric fields are two quite different things, but many of the equations and diagrams are similar.

There are Similarities between Gravitational and Electric Fields...

1)	Gravitational field strength, g, is **force** per **unit mass**.	Electric field strength, E, is **force** per **unit positive charge**.
2)	Newton's law of gravitation for the **force** between two point masses is an **inverse square law**. $F \propto \frac{1}{r^2}$	Coulomb's law for the electric **force** between two point charges is also an **inverse square law**. $F \propto \frac{1}{r^2}$
3)	The **field lines** for a point mass... 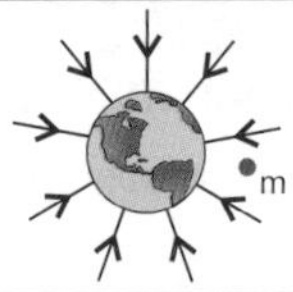	The **field lines** for a **negative** point charge... 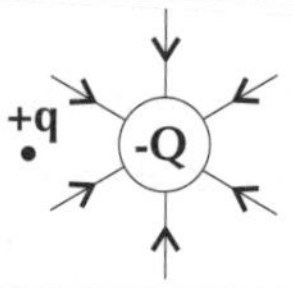
4)	Gravitational potential, V, is **potential energy** per **unit mass**.	Electric potential, V, is **potential energy** per **unit positive charge**.
5)	Absolute potential is **zero** at **infinity** (or where the field strength is so small that it can be neglected).	Absolute potential is **zero** at **infinity** (or where the field strength is so small that it can be neglected).

... and some Differences too

1) Gravitational forces are always **attractive**. Electric forces can be either **attractive** or **repulsive**.
2) Objects can be **shielded** from **electric** fields, but not from gravitational fields.
3) The size of an **electric** force depends on the **medium** between the charges, e.g. plastic or air. For gravitational forces, this makes no difference.

Energy is Transferred when a Mass or Charge Moves in a Field

1) If a charge in an electric field or a mass in a gravitational field moves **along a field line** then **energy** is **converted** from one form to another.
2) The energy change depends only on where the particle **starts** and **finishes**. It **doesn't matter** what **path** it takes to get from A to B.
3) If the particle moves along an **equipotential**, its **energy doesn't change**.

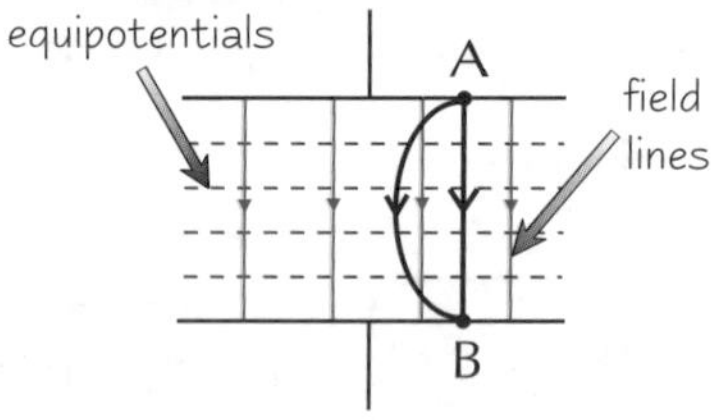

Example in a Gravitational Field

When you throw a ball up in the air you're **doing work** to move the ball against the attractive force of gravity, and **energy** is **converted** from one form to another.
In a **uniform gravitational field**, as at the Earth's surface, the calculations are simple:

1) As the ball rises, it **gains** gravitational **potential energy**: $PE = mg\Delta h$
2) When the ball falls, the gravitational potential energy is converted into **kinetic energy**: $KE = \frac{1}{2}mv^2$
(If there's air resistance some will also be converted to heat.)

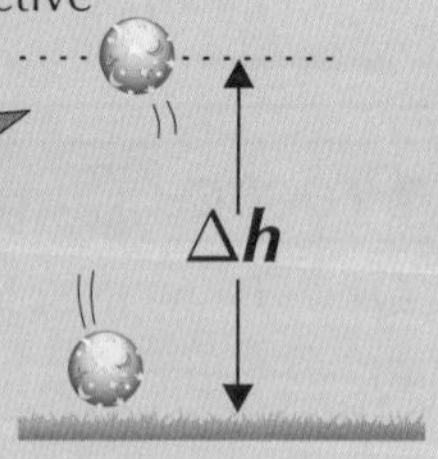

Example in an Electric Field

Two parallel plates have a potential difference of V across them. This creates a **uniform electric field**.

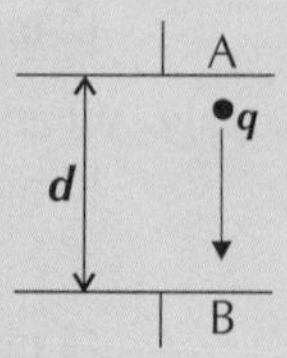

The field strength is $E = \frac{V}{d} = \frac{F}{q}$

this gives $Vq = Fd$

1) To move a charge q from A to B, the **work done** = **force** × **distance moved** = Vq
2) So the energy needed to move a charge q against a potential difference V is given by Vq.

Gravitational and Electric Fields

Charged Particles Move Through Uniform Electric Fields Like Projectiles

OCR A only

You'll probably remember from AS that **projectiles** move through a **uniform gravitational field** along a curved path called a **parabola**. **Charged particles** do a similar thing when they move through **uniform electric fields**.

1) A charged particle will experience a **constant force parallel** to the **electric field lines**.
2) If the particle is **positively charged** then the force is in the **same direction** as the field lines. If it's **negatively charged** (e.g. an **electron**), the force is in the **opposite direction** to the field lines.
3) The particle will **accelerate at a constant rate** in the direction of this force — that's just **Newton's second law**.
4) If the particle's **velocity** has a **component** at **right angles** to the field lines, the particle will keep moving in this direction with a **uniform velocity**. That's **Newton's first law**.
5) The combined effect of constant acceleration in one direction and constant velocity at right angles is a **parabola**.

Example A proton enters a uniform field between two charged, parallel metal plates as shown. Sketch the path of the proton and calculate the vertical distance moved by the proton while it is between the plates. (Charge on a proton = 1.6×10^{-19} C, mass of proton = 1.7×10^{-27} kg.)

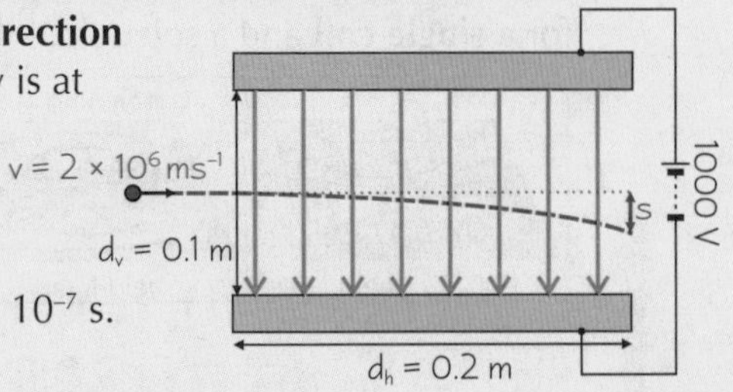

Protons are **positively charged**, so the force on the proton is in the **same direction** as the field (i.e. **downwards**). When the proton enters the field, its velocity is at **right angles** to the field, so it will move in a **parabola**, as shown.

To find the distance the proton moves downward, you need to know **how long** it spends in the field, and the **vertical acceleration.**

The **time** the proton spends in the field is $t = d_h \div v = 0.2 \div (2 \times 10^6) = 1 \times 10^{-7}$ s.

The **field strength** is given by $E = V \div d_v = 1000 \div 0.1 = 10\,000$ NC^{-1}.
So, the **force** on the proton is $F = qE = 1.6 \times 10^{-19} \times 10\,000 = 1.6 \times 10^{-15}$ N, and using $F = ma$, the **vertical acceleration** is $a = F \div m = 1.6 \times 10^{-15} \div 1.7 \times 10^{-27} = 9.4 \times 10^{11}$ ms^{-2}.

Now you can use the equation $s = ut + \frac{1}{2}at^2$ (that you learnt at AS) to find the vertical distance, **s**, moved by the proton: $s = 0 \times 1 \times 10^{-7} + \frac{1}{2} \times 9.4 \times 10^{11} \times (1 \times 10^{-7})^2 = \mathbf{4.7 \times 10^{-3}}$ **m**

Practice Questions

Q1 Describe three similarities and three differences between gravitational and electric fields.

Exam Questions

Q1 Compare the magnitude and direction of the gravitational and electric forces between two electrons which are 8×10^{-10} m apart.
(Use $m_e = 9.11 \times 10^{-31}$ kg, $e = 1.60 \times 10^{-19}$ C, $k = 9.0 \times 10^9$ Nm^2C^{-2} and $G = 6.67 \times 10^{-11}$ Nm^2kg^{-2}.) [3 marks]

Q2 A negatively charged oil drop is held stationary between two charged plates which are 3 cm apart vertically, and have a potential difference of 5000 V across them.

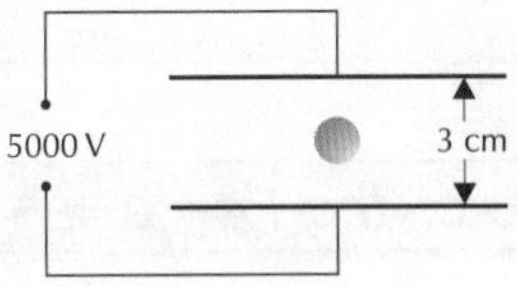

(a) The oil drop has a mass of 1.5×10^{-14} kg. Calculate the size of its charge. [3 marks]
(b) If the polarity of the plates was reversed, what would happen to the oil drop? [1 mark]

Q3 The diagram shows the path followed by a beam of electrons as it passes between two parallel plates.

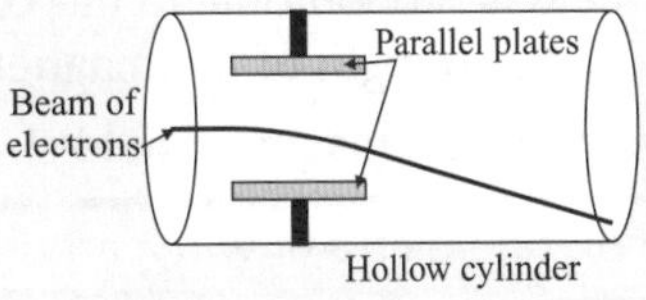

Describe and *explain*:
(a) the direction and nature of the electric field between the plates. [3 marks]
(b) why the path is curved as the beam passes between the plates. [4 marks]

Save energy — stand on a chair...

Eh? But think about this. When someone says, "you've got great potential", they're probably lying. As we all know, gravitational potential is negative at the Earth's surface, and only reaches zero at infinity. Now there's something to aim for.

Magnetic Fields

These pages are for AQA A Unit 4, Edexcel Unit 4, OCR A Unit 5 and OCR B Unit 5.

Magnetic fields — making pretty patterns with iron filings before spending an age trying to pick them off the magnet.

*A **Magnetic Field** is a **Region** Where a **Force** is Exerted on **Magnetic Materials***

1) Magnetic fields can be represented by **field lines**.
2) Field lines go from **north to south**.
3) The **closer** together the lines, the **stronger** the field.

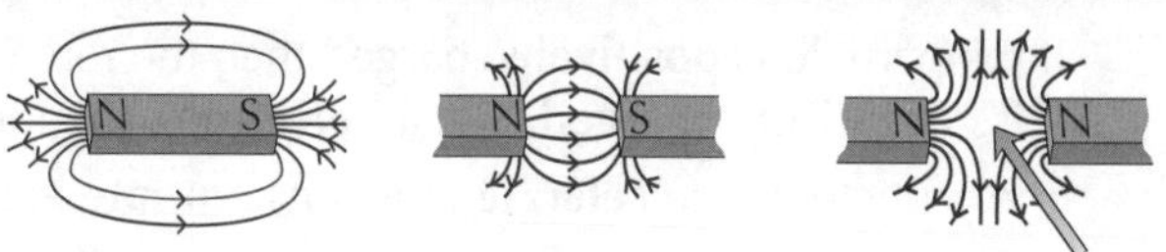

At a neutral point magnetic fields cancel out.

*There is a **Magnetic Field** Around a **Wire** Carrying **Electric Current***

1) The **direction** of a magnetic **field** around a current-carrying wire can be worked out with the **right-hand rule**.
2) You also need to learn these diagrams for a **single coil** and a **solenoid**.

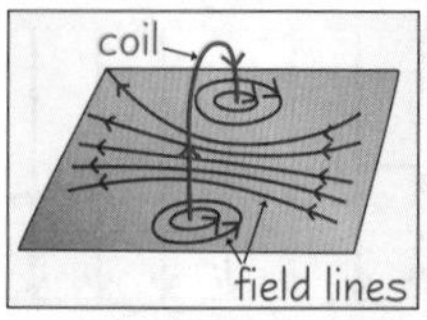

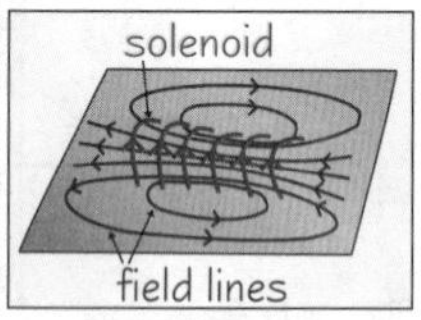

RIGHT-HAND RULE

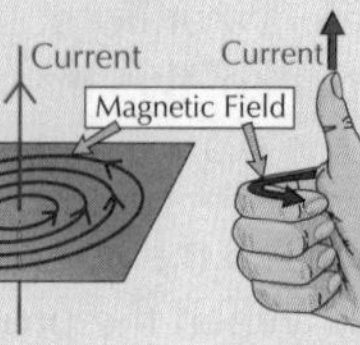

1) Stick your right thumb up, like you're hitching a lift.
2) If your thumb points in the direction of the current...
3) ...your curled fingers point in the direction of the field.

*A **Wire** Carrying a **Current** in a **Magnetic Field** will **Experience** a **Force***

1) If you put a **current-carrying wire** into an **external** magnetic field (e.g. between two magnets), the field around the wire and the field from the magnets **interact**. The field lines from the magnet **contract** to form a **'stretched catapult'** effect where the flux lines are closer together.
2) This causes a **force** on the wire.
3) If the current is **parallel** to the flux lines, **no force** acts.
4) The **direction** of the force is always **perpendicular** to both the **current** direction and the **magnetic field** — it's given by **Fleming's left-hand rule**...

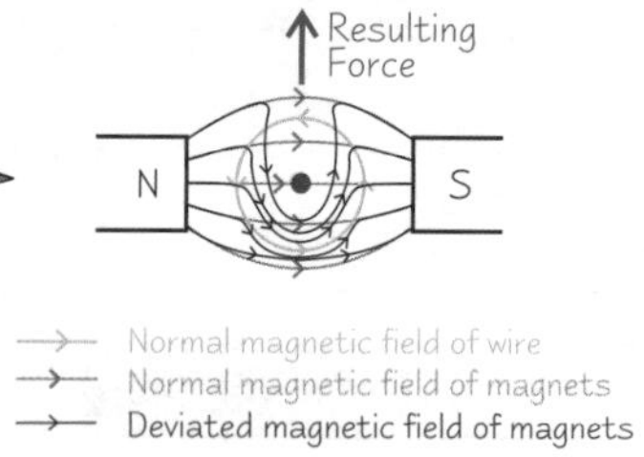

Fleming's Left-Hand Rule

The First finger points in the direction of the uniform magnetic Field, the seCond finger points in the direction of the conventional Current. Then your thuMb points in the direction of the force (in which Motion takes place).

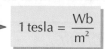

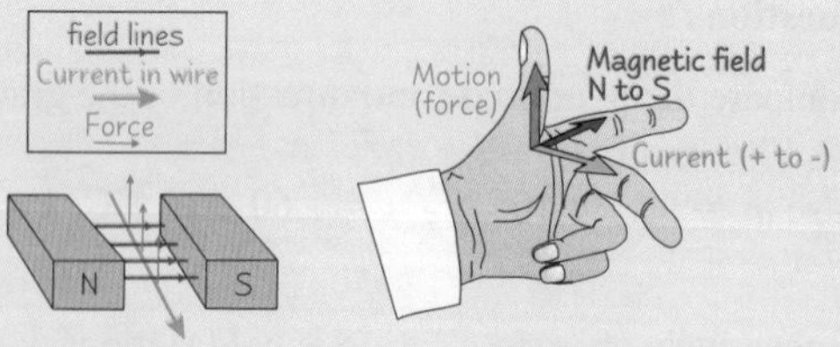

*The **Size** of the **Force** can be **Calculated...***

1) The size of the **force**, F, on a current-carrying wire at right-angles to a magnetic field is proportional to the **current**, I, the **length of wire** in the field, l, and the **strength of the magnetic field**, B. This gives the equation: $F = BIl$
2) In this equation, the **magnetic field strength**, B, is defined as:

The **force** on **one metre** of wire carrying a **current** of **one amp** at **right angles** to the **magnetic field.**

3) **Magnetic field strength** is also called **flux density** and it's measured in **teslas, T**. $1 \text{ tesla} = \frac{\text{Wb}}{\text{m}^2}$
4) Magnetic field strength is a **vector** quantity with both a **direction** and **magnitude**.

It helps to think of flux density as the number of flux lines (measured in webers (Wb), see p. 28) per unit area.

Magnetic Fields

The Force is Greatest when the Wire and Field are Perpendicular...

Edexcel and OCR A

1) The **force** on a current-carrying wire in a magnetic field is caused by the **component** of field strength which is **perpendicular** to the wire, $B \sin\theta$.
2) So, for a wire at an **angle θ** to the field, the **force** acting on the wire is given by:

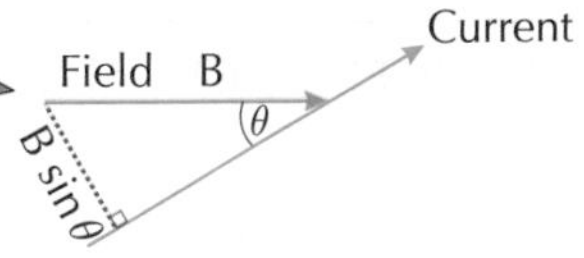

$$F = BIl \sin\theta$$

Examples:

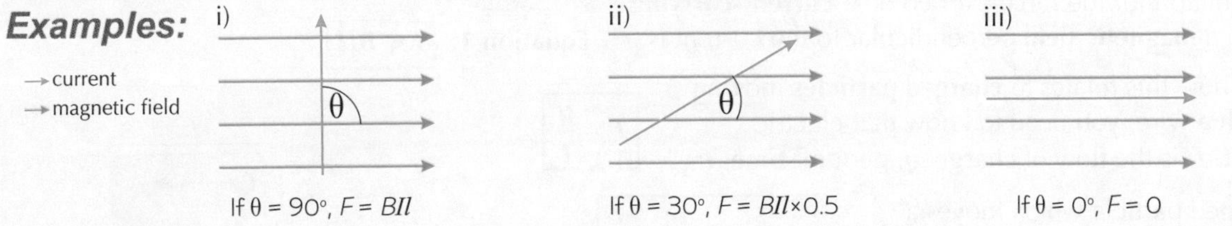

The Forces on a Loop can be Used to Make a Motor

OCR B only

1) If a **current-carrying loop** is placed in a **magnetic field**, the **forces** on the side arms will tend to make the loop **rotate**.
2) By using a **split-ring commutator**, the current in a loop can be **reversed** each time the loop becomes **vertical** (i.e. every **half turn**).
3) This allows the loop to **rotate steadily** — which is otherwise known as a **motor**.

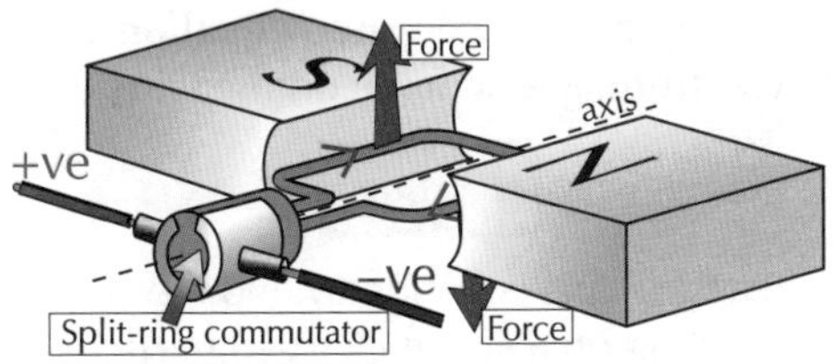

4) This isn't the only way you can use magnetism to make a motor. **Induction motors** operate by altering the magnetic field around a coil of wire that is free to move, which induces a current in the wire, causing it to rotate. Don't worry about it too much for now — the thrills of electromagnetic induction await you on page 28.

Practice Questions

Q1 Describe why a current-carrying wire at right angles to an external magnetic field will experience a force.

Q2 Write down the equation you would use to find the force on a current-carrying wire that is at an angle of 30° to an external uniform field.

Q3 Sketch the magnetic fields around a long straight current-carrying wire and a solenoid. Show the direction of the current and magnetic field on each diagram.

Q4 A copper bar can roll freely on two copper supports, as shown in the diagram. When current is applied in the direction shown, which way will the bar roll?

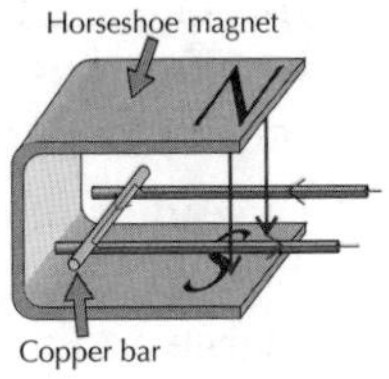

Exam Question

Q1 A 4 cm length of wire carrying a current of 3 A runs perpendicular to a magnetic field of strength 2×10^{-5} T.

(a) Calculate the magnitude of the force on the wire. [2 marks]

(b) If the wire is rotated so that it is at 30° to the field, what would the size of the force be? [2 marks]

I revised the right-hand rule by the A69 and ended up in Newcastle...

Fleming's left-hand rule is the key to this section — so make sure you know how to use it and understand what it all means. Remember that the direction of the magnetic field is from N to S, and that the current is from +ve to −ve — this is as important as using the correct hand. You need to get those right or it'll all go to pot...

Charged Particles in Magnetic Fields

This page is for AQA A Unit 4, Edexcel Unit 4, OCR A Unit 5 and OCR B Unit 5.

Magnetic fields are used a lot when dealing with particle beams — you'll be learning more about their uses in Section 4.

Forces Act on Charged Particles in Magnetic Fields

Electric current in a wire is caused by the **flow** of negatively **charged** electrons. These charged particles are affected by **magnetic fields** — so a current-carrying wire experiences a **force** in a magnetic field (see pages 24–25).

1) The equation for the **force** exerted on a **current-carrying wire** in a **magnetic field** perpendicular to the current is: **Equation 1:** $F = BIl$
2) To see how this relates to **charged particles** moving through a wire, you need to know that electric **current**, I, is the flow of **charge**, q, per unit **time**, t: $I = \frac{q}{t}$
3) A charged particle which moves a **distance** l in **time** t has a **velocity**, v: $v = \frac{l}{t} \Rightarrow t = \frac{l}{v}$
4) So, putting the two equations **together** gives the **current** in terms of the **charge** flowing through the **wire**:

   Equation 2: $I = \frac{qv}{l}$

5) Putting **equation 2** back into **equation 1** gives the **electromagnetic force** on the wire as:

   $F = Bqv$

6) You can use this equation to find the **force** acting on a **single charged particle moving through a magnetic field.**

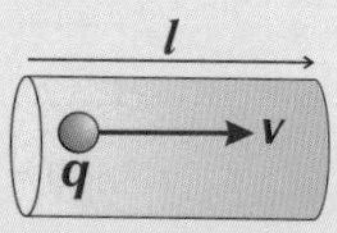

In many exam questions, q is the size of the charge on the electron, which is 1.6×10^{-19} coulombs.

Example

What is the force acting on an electron travelling at 2×10^4 ms^{-1} through a uniform magnetic field of strength 2 T? (The magnitude of the charge on an electron is 1.6×10^{-19} C.)

$F = Bqv$

so, $F = 2 \times 1.6 \times 10^{-19} \times 2 \times 10^4$

so, $F = 6.4 \times 10^{-15}$ N

Edexcel only If you start off with the more general equation for a current-carrying wire at any angle to the magnetic field, $F = BIl \sin\theta$, you just get an extra $\sin\theta$: $F = Bqv \sin\theta$

Charged Particles in a Magnetic Field are Deflected in a Circular Path

1) By **Fleming's left-hand rule** the force on a **moving charge** in a magnetic field is always **perpendicular** to its **direction of travel**.
2) Mathematically, that is the condition for **circular** motion.
3) This effect is used in **particle accelerators** such as **cyclotrons** and **synchrotrons** (see pages 68–69), which use **magnetic fields** to accelerate particles to very **high energies** along circular paths.
4) The **radius of curvature** of the **path** of a charged particle moving through a magnetic field gives you information about the particle's **charge** and **mass** — this means you can **identify different particles** by studying how they're **deflected** (see pages 65–67).

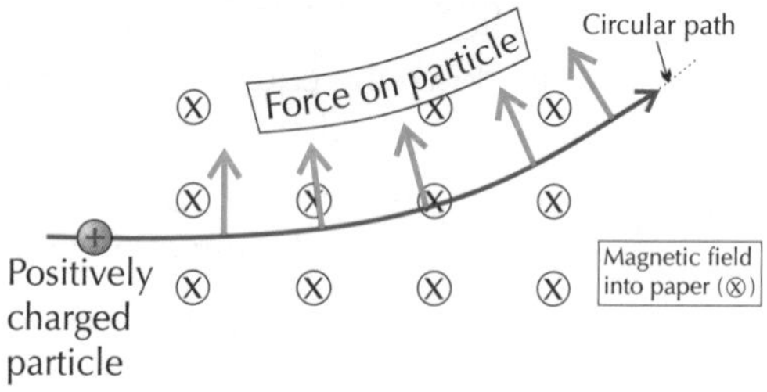

Centripetal Force Tells Us About a Particle's Path

OCR A only

The centripetal force and the electromagnetic force are equivalent for a charged particle travelling along a circular path.

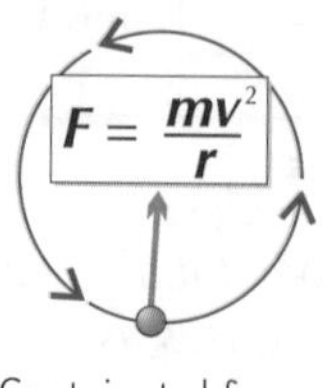

Centripetal force

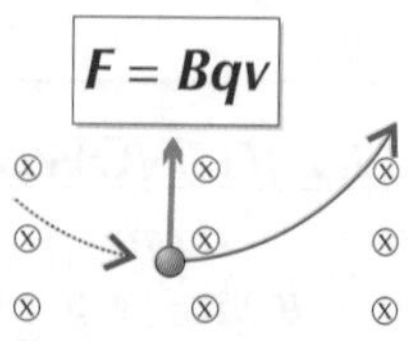

Electromagnetic force

1) For uniform circular motion **Newton's second law** gives: $F = \frac{mv^2}{r}$
2) So, for a **charged particle** following a **circular** path in a **magnetic field** (where $F = Bqv$): $Bqv = \frac{mv^2}{r}$
3) Rearranging gives: $r = \frac{mv}{Bq}$

Where: m is the mass of the particle, v is its speed and r is the radius of the circular path.

Charged Particles in Magnetic Fields

Scientists use Mass Spectrometers to Analyse Samples

1) **Mass spectrometers** are used to **analyse samples** to find out what **chemicals** are present within them and the **relative proportions** of each one.
2) First, the sample is **vaporised** (i.e. turned to gas) and **ionised** before passing along the **spectrometer tube**.
3) The ions travel through **electric** and **magnetic fields** to a **detector**, which is connected to a **computer**.
4) The **identity** of the **ions** reaching the **detector** can be determined from their **mass to charge ratio**.

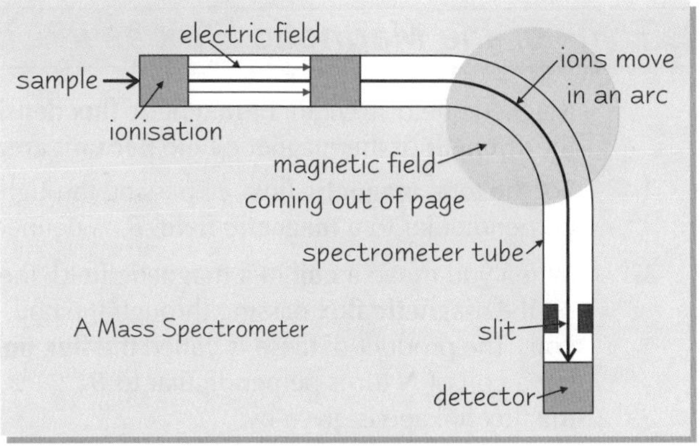

The Electric Field Accelerates the Ions...

1) The **ions** are **charged**, so they experience a **force** as they travel through the **electric field**.
2) This force **accelerates** the ions along the **evacuated spectrometer tube** towards the magnetic field.
3) The **velocity** of the ions depends on the **electric field strength** — **increasing** the **field strength** increases the **force** on the ions, so **increases** their **acceleration** and final **velocity**.

... And the Magnetic Field Deflects the Ions in a Circular Path

The field had deflected the lions onto a circular path.

1) The **magnetic field** deflects the ions in a **circular path** (see the previous page).
2) The **radius** of the path of each **ion** depends on its **mass to charge ratio**, its **velocity** and the strength of the **magnetic field** — see the equation at the bottom of the previous page.
3) The **velocity** of the ions and the **magnetic field strength** can be **controlled** by the user.
4) Only the **ions** moving in an arc of a particular **radius** can pass through the slit into the **detector**.
5) This means that only ions with a particular **mass to charge ratio** reach the detector at any one time.
6) The detector is connected to a **computer**, which **identifies the ions** from their **mass to charge ratio** and the spectrometer settings, and records the **amount** of each ion.

Practice Questions

Q1 Derive the formula for the force on a charged particle in a magnetic field, $F = Bqv$, from $F = BIl$.

Q2 Give two examples of how magnetic fields can be used.

Q3 Outline the role of the electric and magnetic fields in a mass spectrometer.

Exam Questions

Q1 (a) What is the force on an electron travelling at a velocity of 5×10^6 ms^{-1} through a perpendicular magnetic field of 0.77 T? [The charge on an electron is -1.6×10^{-19} C.] [2 marks]

(b) Explain why it follows a circular path while in the field. [1 mark]

Q2 What is the radius of the circular path of an electron with a velocity of 2.3×10^7 ms^{-1} moving perpendicular to a magnetic field of 0.6 mT? [The mass of an electron is 9.11×10^{-31} kg and its charge is -1.6×10^{-19} C.] [3 marks]

Q3 A sample of sodium chloride is analysed using a mass spectrometer. The magnetic field is initially set to 0.20 T and ions of the isotope Cl-35 (mass 35 u) reach the detector. What magnetic field strength would you need for Cl-37 ions (mass 37 u) to reach the detector? Assume that the detector remains in the same place, the electric field remains constant and that both types of ion have the same size charge as an electron. [3 marks]

Hold on to your hats folks — this is starting to get tricky...

Basically, the main thing you need to know here is that both electric and magnetic fields will exert a force on a charged particle. There's even a handy equation to work out the force on a charged particle moving through a magnetic field — it might not impress your friends, but it will impress the examiner, so learn it.

Electromagnetic Induction

These pages are for AQA A Unit 4, Edexcel Unit 4, OCR A Unit 5 and OCR B Unit 5.

Producing electricity by waggling a wire about in a magnetic field sounds like monkey magic — but it's real physics...

Think of the **Magnetic Flux** as the Total **Number** of **Field Lines**...

1) Magnetic field strength, or **magnetic flux density**, ***B***, is a measure of the **strength** of the magnetic field **per unit area**.
2) So, the total **magnetic flux**, ϕ, passing through an **area**, ***A***, perpendicular to a **magnetic field**, ***B***, is defined as:

$$\phi = BA$$

3) When you move a **coil** in a magnetic field, the size of the e.m.f. induced depends on the **magnetic flux** passing through the coil, ϕ, and the **number of turns** on the coil. The product of these is called the **flux linkage**, Φ.
For a coil of ***N*** turns perpendicular to ***B***, the flux linkage is given by:

$$\Phi = N\phi = BAN$$

ϕ is the little Greek letter 'phi', and Φ is a capital 'phi'.

4) The unit of both ϕ and Φ is the **weber**, **Wb**.

A change in flux of one weber per second will induce an electromotive force of 1 volt in a loop of wire.

Jack thought the induction ceremony to get in the rugby club went a bit too far...

Example

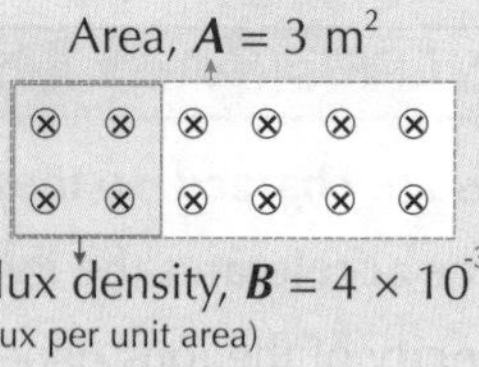

$\phi = BA = 4 \times 10^{-3} \times 3 = 1.2 \times 10^{-2}$ Wb

If this is the magnetic flux inside a solenoid of 10 turns, the flux linkage will be $\Phi = N\phi = 0.12$ Wb

AQA A and OCR A

If the magnetic flux is **not** perpendicular to B, you can find the magnetic flux using this equation:

$$\phi = BA\cos\theta$$

where θ is the angle between the field and the normal to the plane of the wire.

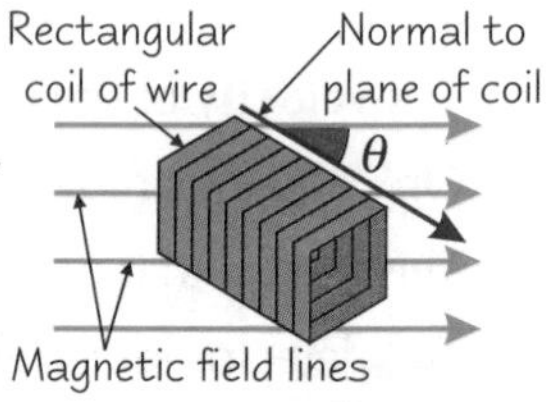

AQA A only

So for a coil with N turns in a uniform magnetic field B, you can find the flux linkage using this equation:

$$\Phi = BAN\cos\theta$$

Example

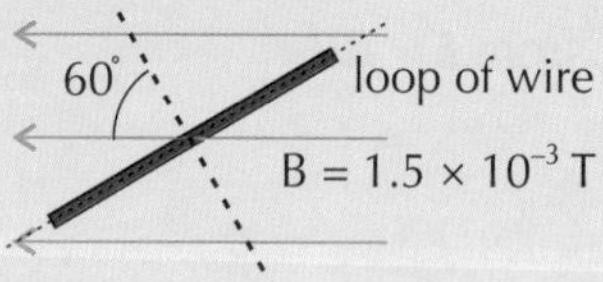

A rectangular coil with 20 turns, each with an area of 0.2 m², is placed in a 1.5×10^{-3} T magnetic field. The angle between the field and the normal of the plane of the coil is 60°. Find the flux linkage in the coil.

$$\Phi = BAN\cos\theta = 1.5\times10^{-3}\times0.2\times20\times\cos60 = 3\times10^{-3}\text{Wb}$$

Charges Accumulate on a **Conductor** Moving Through a **Magnetic Field**

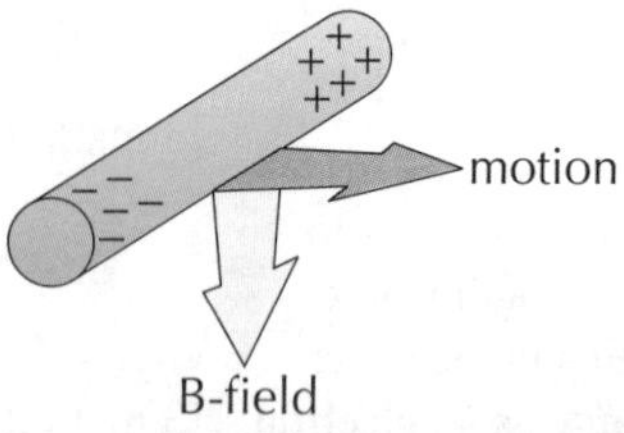

1) If a **conducting rod** moves through a magnetic field its **electrons** will experience a **force** (see p. 24), which means that they will **accumulate** at one end of the rod.
2) This **induces** an **e.m.f.** (**electromotive force**) across the ends of the rod exactly as a **battery** would.
3) If the rod is part of a complete **circuit**, then an induced **current** will **flow** through it — this is called **electromagnetic induction**.
4) An **electromotive force** (**e.m.f.**) is **induced** when there is **relative motion** between a **conductor** and a **magnet**.
5) The **conductor** can **move** and the **magnetic field** stay **still** or the **other way round** — you get an e.m.f. either way.
6) An **e.m.f.** is **produced** whenever **lines of force** (flux) are **cut**.
7) **Flux cutting** always induces e.m.f. but will only **induce** a **current** if the **circuit** is complete.

Electromagnetic Induction

These Results are Summed up by *Faraday's Law...*

FARADAY'S LAW: The **induced e.m.f.** is **directly proportional** to the **rate of change of flux linkage**.

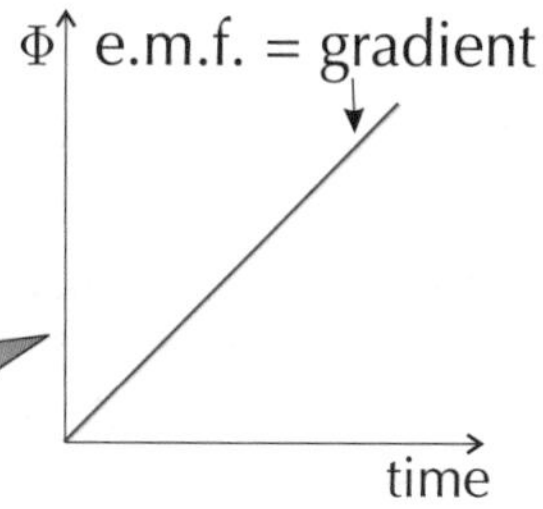

1) **Faraday's law** can be written as:

$$\text{Induced e.m.f.} = \frac{\text{flux change}}{\text{time taken}} = \frac{\Delta\Phi}{\Delta t} = N\frac{\Delta\phi}{\Delta t}$$

2) The **size** of the e.m.f. is shown by the **gradient** of a graph of Φ against time.
3) The **area under** the graph of e.m.f. against time gives the **flux change**.

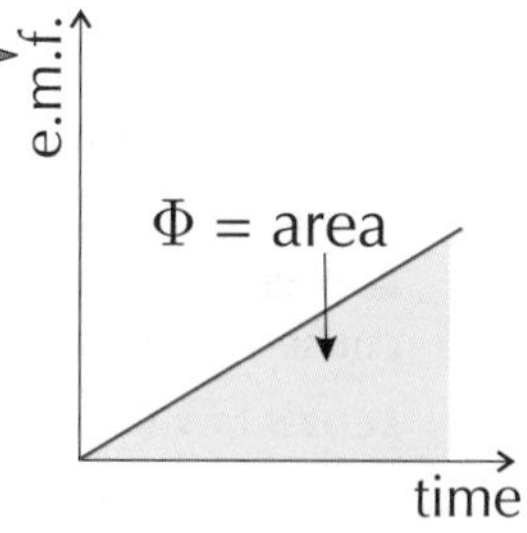

Example

A conducting rod of **length l** moves a **distance x** through a perpendicular magnetic field.

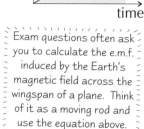

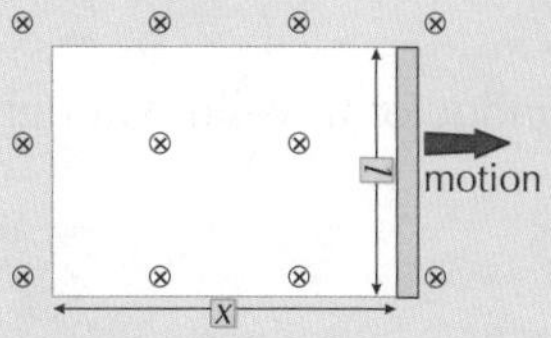

a) What is the flux cut by the rod in terms of l and x?

$\phi = BA = Blx$

b) What is the induced e.m.f. in the rod, in terms of the rod's velocity, v?

$$\text{Induced e.m.f.} = \frac{\text{flux change}}{\text{time taken}} = \frac{Blx}{t} = Blv$$

(since $v = x \div t$)

Exam questions often ask you to calculate the e.m.f. induced by the Earth's magnetic field across the wingspan of a plane. Think of it as a moving rod and use the equation above.

Practice Questions

Q1 What is the difference between magnetic flux density, magnetic flux and magnetic flux linkage?

Q2 State Faraday's law.

Q3 A coil consists of N turns, each of area A. If it is placed at right angles to a uniform magnetic field, what is its flux linkage?

Q4 Explain how you can find the direction of an induced e.m.f. in a copper bar moving at right angles to a magnetic field.

Exam Questions

Q1 A coil of area 0.23 m^2 is placed at right angles to a magnetic field of 2×10^{-3} T.

(a) What is the magnetic flux passing through the coil? [2 marks]

(b) If the coil has 150 turns, what is the magnetic flux linkage in the coil? [2 marks]

(c) Over a period of 2.5 seconds the magnetic field is reduced uniformly to 1.5×10^{-3} T. What is the size of the e.m.f. induced across the ends of the coil? [3 marks]

Q2 A 0.01 m^2 coil of 500 turns is perpendicular to a magnetic field of 0.9 T.

(a) What is the magnetic flux linkage in the coil? [2 marks]

(b) The coil is rotated until the normal to the plane of the coil is at 90° to the direction of the magnetic field. The movement is uniform and takes 0.5 s. Calculate the e.m.f. induced by this movement. [4 marks]

Beware — physics can induce extreme confusion...

OK... I know that might have seemed a bit scary... but the more you go through it, the more it stops being a big scary monster of doom and just becomes another couple of equations you have to remember. Plus it's one of those things that makes you sound well clever... "What did you learn today, Jim?", "Oh, just magnetic flux linkage in solenoids, Mum..."

Electromagnetic Induction

These pages are for AQA A Unit 4, Edexcel Unit 4, OCR A Unit 5 and OCR B Unit 5.

E.m.f. is a bit of a rebel... it always opposes the change that caused it.

The Direction of the Induced E.m.f. and Current are given by Lenz's Law...

LENZ'S LAW: The **induced e.m.f.** is always in such a **direction** as to **oppose** the **change** that caused it.

1) **Lenz's law** and **Faraday's law** can be **combined** to give one formula that works for both:

$$\text{Induced e.m.f.} = -\frac{\Delta\Phi}{\Delta t} = -N\frac{\Delta\phi}{\Delta t}$$

Or as a differential equation (for **Edexcel** and **OCR B**):

$$\text{Induced e.m.f.} = -\frac{d\Phi}{dt} = -\frac{d(N\phi)}{dt}$$

2) The **minus sign** shows the direction of the **induced e.m.f.**
3) The idea that an induced e.m.f. will **oppose** the change that caused it agrees with the principle of the **conservation of energy** — the **energy used** to pull a conductor through a magnetic field, against the **resistance** caused by magnetic **attraction**, is what **produces** the **induced current**.
4) **Lenz's law** can be used to find the **direction** of an **induced e.m.f.** and **current** in a conductor travelling at right angles to a magnetic field...

1) **Lenz's law** says that the **induced e.m.f.** will produce a force that **opposes** the motion of the conductor — in other words a **resistance**.
2) Using **Fleming's left-hand rule** (see p. 24), point your thumb in the direction of the force of **resistance** — which is in the **opposite direction** to the motion of the conductor.
3) Your **second finger** will now give you the direction of the **induced e.m.f.**
4) If the conductor is **connected** as part of a **circuit**, a current will be induced in the **same direction** as the induced e.m.f.

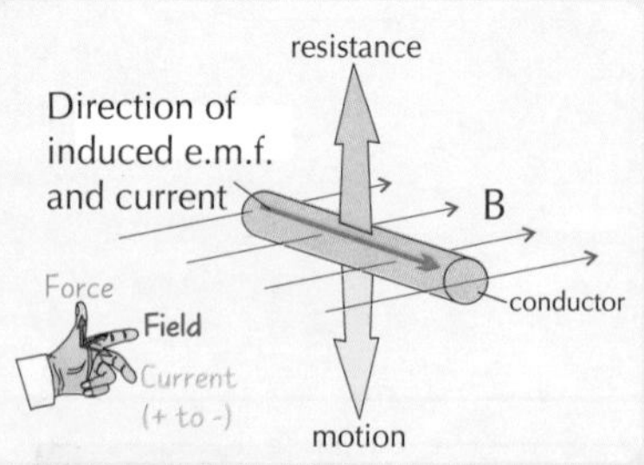

Flux Linkage and Induced Voltage are 90° Out of Phase

AQA A only

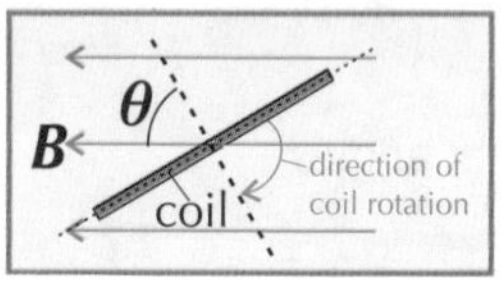

1) The amount of flux cut by the coil (**flux linkage**) is: $\Phi = BAN\cos\theta$ See page 28
(θ is the angle between the normal to the coil and the flux lines)
2) As the coil rotates, θ changes so the **flux linkage** varies **sinusoidally** between $+BAN$ and $-BAN$.
3) How fast θ changes depends on the angular speed, ω, of the coil (see page 8), $\theta = \omega t$. So you can write:

$$\Phi = BAN\cos\omega t$$

4) The **induced e.m.f.**, ε, depends on the **rate of change** of **flux linkage** (Faraday's law), so it also varies **sinusoidally**. The equation for the e.m.f. at time t is:

$$\varepsilon = BAN\omega\sin\omega t$$

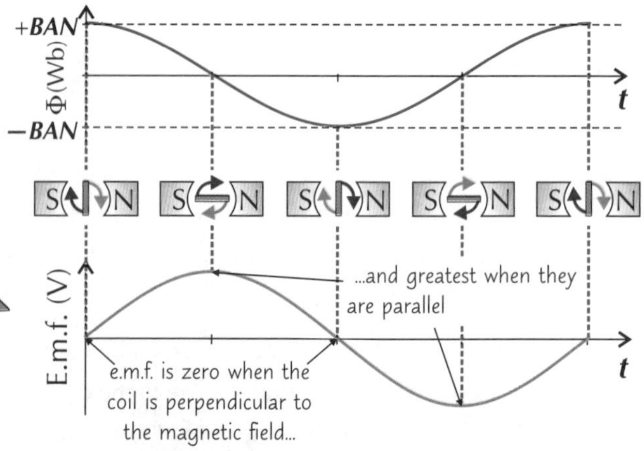

Example

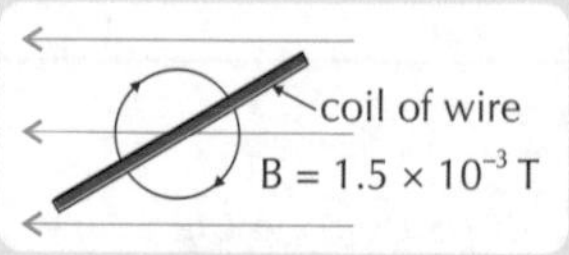

A rectangular coil with 20 turns, each with an area of 0.2 m, is rotated at 20 rad s^{-1} in a uniform 1.5 mT magnetic field. Calculate the maximum e.m.f induced in the coil.

$\varepsilon = BAN\omega\sin\omega t$. So, ε will be greatest when $\sin\omega t = \pm 1$, which gives $\varepsilon = 1.5 \times 10^{-3} \times 0.2 \times 20 \times 20 \times \pm 1 = \pm 0.12$ V

Electromagnetic Induction

You Can Change the Amount of E.m.f. Induced in a Coil

You can change the voltage induced in the coil by changing one (or more) of the following factors:

1) The **angle between the coil and the field** — the more aligned the coil is to the field, the fewer field lines it will cut through, so the smaller the e.m.f. induced.
2) The **number of turns of the coil** — the higher the number of turns, the more points in the coil will cut each flux line, so the higher the e.m.f. induced in the coil.
3) The **area of the coil** — the larger the area of the coil, the more flux lines will pass though it and so the higher the e.m.f. induced.
4) The **magnetic field strength** (**flux density**) — the higher the flux density, the more flux lines there will be per unit area, so the coil will cut more flux, inducing a greater e.m.f.
5) The **angular speed** of the coil — increasing the rate the coil rotates at increases the number of flux lines cut by the coil in a given time, and so increases the voltage induced in the coil.

An Alternator is a Generator of Alternating Current

1) **Generators**, or dynamos, **convert** kinetic energy into **electrical energy** — they **induce** an electric **current** by **rotating** a **coil** in a magnetic field.
2) A simple **alternator** looks similar to a **motor** but with **slip rings** and **brushes** instead of a split-ring commutator.
3) The output **voltage** and **current** change direction with every **half rotation** of the coil, producing **alternating current** (**AC**).

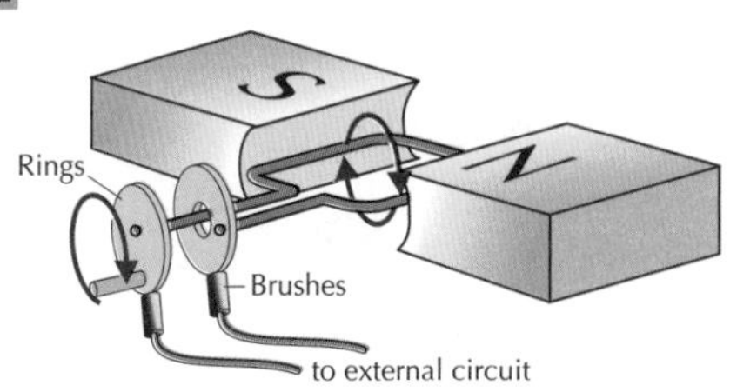

Practice Questions

Q1 State Lenz's law.

Q2 Show that flux linkage and induced voltage are 90° out of phase.

Q3 Give two ways you could increase the e.m.f. induced in a coil of wire moved through a uniform magnetic field.

Exam Questions

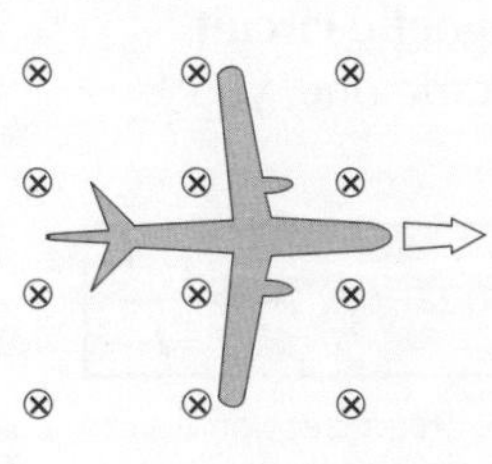

Q1 An aeroplane with a wingspan of 30 m flies at a speed of 100 ms^{-1} perpendicular to the Earth's magnetic field, as shown. The Earth's magnetic field at the aeroplane's location is 60×10^{-6} T.

(a) Calculate the induced e.m.f. between the wing-tips. [2 marks]

(b) Complete the diagram to show the direction of the induced e.m.f. between the wing-tips. [1 mark]

Q2 The graph shows how the flux through a coil varies over time. Sketch a graph to show how the induced e.m.f. in the coil varies over this same time period.

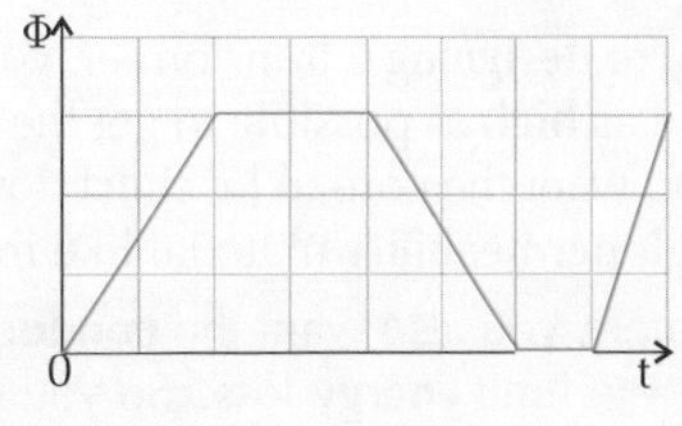

[3 marks]

You're nearly there... I can almost smell the transformer finale...

Make sure you know the difference between flux and flux linkage, and that you can calculate both. Then all you need to learn is that the induced e.m.f. is proportional to minus the rate of change of flux linkage — and that's it. Remember when you're using Fleming's left-hand rule to work out the direction of the induced e.m.f. that you need to point your thumb in the opposite direction to the direction the conductor is moving in...

Transformers

These pages are for AQA A Unit 4, OCR A Unit 5 and OCR B Unit 5.

Transformers are like voltage aerobics instructors. They say step up, the voltage goes up. They say step down, the voltage goes down. They say star jump, and the voltage does nothing because neither of them are alive — it's just induction.

Transformers Work by Electromagnetic Induction

1) **Transformers** are devices that make use of electromagnetic induction to **change** the size of the **voltage** for an **alternating current**. They use the principle of flux linking using two coils of wire.

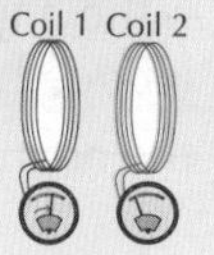

For example, if the **voltage** in **Coil 1** is **increased**, an **e.m.f.** and a **current** will be **induced** in **Coil 2**.

2) An alternating current flowing in the **primary** (or input) **coil** produces **magnetic flux**.
3) The **magnetic field** is passed through the **iron core** to the **secondary** (or output) coil, where it **induces** an alternating **voltage** of the same frequency.
4) From Faraday's law, the **induced** e.m.f.s in both the **primary** and **secondary** coils can be calculated:

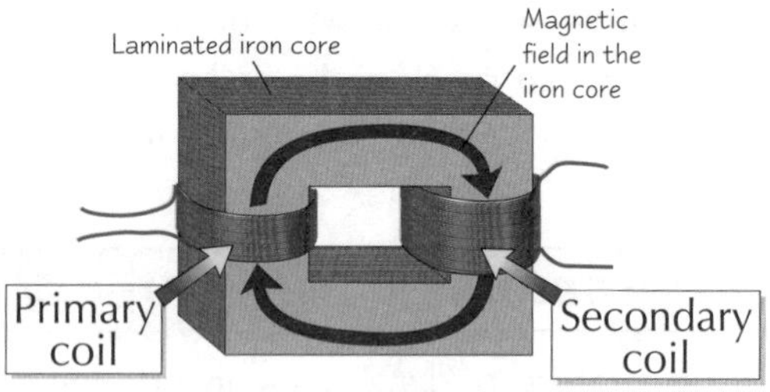

Primary coil: $V_p = N_p \dfrac{d\Phi}{dt}$

Secondary coil: $V_s = N_s \dfrac{d\Phi}{dt}$

These can be combined to give the equation for an **ideal transformer**:

$$\frac{V_p}{V_s} = \frac{N_p}{N_s}$$

(where N is the number of turns in a coil)

5) **Step-up** transformers **increase** the **voltage** by having **more turns** on the **secondary** coil than the primary. **Step-down** transformers **reduce** the voltage by having **fewer** turns on the secondary coil.

Example What is the output voltage for a transformer with a primary coil of 100 turns, a secondary coil of 300 turns and an input voltage of 230 V?

$$\frac{V_p}{V_s} = \frac{N_p}{N_s} \Rightarrow \frac{230}{V_s} = \frac{100}{300} \Rightarrow V_s = \frac{230 \times 300}{100} = 690 \text{ V}$$

Permeability and Conductivity Affect Transformer Dimensions

OCR B only

1) Magnetic flux always forms a **closed loop**, so you can think of a magnetic field as a **magnetic circuit** (although nothing actually flows anywhere). Comparing a magnetic circuit with an electric one, you can think of the **magnetic flux** as the 'current' and the **permeance** as the 'conductance'.
2) The **permeance** of a material is the **amount of flux induced** in it for a given number of current turns that surround it. The **higher** the **permeance** of a material, the **greater** the **amount of flux** induced.
3) Both permeance and conductance are **inversely proportional** to the **length** of the material, and **proportional** to the **cross-sectional area**.

$$\text{permeance, } \Lambda = \frac{\mu A}{L}$$

Where A is the cross-sectional area, L is the length and μ is the permeability of the material.

4) When you're **designing** a transformer, you want to make the **permeance** of the core as **high** as possible to get the maximum flux induced in it. Ideally you want the core to be **short** (**low L**) and **fat** (**high A**) and made from a **high permeability** material like **iron**.

The permeability of a material, μ, is the permeance per unit cross-section of a unit length of material.

5) Unfortunately, you also want the **conductance** of the **copper coils** used on a transformer to be as **high** as possible — to limit **energy loss**. So you want to make the right **number of turns** with the **shortest** piece of wire possible, i.e. use small-radius (tight) coils. This doesn't really work when you have a fat core to wrap them around, so you have to try to get a **balance** in **dimensions** to get the **best** overall transformer performance.
6) Unlike an electric circuit, a magnetic circuit will still work if there's an **air** (or vacuum) **gap** in it. So in the case of transformers, if there's an air gap in an otherwise iron core, magnetic flux stills 'flows' around the circuit. But because air has a very **low permeability** compared to iron, the amount of flux in the circuit would be **dramatically lower** than without the air gap.

Transformers

Transformers are **Not 100% Efficient**

1) If a transformer was **100% efficient** the **power in** would **equal** the **power out**.
2) This means that for an **ideal transformer**: $V_pI_p = V_sI_s$ or $\frac{V_p}{V_s} = \frac{I_s}{I_p}$
3) However, in practice there will be **small losses** of **power** from the transformer, mostly in the form of **heat**.
4) **Heat** can be produced by **eddy currents** in the transformer's iron core — currents **induced** by the changing magnetic flux in the core. This effect is reduced by **laminating** the core with layers of **insulation**.
5) Heat is also generated by **resistance** in the coils — to minimise this, **thick copper wire** is used, which has a **low resistance**.

You can put the two ideal transformer equations together to give:

$$\frac{V_p}{V_s} = \frac{N_p}{N_s} = \frac{I_s}{I_p}$$

*AQA A **only***

The **efficiency** of a transformer is simply the **ratio** of **power out** to **power in**, so:

$$\text{efficiency} = \frac{V_sI_s}{V_pI_p}$$

Transformers are an **Important** Part of the **National Grid**...

1) **Electricity** from power stations is sent round the country in the **National Grid** at the **lowest** possible current, because **losses** due to the **resistance** in the cables are proportional to I^2 — so if you double the transmitted current, you quadruple the power lost.
2) Since **power** = **current** × **voltage**, a **low current** means a **high voltage**.
3) **Transformers** allow us to **step up** the voltage to around **400 000 V** for **transmission** through the national grid, and then **reduce** it again to **230 V** for domestic use.

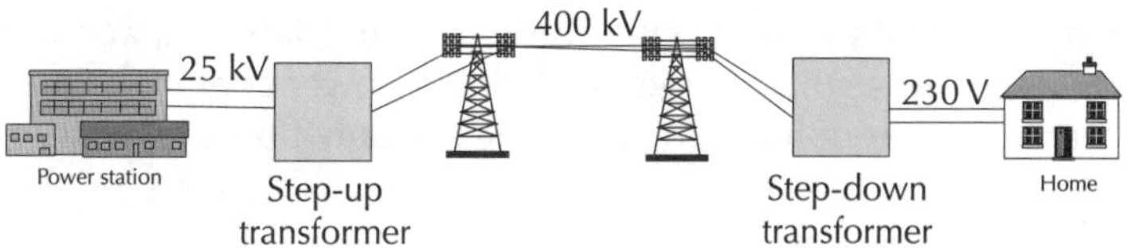

... robots in disguise

Practice Questions

Q1 Draw a diagram of a simple transformer. What is meant by a step-down transformer?

Q2 Describe how you could minimise heat loss in a transformer core due to eddy currents.

Q3 What is meant by the permeance of a material? Describe what considerations you need to take into account when designing the shape of a transformer.

Exam Questions

Q1 A transformer with 150 turns in the primary coil has an input voltage of 9 V.

(a) How many turns are needed in the secondary coil to step up the voltage to 45 V? [2 marks]

(b) The input current for the transformer is 1.5 A. If the transformer is ideal, what is the output current? [2 marks]

(c) What is the efficiency of the transformer if the power output is measured as 10.8 W? [2 marks]

Q2 Using Lenz's law, explain why eddy currents are set up in real transformers, and why they alter the flux in the transformer core.
(Marks will be given for the quality of your written communication.) [4 marks]

Arrrrrrrrggggggghhhhhhh...

Breathe a sigh of relief, pat yourself on the back and make a brew — well done, you've reached the end of Section Two. That was pretty nasty stuff, but don't let all of those equations get you down — once you've learnt the main ones and can use them blindfolded, even the trickiest-looking exam question will be a walk in the park...

Capacitors

These pages are for AQA A Unit 4, Edexcel Unit 4, OCR A Unit 5 and OCR B Unit 4.

Capacitors are things that store electrical charge — like a charge bucket. The capacitance of one of these things tells you how much charge the bucket can hold. Sounds simple enough... ha... ha, ha, ha...

Capacitance is Defined as the Amount of Charge Stored per Volt

$$C = \frac{Q}{V}$$

where Q is the **charge** in coulombs, V is the **potential difference** in volts and C is the **capacitance** in **farads (F) — 1 farad = 1 C V^{-1}**.

A farad is a **huge** unit so you'll usually see capacitances expressed in terms of:

μF — microfarads (× 10^{-6})
nF — nanofarads (× 10^{-9})
pF — picofarads (× 10^{-12})

Capacitors are used in Flash Photography and Nuclear Fusion

Capacitors are found in loads of **electronic devices** — they're useful because they **store** up electric charge for use when you want it. What's more, the **amount of charge** that can be stored and the **rate** at which it's **released** can be controlled by the type of capacitor chosen — for example:

1) **Flash photography** — when you take a picture, charge stored in a **capacitor** flows through a tube of xenon gas which emits a **bright light**. In order to give a **brief flash** of bright light, the capacitor has to discharge really quickly to give a **short pulse** of high current.
2) **Nuclear fusion** — an enormous amount of **energy** is needed to start a nuclear fusion reaction (see page 57) — one way to deliver this is using **lasers** controlled by **capacitors**. Capacitors that release a huge amount of charge in a tiny fraction of a second are used to **maximise** the amount of energy in each pulse of laser-light.
3) **Back-up power supplies** — **computers** are often connected to back-up power supplies to make sure that you don't lose any data if there's a **power cut**. These often use **large capacitors** that store charge while the power is on then release that charge slowly if the power goes off. The capacitors are designed to discharge over a number of hours, maintaining a **steady flow** of charge.

You can Investigate the Charge Stored by a Capacitor Experimentally

Investigating the Charge Stored on a Capacitor

1) Set up a **test circuit** to measure current and potential difference:

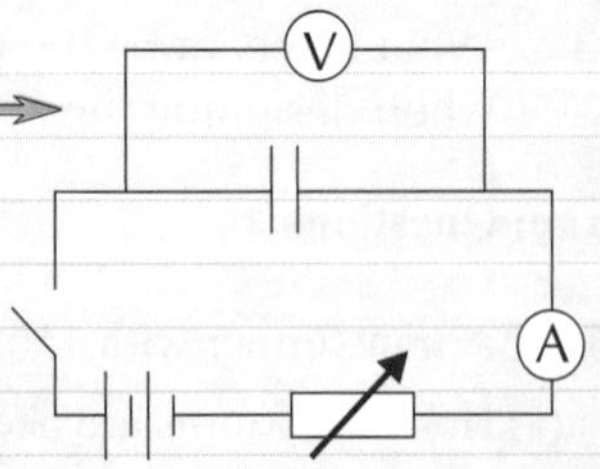

2) Constantly adjust the **variable resistor** to keep the charging current **constant** for as long as you can (it's impossible when the capacitor is nearly fully charged).
3) Record the p.d. at regular intervals until it **equals** the **battery p.d.**
4) From these results, you can plot the following graphs:

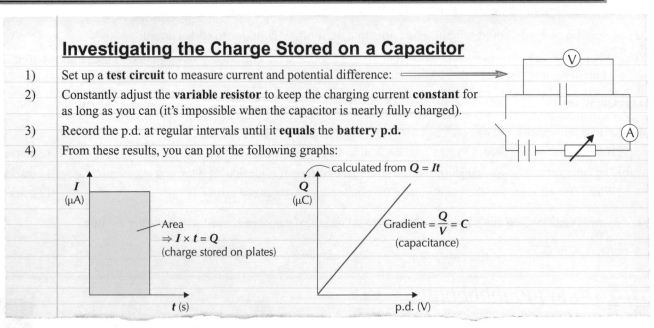

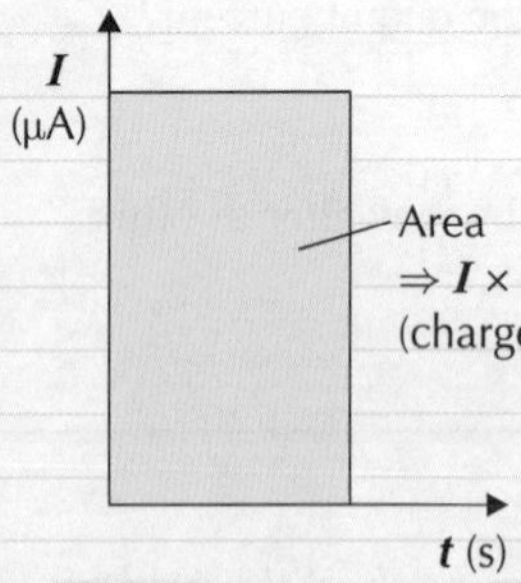

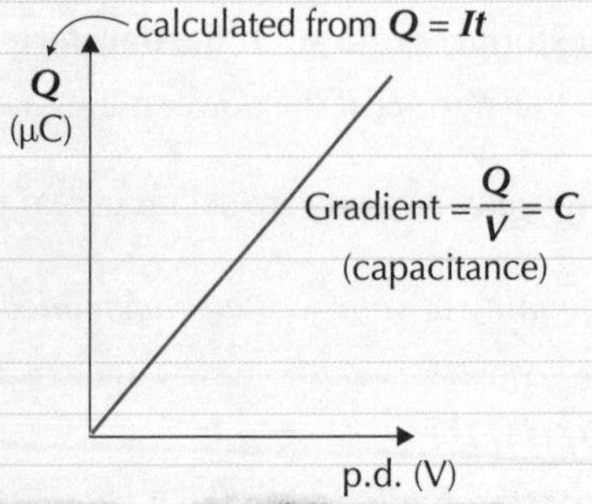

Capacitors

Capacitors in Parallel

*OCR A **only***

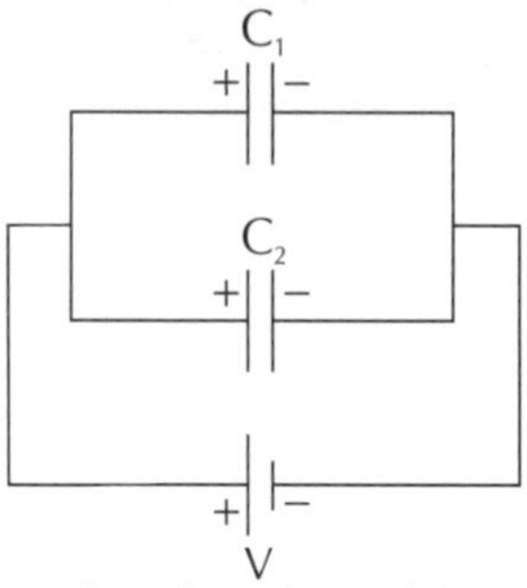

Capacitors in parallel

1) Adding **capacitors** in **parallel** is like **adding resistors** in **series**.
2) In a **parallel circuit**, the **p.d.** across each component is the **same**.
3) So the **charge** stored on **each** capacitor is: $Q = CV$
4) And the **total charge** stored is: $Q_{total} = Q_1 + Q_2 = C_1V + C_2V$

Total capacitance of capacitors in **parallel** — just **add them up**: $C_{total} = C_1 + C_2$

Capacitors in Series

*OCR A **only***

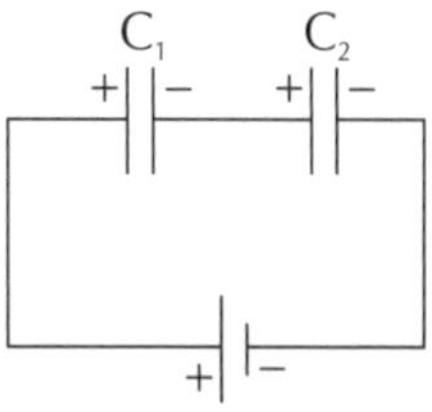

Capacitors in series

1) Connecting **capacitors** in **series** is like adding **resistors** in **parallel**.
2) When capacitors are connected in series, their **combined capacitance decreases**.

$$\frac{1}{C_{total}} = \frac{1}{C_1} + \frac{1}{C_2}$$

Capacitors Store Energy

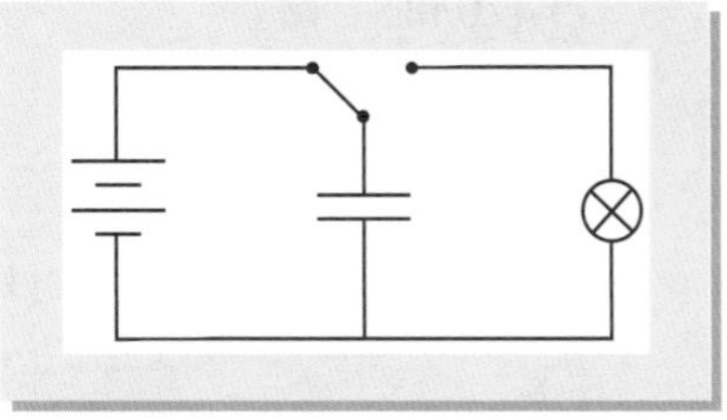

1) In this circuit, when the switch is flicked to the **left**, **charge** builds up on the plates of the **capacitor**. **Electrical energy**, provided by the battery, is **stored** by the capacitor.
2) If the switch is flicked to the **right**, the energy stored on the plates will **discharge** through the **bulb**, converting electrical energy into light and heat.
3) **Work** is done **removing charge** from **one plate** and depositing **charge** onto the other one. The energy for this must come from the **electrical energy** of the **battery**, and is given by **charge × p.d.**
4) You can find the **energy stored** in a capacitor from the **area** under a **graph** of **potential difference** against **charge stored** on the capacitor.

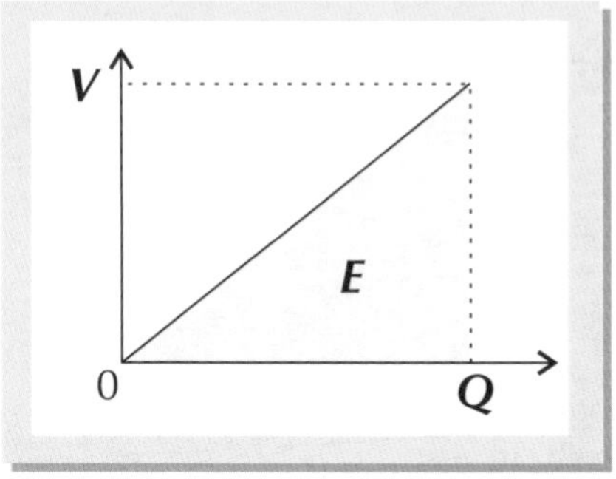

The p.d. across the capacitor is **proportional** to the charge stored on it (see p. 34), so the graph will be a **straight line** through the origin. The **energy stored** is given by the **yellow triangle**.

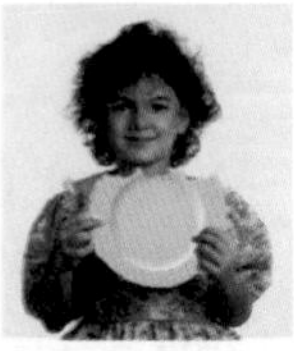
Jane had heard there was energy stored on plates.

5) **Area of triangle = ½ × base × height**, so the energy stored by the capacitor is: $E = \frac{1}{2}QV$

You need to remember where this equation comes from.

Capacitors

There are **Three** Expressions for the **Energy Stored** by a Capacitor

1) You know the first one already: $E = \frac{1}{2}QV$

2) $C = \frac{Q}{V}$, so $Q = CV$. Substitute that into the energy equation: $E = \frac{1}{2}CV \times V$. So: $E = \frac{1}{2}CV^2$

3) $V = \frac{Q}{C}$, so $E = \frac{1}{2}Q \times \frac{Q}{C}$. Simplify: $E = \frac{Q^2}{2C}$

Example *A 900 μF capacitor is charged up to a potential difference of 240 V. Calculate the energy stored by the capacitor.*

First, choose the best equation to use — you've been given **V** and **C**, so you need $E = \frac{1}{2}CV^2$.

Substitute the values in: $E = \frac{1}{2} \times 9 \times 10^{-4} \times 240^2 = 25.92$ J

Practice Questions

Q1 Define capacitance.

Q2 What is the relationship between charge, voltage and capacitance?

Q3 Write the following in standard form: a) 220 μF b) 1000 pF c) 470 nF.

Exam Questions

Q1 Capacitors are found in many electronic devices, including cameras.

(a) Outline how capacitors are used in cameras. [1 mark]

(b) Explain why a capacitor is a suitable component for this use. [2 marks]

Q2 From the graphs below, calculate the capacitance of the capacitor and the charge stored on its plates.

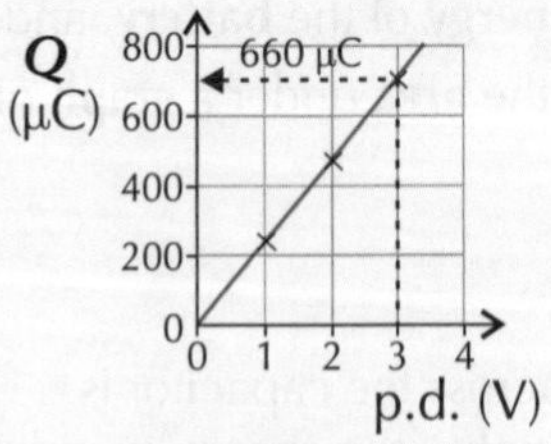

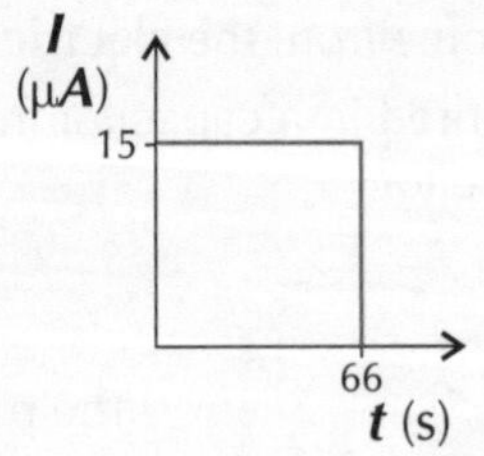

[4 marks]

Q3 A 500 mF capacitor is fully charged up from a 12 V supply.

(a) Calculate the total energy stored by the capacitor. [2 marks]

(b) Calculate the charge stored by the capacitor. [2 marks]

Q4 Explain why a circuit with two 470 mF capacitors in parallel would store more charge than a circuit with two 470 mF capacitors in series, when the same voltage is applied to both circuits.
(Marks will be awarded for the quality of your written communication.) [4 marks]

Capacitance — fun, it's not...

Capacitors are really useful in the real world. Pick an appliance, any appliance, and it'll probably have a capacitor or several. If I'm being honest though, the only saving grace of these pages for me is that they're not especially hard...

Charging and Discharging

These pages are for AQA A Unit 4, Edexcel Unit 4, OCR A Unit 5 and OCR B Unit 4.

Charging and discharging — sounds painful...

You can Charge a Capacitor by Connecting it to a Battery

1) When a capacitor is connected to a **battery**, a **current** flows in the circuit until the capacitor is **fully charged**, then **stops**.
2) The electrons flow onto the plate connected to the **negative terminal** of the battery, so a **negative charge** builds up.
3) This build-up of negative charge **repels** electrons off the plate connected to the **positive terminal** of the battery, making that plate positive. These electrons are attracted to the positive terminal of the battery.

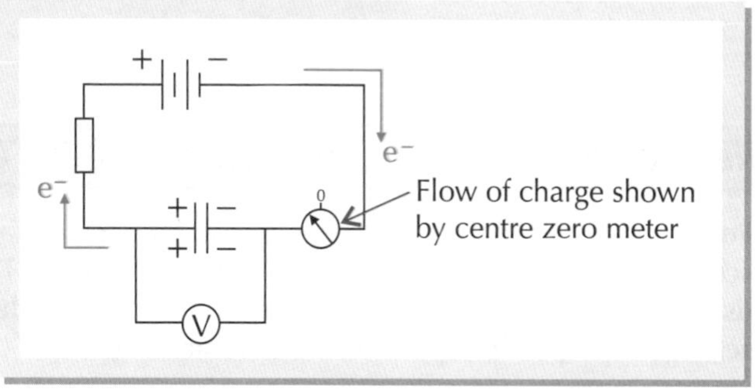

4) An **equal** but **opposite** charge builds up on each plate, causing a **potential difference** between the plates. Remember that **no charge** can flow **between** the plates because they're **separated** by an **insulator** (dielectric).
5) Initially the **current** through the circuit is **high**. But, as **charge** builds up on the plates, **electrostatic repulsion** makes it **harder** and **harder** for more electrons to be deposited. When the p.d. across the **capacitor** is equal to the p.d. across the **battery**, the **current** falls to **zero**. The capacitor is **fully charged**.

an equal but opposite charge

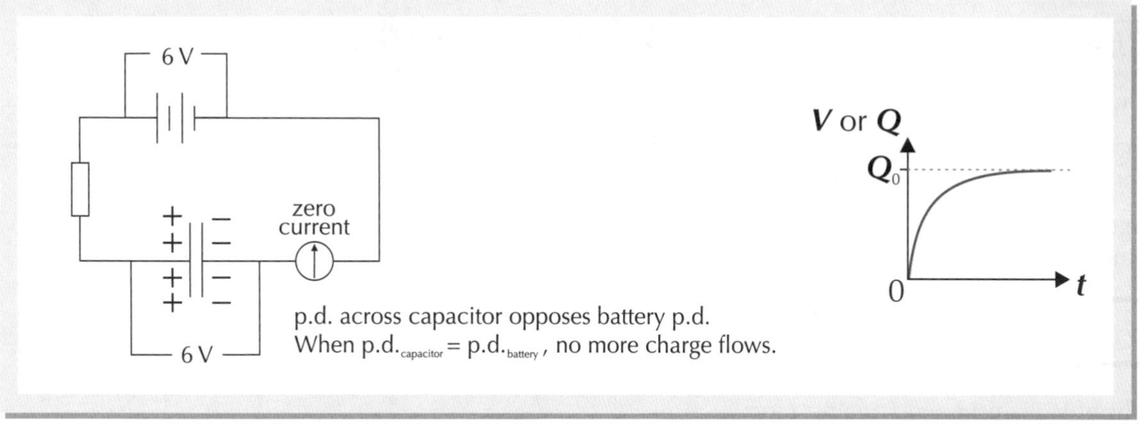

To Discharge a Capacitor, Take Out the Battery and Reconnect the Circuit

1) When a **charged capacitor** is connected across a **resistor**, the p.d. drives a **current** through the circuit.
2) This current flows in the **opposite direction** from the **charging current**.
3) The capacitor is **fully discharged** when the **p.d.** across the plates and the **current** in the circuit are both **zero**.

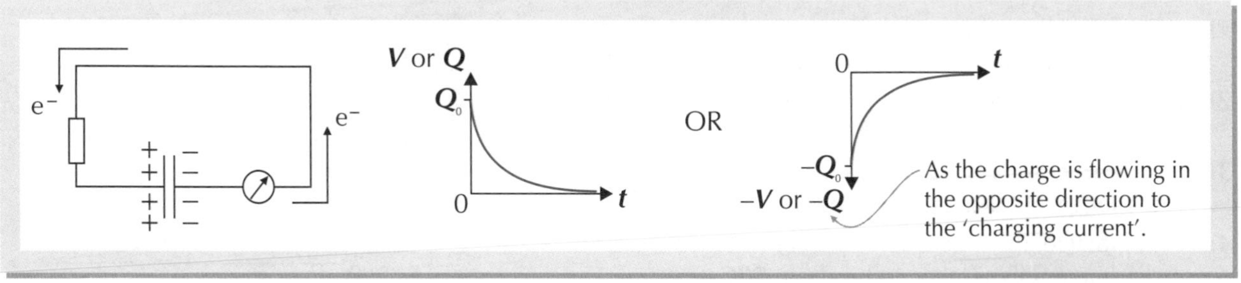

Charging and Discharging

The Time Taken to Charge or Discharge Depends on Two Factors

The **time** it takes to charge up or discharge a capacitor depends on:

1) The **capacitance** of the capacitor (**C**). This affects the amount of **charge** that can be transferred at a given **voltage**.
2) The **resistance** of the circuit (**R**). This affects the **current** in the circuit.

Discharge Rate is Proportional to the Charge Remaining

OCR B only

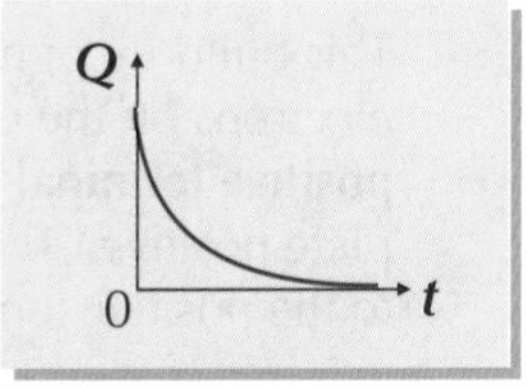

If you measure the amount of **charge remaining** on the plates of a capacitor while it is **discharging**, you'll get a **graph** like the one on the **right**. The amount of charge **initially falls quickly**, but the rate **slows** as the amount of **charge decreases** — the **rate of discharge** is **proportional** to the **charge remaining**.

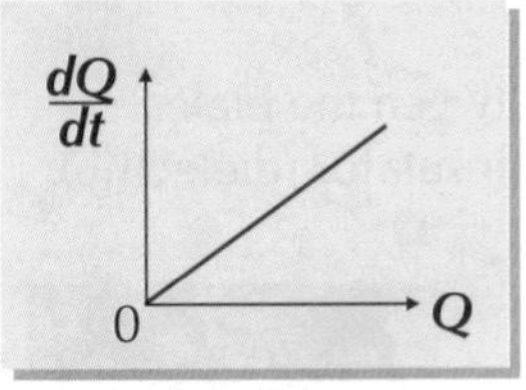

You can show this **relationship** by drawing a **graph** of the rate of discharge (***dQ/dt***) against the charge remaining (***Q***) — you get a lovely straight line through the origin (see left).

It also means that you can write an **equation** for the **rate of discharge** of a capacitor:

The solution of this equation is the exponential equation given below.

$$\frac{dQ}{dt} = -\frac{Q}{RC}$$

where ***Q*** is the **charge remaining** (C), ***R*** is the **resistance** of the circuit (Ω) and ***C*** is the **capacitance** of the capacitor (F).

The Charge on a Capacitor Decreases Exponentially

1) When a capacitor is **discharging**, the amount of **charge** left on the plates falls **exponentially with time**.
2) That means it always takes the **same length of time** for the charge to **halve**, no matter **how much charge** you start with — like radioactive decay (see p. 48).

The charge left on the plates of a capacitor discharging from full is given by the equation:

$$Q = Q_0 e^{-\frac{t}{RC}}$$

where Q_0 is the charge of the capacitor when it's fully charged.

The graphs of ***V*** against ***t*** and ***I*** against ***t*** for charging and discharging are also exponential.

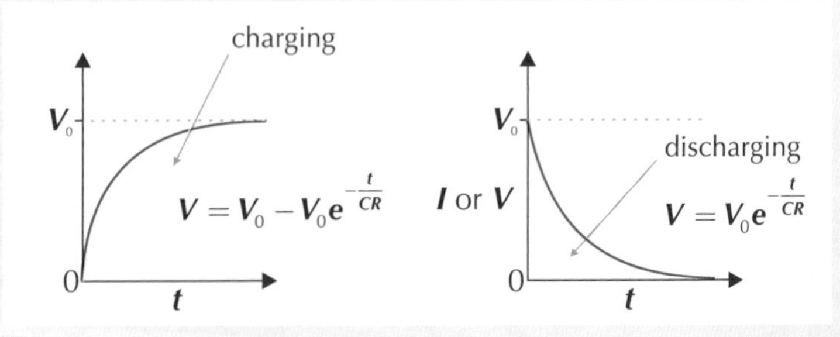

Time Constant τ = RC

τ is the Greek letter 'tau'

If $t = \tau = RC$ is put into the equation above, then $Q = Q_0 e^{-1}$. So when $t = \tau$: $\frac{Q}{Q_0} = \frac{1}{e}$, where $\frac{1}{e} \approx \frac{1}{2.718} \approx 0.37$.

1) So τ, the **time constant**, is the time taken for the charge on a discharging capacitor (Q) to **fall** to **37%** of Q_0.
2) It's also the time taken for the charge of a charging capacitor to **rise** to **63%** of Q_0.
3) The **larger** the **resistance** in series with the capacitor, the **longer it takes** to charge or discharge.
4) In practice, the time taken for a capacitor to charge or discharge **fully** is taken to be about 5***RC***.

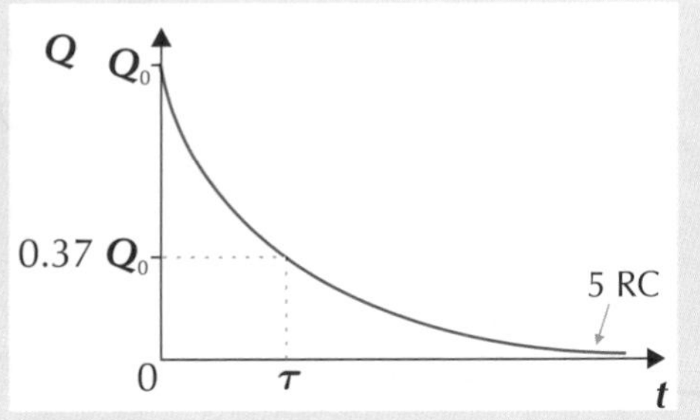

Charging and Discharging

You Can Solve Differential Equations Using Iterative Methods

OCR B only

1) A differential equation shows how the **rate of change of a quantity** depends on the **value** of the quantity itself.
2) $\frac{dQ}{dt} = -\frac{Q}{RC}$ is a **differential equation** — the **rate charge leaves** the plates is **proportional** to the **charge** left.
3) Scientists often use **iterative methods** to solve differential equations. Iterative methods work for **every type** of differential equation and are easy to do with a **computer**. However, the answers are only **approximate**.

You can solve differential equations using graphical methods too — see page 51 for an example.

An iterative method for solving $\frac{dQ}{dt} = -\frac{Q}{RC}$:

1) Start with the **initial value of *Q*** (or use the value you have worked out in step 5).
2) **Substitute** the value of ***Q*** into the equation to work out the value of ***dQ/dt***.
3) Increase the **time** by a small **interval** (the smaller the interval, the more accurate your answer).
4) Estimate the **change in *Q*** over this time interval by multiplying ***dQ/dt*** by the time interval.
5) Find the value of ***Q* after** the time interval by **adding the change** to the old value of ***Q***, then go back to step 1 and **repeat the process** until you get to the time that you want.

Example A 150 μF capacitor is charged until it stores 1.8 C of charge, then discharged through a resistance of 40 kΩ. Use an iterative method to find the charge remaining on the capacitor after 0.4 s of discharging. Use a time interval of 0.2 s for each iteration.

A table is useful for answering this type of question — start by filling in the time column and the first value of ***Q***. Then divide **−*Q*** by ***RC*** to find the first value of ***dQ/dt*** and add this to the table. Next, multiply ***dQ/dt*** by the time interval (0.2 s), to find **Δ*Q***. Add **Δ*Q*** to the initial value of ***Q*** to find the value of ***Q*** after the time interval. Copy the new value of ***Q*** into the next row and repeat the process to complete the rest of the row. You now have a value for ***Q*** after the time the question asks for (0.4 s) — so the answer is **1.682 C**.

$\frac{-1.8}{40 \times 10^3 \times 150 \times 10^{-6}}$ -0.3×0.2 $1.8 + (-0.06)$

Time (s)	Q (C)	dQ/dt (Cs^{-1})	ΔQ (C)	Q (C)
0	1.8	−0.3	−0.06	1.74
0.2	1.74	−0.29	−0.058	1.682
0.4	1.682			

Practice Questions

Q1 Sketch graphs to show the variation of p.d. across the plates of a capacitor with time for:
a) charging a capacitor, b) discharging a capacitor.

Q2 What two factors affect the rate of charge of a capacitor?

Exam Questions

Q1 A 250 μF capacitor is fully charged from a 6 V battery and then discharged through a 1 kΩ resistor.
(a) Calculate the time taken for the charge on the capacitor to fall to 37% of its original value. [2 marks]
(b) Calculate the percentage of the total charge remaining on the capacitor after 0.7s. [3 marks]
(c) If the charging voltage is increased to 12 V, what effect will this have on:
i) the total charge stored, ii) the capacitance of the capacitor, iii) the time taken to fully charge? [3 marks]

Q2 A 10 μF capacitor is discharged through a resistance of 200 kΩ. The capacitor initially stores 5.0×10^{-2} C.
Complete the table below to work out the charge after 2.0 s. Use a time interval of 0.5 s for each iteration. [5 marks]

Time (s)	Charge (C)	dQ/dt (Cs^{-1})	ΔQ (C)	New Charge (C)

An analogy — consider the lowly bike pump...

One way to think of the charging process is like pumping air into a bike tyre. To start with, the air goes in easily, but as the tyre pressure increases, it gets harder and harder to squeeze more air in. The analogy works just as well for discharging...

Scattering to Determine Structure

This page is for AQA A Unit 5, Edexcel Unit 4, OCR A Unit 5 and OCR B Unit 5.

By firing radiation at different materials, you can take a sneaky beaky at their internal structures...

Alpha Particle Scattering Lets Us See Inside the Atom

1) If a beam of **positively charged alpha particles** is directed at a thin gold film, most **pass straight through**. However, if an alpha particle is travelling straight towards, or close by, a nucleus, its path will be **deflected**.
2) **Experimental evidence** shows that some of these alpha particles are deflected by **more than 90°** — in other words they '**bounce**' back.

Rutherford Scattering

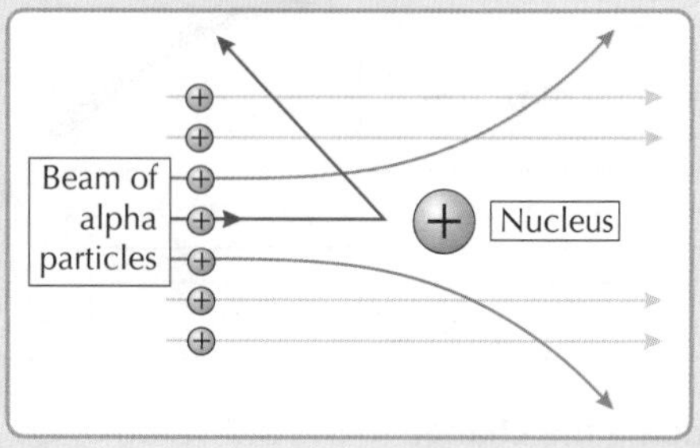

3) This evidence means that inside the atoms there must be **small positively charged nuclei**, which **repel** the passing alpha particles.
4) The nucleus must be **small** since very few alpha particles are deflected by much.
5) It must be **positive** to repel the positively charged alpha particles.

You can Estimate the Closest Approach of a Scattered Particle

1) When you fire an alpha particle at a gold nucleus, you know its **initial kinetic energy**.
2) An alpha particle that 'bounces back' and is deflected through 180° will have stopped a short distance from the nucleus. It does this at the point where its **electrical potential energy** (see p. 21) **equals** its **initial kinetic energy**.

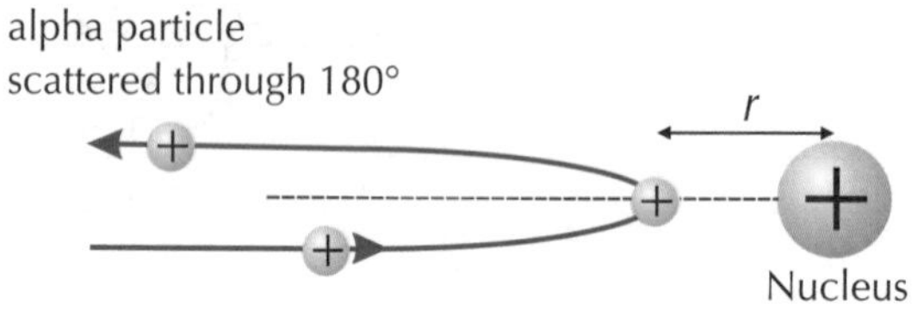

$$\text{Initial K.E.} = E_{elec} = \frac{Q_{gold}q_{alpha}}{4\pi\varepsilon_0 r}$$

ε_0 is the permittivity of free space

3) It's just conservation of energy — and you can use it to find how close the particle can get to the nucleus.
4) To find the charge of a nucleus you need to know the atom's **proton number, Z** — that tells you how many protons are in the nucleus (surprisingly).
A proton has a charge of **+e** (where e is the charge on an electron), so the charge of a nucleus must be **+Ze**.

Example An alpha particle with an initial kinetic energy of 6 MeV (see p.68) is fired at a gold nucleus. Find the closest approach of the alpha particle to the nucleus.

Initial particle energy $= 6\text{ MeV} = 6\times10^6\text{ eV}$

Convert energy into joules: $6\times10^6\times1.6\times10^{-19} = 9.6\times10^{-13}\text{ J}$

So, electrical potential energy $= E_{elec} = \dfrac{Q_{gold}q_{alpha}}{4\pi\varepsilon_0 r} = 9.6\times10^{-13}\text{ J}$ at closest approach.

Rearrange to get $r = \dfrac{(+79e)(+2e)}{4\pi\varepsilon_0(9.6\times10^{-13})}$

$$= \frac{2\times79\times(1.6\times10^{-19})^2}{4\pi\times8.9\times10^{-12}\times9.6\times10^{-13}} = \mathbf{3.8\times10^{-14}\ m}$$

Scattering to Determine Structure

This page is for AQA A only.

You can also use **Electron Diffraction** to **Estimate Nuclear Diameter**

1) **Electrons** are a type of particle called a **lepton**. Leptons **don't interact** with the **strong nuclear force** (see p. 44) (whereas neutrons and alpha particles do). Because of this, electron diffraction is the **most accurate** method for getting a picture of a crystal's **atomic structure**.
2) Like other particles, electrons show **wave-particle duality** (see p. 132) — so **electron beams** can be diffracted.
3) A beam of moving electrons has an associated **de Broglie wavelength**, λ, which at high speeds (where you have to take into account relativistic effects (see p. 134)) is approximately: $\lambda \simeq \frac{hc}{E}$
(***h*** is Planck's constant, which is 6.6×10^{-34} Js^{-1})
4) If a beam of **high-energy electrons** is directed onto a thin film of material in front of a screen, a **diffraction pattern** will be seen on the screen.
5) As with light diffraction patterns, the first minimum appears where:

$$\sin\theta \simeq \frac{1.22\lambda}{d}$$

d is the diameter of the nucleus it has been scattered by.

6) Using measurements from this diffraction pattern, the **size and spacing** of the material's atomic **nuclei** can be worked out.

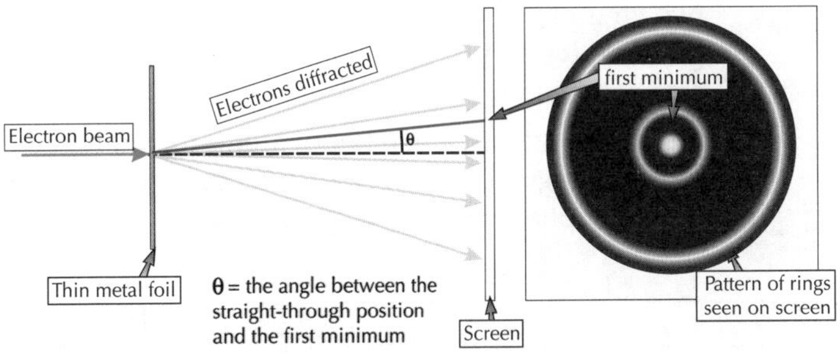

Example A beam of 300 MeV electrons is fired at a piece of thin foil, and produces a diffraction pattern on a fluorescent screen. The first minimum of the diffraction pattern is at an angle of 30° from the straight-through position. Estimate the diameter of the nuclei the electrons were diffracted by.

$$E = 300 \text{ MeV} = 3.00\times10^{8}\times1.6\times10^{-19} = 4.8\times10^{-11}\text{J},\ \lambda \simeq \frac{hc}{E} = \frac{6.6\times10^{-34}\times3.0\times10^{8}}{4.8\times10^{-11}} = 4.125\times10^{-15}\text{m}$$

$$\text{So } d \simeq \frac{1.22\lambda}{\sin\theta} = \frac{1.22\times4.125\times10^{-15}}{\sin30^\circ} = 2\times1.22\times4.125\times10^{-15} = \mathbf{1.0\times10^{-14}\ m}$$

Practice Questions

Q1 Explain how alpha particle scattering shows that a nucleus is both small and positively charged.

Q2 Why are X-rays a suitable electromagnetic wave to investigate atomic sizes?

Exam Questions

Q1 A beam of alpha particles is directed onto a very thin gold film.
(a) Explain why the majority of alpha particles are not scattered. [2 marks]
(b) Explain how alpha particles are scattered by atomic nuclei. [3 marks]

Q2 Various particles can be used to investigate the structure of matter.
(a) Why do particles such as electrons produce diffraction patterns? [2 marks]
(b) Why is electron-beam diffraction the most accurate method for finding out about the atomic structure of a crystal? [1 mark]
(c) When electrons are directed at a larger nucleus, the beam suffers less diffraction. Why does this happen? [2 marks]

Alpha scattering — It's positively repulsive...

Scattering and diffraction are the key ideas you need to understand for questions about atomic size and structure. Remember, particles like electrons have wave-like properties, so if you fire them at crystal structures they make a diffraction pattern. This lets you work out size, spacing etc...

Nuclear Radius and Density

These pages are for AQA A Unit 5 and OCR A Unit 5 only.

The tiny nucleus — such a weird place, but one that you need to become ultra familiar with. Lucky you...

The Nucleus is a Very Small Part of a Whole Atom

1) By **probing atoms** using scattering and diffraction methods, we know that the **diameter of an atom** is about 0.1 nm (1×10^{-10} m) and the diameter of the smallest **nucleus** is about 2 fm (2×10^{-15} m — pronounced "femtometres").
2) So basically, **nuclei** are really, really **tiny** compared with the size of the **whole atom**.
3) To make this **easier to visualise**, try imagining a **large Ferris wheel** (which is pretty darn big) as the size of **an atom**. If you then put a **grain of rice** (which is rather small) in the centre, this would be the size of the atom's **nucleus**.
4) **Molecules** are just a number of **atoms joined together**. As a rough guide, the size of a molecule equals the number of atoms in it multiplied by the size of one atom.

The Nucleus is Made Up of Nucleons

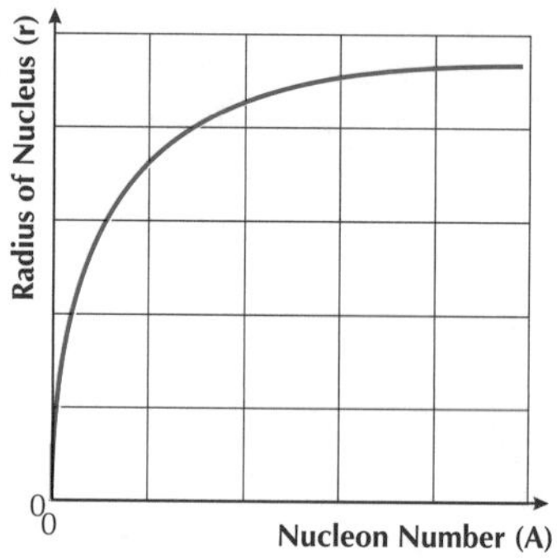

1) The **particles** that make up the nucleus (i.e. **protons** and **neutrons**) are called **nucleons**.
2) The **number of nucleons** in an atom is called the **mass** (or **nucleon**) **number, *A***.
3) As **more nucleons** are added to the nucleus, it gets **bigger**.
4) And as we all know by now, you can measure the size of a nucleus by firing particles at it (see p. 40-41).

See p. 52 for more on the mass number and how this is used to represent atomic structure in standard notation.

Nuclear Radius is Proportional to the Cube Root of the Mass Number

AQA A only

The **nuclear radius** increases roughly as the cube root of the mass (nucleon) number.

1) This **straight-line graph** shows that the **nuclear radius** (***r***) is **directly proportional** to the cube root of the **nucleon number** (*A*).
2) This relationship can be written as: $r \propto A^{1/3}$.
3) We can make this into an equation by introducing a constant, r_0, giving:

$$r = r_0 A^{1/3}$$

Where r_0 is the value of r when $A = 1$, i.e. for a proton (hydrogen nucleus). The value of r_0 is about 1.4 fm.

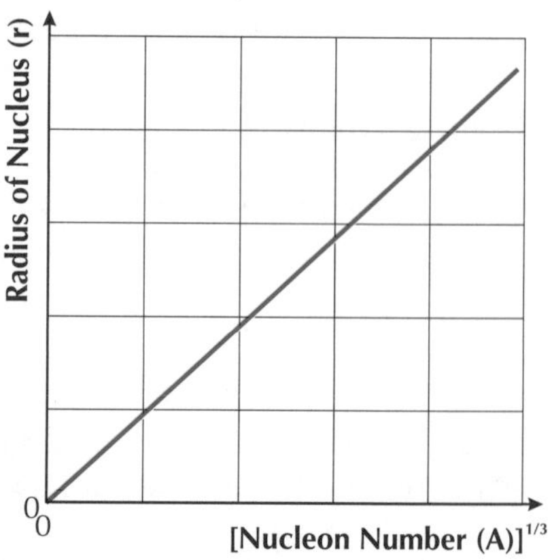

Example Calculate the radius of an oxygen nucleus which has 16 nucleons.

$$r = r_0 A^{1/3} = 1.4 \times 10^{-15} \times (16)^{1/3}$$
$$= 3.5 \times 10^{-15} \text{ m (or 3.5 fm)}$$

Nuclear Radius and Density

The Density of Nuclear Matter is Enormous

1) The **volume** that each nucleon (i.e. a **proton** or a **neutron**) takes up in a nucleus is about the **same**.
2) Because protons and neutrons have nearly the **same mass**, it means that all nuclei have a **similar density** (ρ).
3) But nuclear matter is **no ordinary** stuff. Its density is **enormous**. A **teaspoon** of pure nuclear matter would have a mass of about **five hundred million tonnes**. (Just to make you gasp in awe and wonder, out in space nuclear matter makes up neutron stars, which are several kilometres in diameter.)

The following examples show how **nuclear density** is pretty much the **same**, **regardless of the element**.

Example 1

Work out the density of a carbon nucleus given that its mass is 2.00×10^{-26} kg and **A** = 12.

1) The **radius** (r) of a carbon nucleus $\approx$ **3.2 × 10⁻¹⁵ m**
2) So, the **volume** (V) of the nucleus $= \frac{4}{3}\pi r^3$ $= \mathbf{1.37 \times 10^{-43}\ m^3}$
3) This gives the **density** (ρ) of a carbon nucleus as:

$$\rho = \frac{m}{V} = \frac{2.00 \times 10^{-26}}{1.37 \times 10^{-43}} = 1.46 \times 10^{17}\ \text{kg m}^{-3}$$

Example 2

Work out the density of a gold nucleus given that its mass is 3.27×10^{-25} kg and **A** = 197.

1) The **radius** (r) of a gold nucleus $\approx \mathbf{8.1 \times 10^{-15}\ m}$
2) So, the **volume** (V) of the nucleus $= \frac{4}{3}\pi r^3$ $= \mathbf{2.23 \times 10^{-42}\ m^3}$
3) This gives the **density** (ρ) of a gold nucleus as:

$$\rho = \frac{m}{V} = \frac{3.27 \times 10^{-25}}{2.23 \times 10^{-42}} = 1.47 \times 10^{17}\ \text{kg m}^{-3}$$

Nuclear density is significantly larger than atomic density — this suggests three important facts about the structure of an atom:
a) Most of an atom's mass is in its nucleus.
b) The nucleus is small compared to the atom.
c) An atom must contain a lot of empty space.

Practice Questions

Q1 What is the approximate size of an atom?

Q2 What are nucleons?

Q3 What is the relationship between the nuclear radius and mass number?

Q4 In the formula $r = r_o A^{1/3}$, what does r_o represent?

Q5 Explain why the density of ordinary matter is much less than that of nuclear matter.

Exam Questions

Q1 The radius (r) of a nucleus with A nucleons can be calculated using the equation $r = r_o A^{1/3}$.
(a) If a carbon nucleus containing 12 nucleons has a radius of 3.2×10^{-15} m, show that $r_o = 1.4 \times 10^{-15}$ m. [2 marks]
(b) Calculate the radius of a radium nucleus containing 226 nucleons. [1 mark]
(c) Calculate the density of the radium nucleus if its mass is 3.75×10^{-25} kg. [2 marks]

Q2 A sample of pure gold has a density of 19 300 kg m^{-3}. If the density of a gold nucleus is 1.47×10^{17} kg m^{-3}, discuss what this implies about the structure of a gold atom. [4 marks]

Nuclear and particle physics — heavy stuff...

So basically the nucleus is a tiny part of the atom, but it's incredibly dense. The density doesn't change much from element to element, and the radius depends on the mass number. Learn the theory like your own backyard, but don't worry about remembering equations and values — those friendly examiners have popped them in the exam paper for you. How nice...

The Strong Nuclear Force

These pages are for OCR A Unit 5 only

Keeping the nucleus together requires a lot of effort — a bit like A2 Physics then...

There are *Forces* at Work *Inside* the *Nucleus...*

There are several different **forces** acting on the nucleons in a nucleus. To understand these forces you first need to take a look at the **electrostatic** forces due to the protons' electric charges, and also the **gravitational** forces.

1) The **electrostatic force**

All protons have an equal, **positive electric charge**. So, packed close together inside a nucleus, these protons will **repel** each other. You can work out the size of this **force of repulsion** using **Coulomb's law**. Assuming that two protons are 1×10^{-14} m apart, the force of repulsion F_R will be:

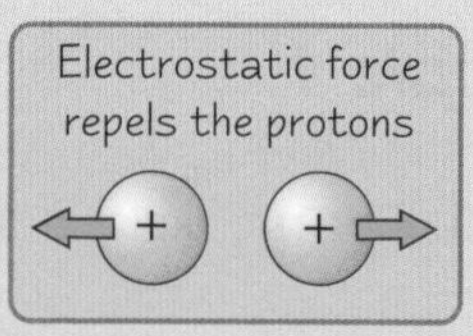

$$F_R = \frac{1}{4\pi\varepsilon_o}\frac{Q_1Q_2}{r^2} = \frac{1}{4\pi(8.85\times10^{-12})}\frac{(1.6\times10^{-19})(1.6\times10^{-19})}{(1\times10^{-14})^2} = 2.3\text{ N}$$

In this example: Q_1 and Q_2 are the electric charges on two protons, ε_o is the permittivity of free space, and r is the distance separating the two protons.

2) The **gravitational force**

Newton's law of gravitation says that two **massive** objects will **attract** each other. So, for the same two protons, this **attractive force**, F_A, will be:

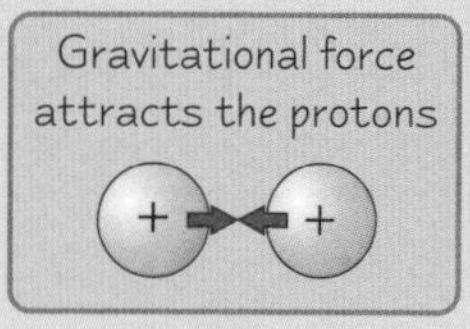

$$F_A = -G\frac{m_1m_2}{r^2} = -(6.67\times10^{-11})\cdot\frac{(1.67\times10^{-27})(1.67\times10^{-27})}{(1\times10^{-14})^2} = -1.86\times10^{-36}\text{ N}$$

In this example: G is the gravitational constant, m_1 and m_2 are the masses of two protons, and r is the distance separating the two protons.

The **electrostatic force** of repulsion is far **bigger** than the **gravitational** attractive force. If these were the only forces acting in the nucleus, the nucleons would **fly apart**. So there must be **another attractive force** that **holds the nucleus together** — called the **strong nuclear force**. (The gravitational force is so small, it's usually ignored.)

The *Strong Nuclear Force* Binds Nucleons Together

Now pay attention please. This bit's rather strange because the **strong nuclear force** is quite **complicated**, but here are the **main points**:

1) To **hold the nucleus together**, the strong nuclear force must be an **attractive force** that is **larger** than the electrostatic force.
2) Experiments have shown that the strong nuclear force between nucleons has a **short range**. It can only hold nucleons together when they are separated by up to **10 fm** — which is the maximum size of a nucleus.
3) The **strength** of the strong nuclear force between nucleons **quickly falls** beyond this distance (see the graph on the next page).
4) Experiments also show that the strong nuclear force **works equally between all nucleons**. This means that the size of the force is the same whether proton-proton, neutron-neutron or proton-neutron.
5) At **very small separations**, the strong nuclear force must be **repulsive** — otherwise there would be nothing to stop it **crushing** the nucleus to a **point**.

lime green, orange and day-glow pink — repulsive at small separations

The Strong Nuclear Force

*The **Size** of the Strong Nuclear Force **Varies with Nucleon Separation***

The **strong nuclear force** can be plotted on a **graph** to show how it changes with the **distance of separation** between **nucleons**. If the **electrostatic force** is also plotted, you can see the **relationship** between these **two forces**.

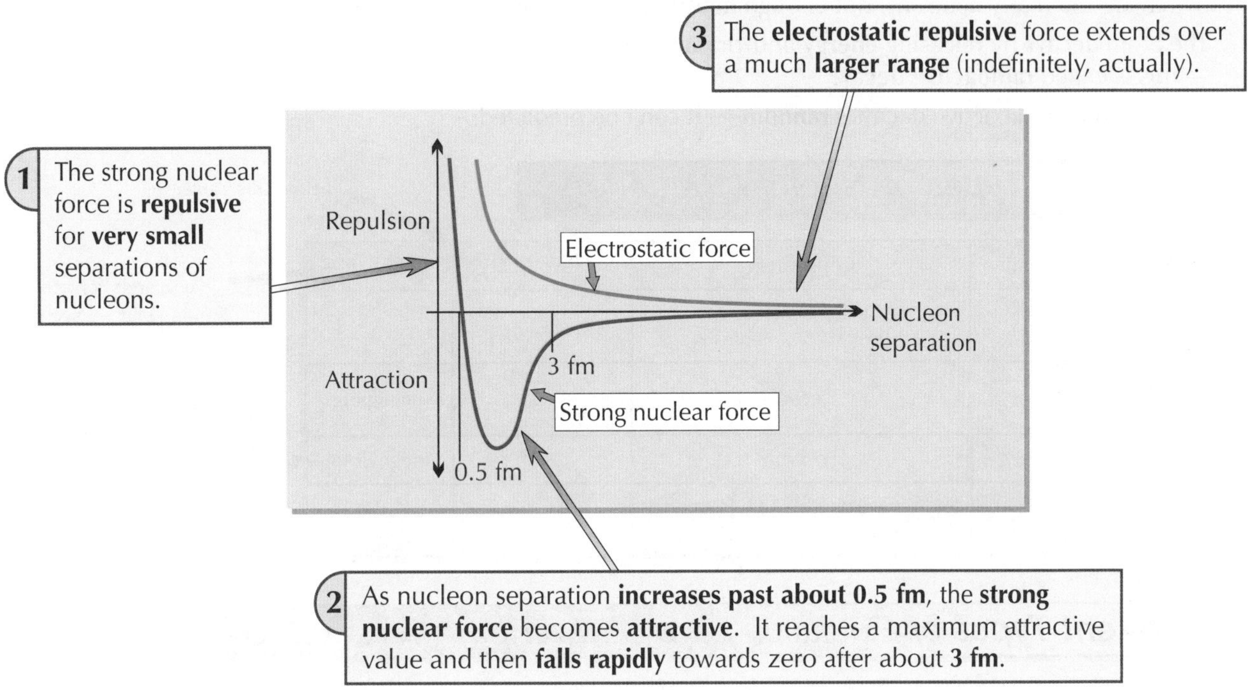

3 The **electrostatic repulsive** force extends over a much **larger range** (indefinitely, actually).
1 The strong nuclear force is **repulsive** for **very small** separations of nucleons.
Repulsion
Electrostatic force
Nucleon separation
3 fm
Attraction
Strong nuclear force
0.5 fm
2 As nucleon separation **increases past about 0.5 fm**, the **strong nuclear force** becomes **attractive**. It reaches a maximum attractive value and then **falls rapidly** towards zero after about **3 fm**.

Practice Questions

Q1 What causes an electrostatic force inside the nucleus?

Q2 Explain why the gravitational forces between nucleons are usually ignored.

Q3 What evidence suggests the existence of a strong nuclear force?

Q4 Is the strong interaction attractive or repulsive at a nucleon separation of 10 fm?

Exam Questions

Q1 Coulomb's law can be used to find the electrostatic force of repulsion between two protons in a nucleus.

$$F = \frac{1}{4\pi\varepsilon_o}\frac{Q_1Q_2}{r^2}$$

The charge, Q, on a proton is $+1.6 \times 10^{-19}$ C and the permittivity of free space, ε_0, is 8.85×10^{-12} Fm^{-1}.

(a) If two protons are separated by a distance, r, of 9×10^{-15} m, calculate the electrostatic force between them. [2 marks]

(b) If the protons move closer together, what effect will this have on the repulsive force? [1 mark]

(c) What is the electrostatic force between a proton and a neutron? Explain your answer. [2 marks]

Q2 The strong nuclear force binds the nucleus together.

(a) Explain why the force must be repulsive at very short distances. [1 mark]

(b) How does the strong interaction limit the size of a stable nucleus? [2 marks]

The strong interaction's like nuclear glue...

Right then, lots of scary looking stuff on these pages, but DON'T PANIC... the important bits can be condensed into a few points: a) the electrostatic force pushes protons in the nucleus apart, b) the strong interaction pulls all nucleons together, c) there's a point where these forces are balanced — this is the typical nucleon separation in a nucleus. Easy eh?...

Radioactive Emissions

These pages are for AQA A Unit 5, Edexcel Unit 5, OCR A Unit 5 and OCR B Unit 5 only.

Unstable Atoms are **Radioactive**

1) If an atom is **unstable**, it will **break down** to **become** more stable. Its **instability** could be caused by having **too many neutrons**, **not enough neutrons**, or just **too much energy** in the nucleus.
2) The atom **decays** by **releasing energy** and/or **particles**, until it reaches a **stable form** — this is called **radioactive decay**.
3) An individual radioactive decay is **random** — it can't be predicted.

There are **Four Types** of **Nuclear Radiation**

Learn this table.

Radiation	Symbol	Constituent	Relative Charge	Mass (u)
Alpha	α	A helium nucleus — 2 protons & 2 neutrons	+2	4
Beta-minus (Beta)	β or β^-	Electron	-1	(negligible)
Beta-plus	β^+	Positron	+1	(negligible)
Gamma	γ	Short-wavelength , high-frequency electromagnetic wave.	0	0

u stands for atomic mass unit — see p. 54.

See p. 60 for more on positrons.

The **Different Types** of Radiation have **Different Penetrations**

When a radioactive particle **hits** an **atom** it can **knock off electrons**, creating an **ion** — so, **radioactive emissions** are also known as **ionising radiation**.

Alpha, **beta** and **gamma** radiation can be **fired** at a **variety of objects** with **detectors** placed the **other side** to see whether they **penetrate** the object.

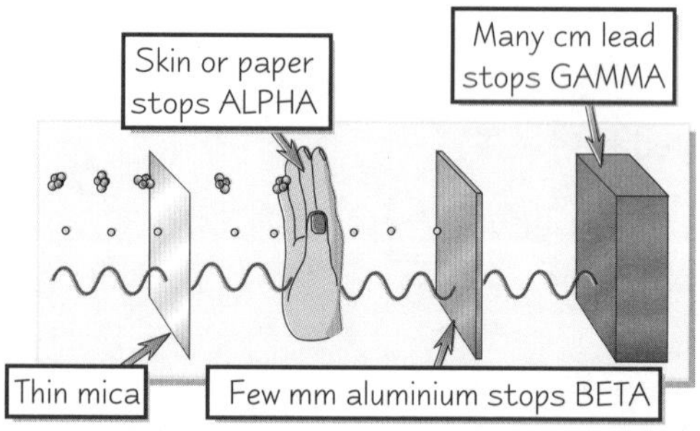

Radiation	Symbol	Ionising	Speed	Penetrating power	Affected by magnetic field
Alpha	α	Strongly	Slow	Absorbed by paper or a few cm of air	Yes
Beta-minus (Beta)	β or β^-	Weakly	Fast	Absorbed by ~3 mm of aluminium	Yes
Beta-plus	β^+	Annihilated by electron — so virtually zero range			
Gamma	γ	Very weakly	Speed of light	Absorbed by many cm of lead, or several m of concrete.	No

Alpha, **Beta** and **Gamma** have **Different Ionising Properties**

What a **radioactive source** can be **used** for often depends on its **ionising properties**.

1) **Alpha** particles are **strongly positive** — so they can **easily pull electrons** off atoms, **ionising** them.
2) Ionising an atom **transfers** some of the **energy** from the **alpha particle** to the **atom**. The alpha particle **quickly ionises** many atoms (about 10 000 ionisations per alpha particle) and **loses** all its **energy**. This makes alpha-sources suitable for use in **smoke alarms** because they allow **current** to flow, but won't **travel very far**.
3) The **beta**-minus particle has **lower mass** and **charge** than the alpha particle, but a **higher speed**. This means it can still **knock electrons** off atoms. Each **beta** particle will ionise about 100 atoms, **losing energy** at each interaction.
4) This **lower** number of **interactions** means that beta radiation causes much **less damage** to body tissue than alpha radiation. This means beta radiation can be used in **medicine** to target and damage **cancerous cells** — since it passes through healthy tissue without causing too many problems.
5) Gamma radiation is even more **weakly ionising** than beta radiation, so will do even **less damage** to body tissue. This means it can be used for **diagnostic techniques** in medicine.
6) The **effective dose** you receive from each type of radiation is called the **dose equivalent**... see p. 123.

Radioactive Emissions

The *Intensity* of *Gamma Radiation* Obeys the *Inverse Square Law*

AQA A only

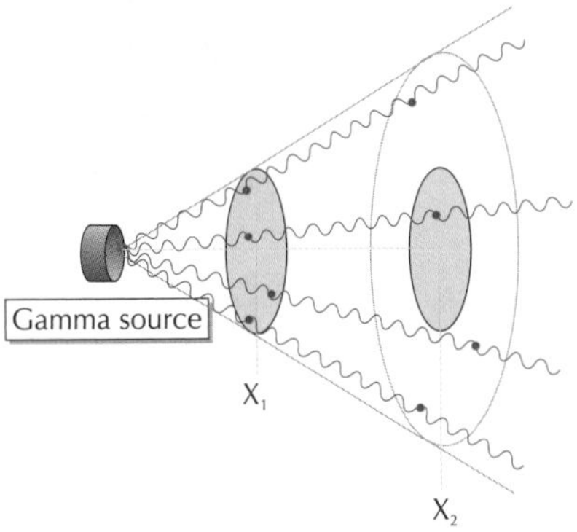

1) A **gamma source** will **emit** gamma **radiation** in **all directions**.
2) This radiation **spreads out** as you get **further away** from the source.
3) However, the amount of **radiation per unit area** (the **intensity**) will **decrease** the further you get from the source.
4) If you took a reading of **intensity**, I, at a **distance**, x, from the source you would find that it **decreases** by the **square of the distance** from the source.
5) This can be written as the equation:

$$I = \frac{kI_o}{x^2}$$

where k is a constant, and I_o is the intensity at the source.

6) This **relationship** can be **proved** by taking **measurements of intensity** at different distances from a gamma source, using a **Geiger-Müller tube** and **counter**.
7) If the **distance** from the source is **doubled** the **intensity** is found to **fall to a quarter** — which **verifies** the inverse square law.

That's why one of the safety precautions when handling a source is to hold it at arm's length, so you lessen the amount of radiation reaching you.

We're *Surrounded* by *Background Radiation*

AQA A and Edexcel.

Put a Geiger-Müller tube **anywhere** and the counter will click — it's detecting **background radiation**.

When you take a **reading** from a radioactive source, you need to **measure** the **background radiation** separately and **subtract** it from your **measurement**.

There are many **sources** of background radiation:

1) **The air:** Radioactive **radon gas** is released from **rocks**. They emit alpha radiation. The concentration of this gas in the atmosphere varies a lot from place to place, but it's usually the largest contributor to the background radiation.
2) **The ground and buildings: All rock** contains radioactive isotopes.
3) **Cosmic radiation:** Cosmic rays are particles (mostly high-energy protons) from **space**. When they collide with particles in the upper atmosphere, they produce nuclear radiation.
4) **Living things:** All plants and animals contain **carbon**, and some of this will be radioactive **carbon-14**.
5) **Man-made radiation:** In most areas, radiation from **medical** or **industrial** sources makes up a tiny, tiny fraction of the background radiation.

Practice Questions

Q1 What makes an atom radioactive?

Q2 Name three types of nuclear radiation and give three properties of each.

Q3 Give three sources of background radiation.

Exam Questions

Q1 Briefly describe an absorption experiment to distinguish between alpha, beta and gamma radiation. You may wish to include a sketch in your answer. [4 marks]

Q2 The count rate detected by a G-M tube, 10 cm from a gamma source, is 240 counts per second. What would you expect the count rate to be at 40 cm from the source? [3 marks]

Radioactive emissions — as easy as α, β, γ...

You need to learn the different types of radiation and their properties. Remember that alpha particles are by far the most ionising and so cause more damage if they get inside your body than the same dose of any other radiation — which is one reason we don't use alpha sources as medical tracers. Learn this all really well, then go and have a brew and a bickie...

Exponential Law of Decay

These pages are for AQA A Unit 5, Edexcel Unit 5, OCR A Unit 5 and OCR B Units 4 and 5.

Oooh look — some maths. Good.

It could be you.

Every Isotope Decays at a Different Rate

1) **Radioactive decay** is completely **random**. You **can't predict which** atom will decay **when**.
2) Although you can't predict the decay of an **individual atom**, if you take a **very large number of atoms**, their **overall behaviour** shows a **pattern**.
3) Any sample of a particular **isotope** has the **same rate of decay**, i.e. the same **proportion** of atoms will **decay** in a **given time**.

Isotopes of an element have the same number of protons, but different numbers of neutrons in their nuclei.

The Rate of Decay is Measured by the Decay Constant

The **activity** of a sample — the **number** of atoms that **decay each second** — is **proportional** to the **size of the sample**. For a **given isotope**, a sample **twice** as big would give **twice** the **number of decays** per second.

The **decay constant** (λ) measures how **quickly** an isotope will **decay** — the **bigger** the value of λ, the faster the rate of decay. Its unit is $\mathbf{s^{-1}}$.

activity = decay constant × number of atoms

Or in symbols: $A = \lambda N$

Don't get λ confused with wavelength.

Activity is measured in **becquerels** (Bq): 1 Bq = 1 decay per second (s^{-1})

You Need to Learn the Definition of Half-Life

The **half-life** ($T_{1/2}$) of an **isotope** is the **average time** it takes for the **number of undecayed atoms** to **halve.**

Measuring the **number of undecayed atoms** isn't the easiest job in the world. **In practice**, half-life isn't measured by counting atoms, but by measuring the **time it takes** the **activity** to **halve**.

The **longer** the **half-life** of an isotope, the **longer** it stays **radioactive**.

The Number of Undecayed Particles Decreases Exponentially

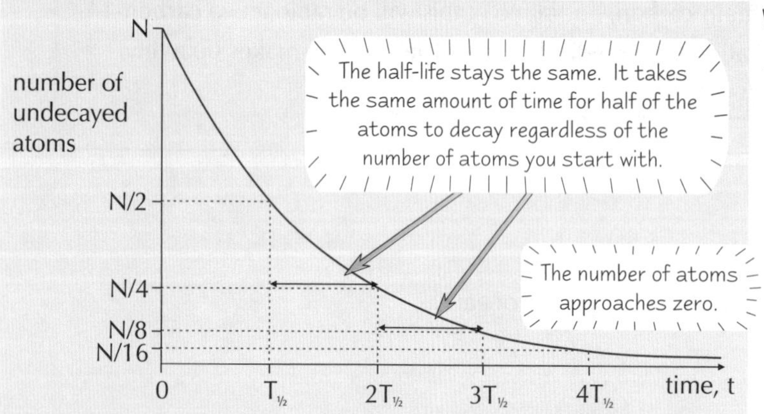
N
number of undecayed atoms
N/2
N/4
N/8
N/16
0
$T_{1/2}$
$2T_{1/2}$
$3T_{1/2}$
$4T_{1/2}$
time, t
The half-life stays the same. It takes the same amount of time for half of the atoms to decay regardless of the number of atoms you start with.
The number of atoms approaches zero.

When you're **measuring** the **activity** and **half-life** of a **source**, you've got to **remember background radiation**. The **background radiation** needs to be **subtracted** from the **activity readings** to give the **source activity**.

You'd be **more likely** to actually meet a **count rate-time graph** or an **activity-time graph**. They're both **exactly the same shape** as the graph above, but with different **y-axes**.

How to find the half-life of an isotope

STEP 1: Read off the value of count rate, particles or activity when t = 0.

STEP 2: Go to half the original value.

STEP 3: Draw a horizontal line to the curve, then a vertical line down to the x-axis.

STEP 4: Read off the half-life where the line crosses the x-axis.

STEP 5: Check the units carefully.

STEP 6: It's always a good idea to check your answer. Repeat steps 1-4 for a quarter the original value. Divide your answer by two. That will also give you the half-life. Check that you get the same answer both ways.

AQA A and OCR B only

Plotting the natural log (ln) of the number of radioactive atoms (or the activity) against time gives a straight-line graph (see p. 138).

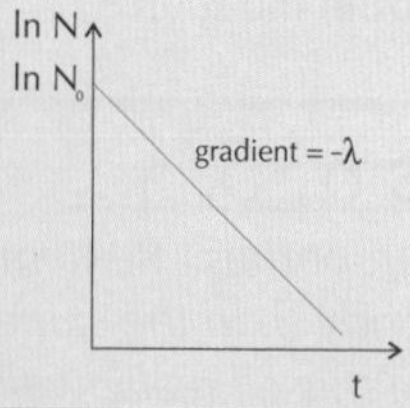
ln N
ln N_0
gradient = $-\lambda$
t

Exponential Law of Decay

You Need to Know the *Equations* for *Half-Life* and *Decay...*

1) The rate of radioactive decay is proportional to the number of nuclei remaining — you can write this as a **differential equation**.

$$\frac{dN}{dt} = -\lambda N$$

See the next page for how to solve this beauty...

2) The **half-life** can be **calculated** using the equation:
(where ln is the natural log)

$$T_{\frac{1}{2}} = \frac{\ln 2}{\lambda} \simeq \frac{0.693}{\lambda}$$

3) The **number of radioactive atoms** remaining, N, depends on the **number originally** present, N_0. The **number remaining** can be calculated using the equation:

$$N = N_0 e^{-\lambda t}$$

Here t = time, measured in seconds.

4) As a sample decays, its **activity** will go down, and there's a handy equation for that too:

$$A = A_0 e^{-\lambda t}$$

Example:
A sample of the radioactive isotope ^{13}N contains 5×10^6 atoms. The decay constant for this isotope is $1.16 \times 10^{-3}\ s^{-1}$.

a) What is the half-life for this isotope?

$$T_{½} = \frac{\ln 2}{1.16 \times 10^{-3}} = 598\ s$$

b) How many atoms of ^{13}N will remain after 800 seconds?

$$N = N_0 e^{-\lambda t} = 5 \times 10^6 e^{-(1.16 \times 10^{-3})(800)} = 1.98 \times 10^6 \text{ atoms}$$

Radioactive Isotopes Have *Many Uses*

1) Radioactive substances are extremely useful. You can use them for all sorts — to diagnose **medical problems** (see p.122), **sterilise** food, and in **smoke alarms**.

2) The radioactive isotope carbon-14 is used in **radiocarbon dating**. Living plants take in carbon dioxide from the atmosphere as part of **photosynthesis**, including the **radioactive isotope carbon-14**. When they **die**, the **activity** of carbon-14 in the plant starts to **fall**, with a **half-life** of around **5730 years**. Archaeological finds made from once living material (like wood) can be tested to find the **current amount** of carbon-14 in them, and date them.

OCR A only
Smoke detectors have a weak source of α-radiation close to two electrodes.
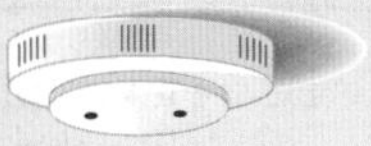
The radiation ionises the air, and a current flows between the electrodes. If there's a fire, smoke absorbs the radiation — the current stops and the alarm sounds.

Practice Questions

Q1 Define radioactive activity. What units is it measured in?

Q2 Sketch a general radioactive decay graph showing the number of undecayed particles against time.

Q3 What is meant by the term 'half-life'?

Q4 Describe how radiocarbon dating works.

Exam Questions

Q1 Explain what is meant by the random nature of radioactive decay. [1 mark]

Q2 You take a reading of 750 Bq from a pure radioactive source. The radioactive source initially contains 50 000 atoms, and background activity in your lab is measured as 50 Bq.

(a) Calculate the decay constant for your sample. [3 marks]

(b) What is the half-life of this sample? [2 marks]

(c) Approximately how many atoms of the radioactive source will there be after 300 seconds? [2 marks]

Radioactivity is a random process — just like revision shouldn't be...

Remember the shape of that graph — whether it's count rate, activity or number of atoms plotted against time, the shape's always the same. This is all pretty straightforward mathsy-type stuff: plugging values in equations, reading off graphs, etc. Not very interesting, though. Ah well, once you get onto relativity you'll be longing for a bit of boredom.

Modelling Decay

These pages are for AQA A Unit 5, OCR A Unit 5 and OCR B Unit 4.

Who'd have thought that capacitors and radioactive isotopes could have so much in common? Read on...

Capacitors and Radioactive Isotopes Have Similar Decay Equations

OCR A and OCR B

Radioactive isotopes might seem very different from **capacitors** in R-C circuits (see page 38), but their **decay equations** are actually **very similar**. This **table** shows the **similarities** and **differences** between the equations.

	Discharging Capacitors	Radioactive Isotopes
1)	Decay equation is $Q = Q_0 e^{-t/RC}$.	Decay equation is $N = N_0 e^{-\lambda t}$.
2)	The **quantity** that decays is Q, the amount of charge left on the plates of the capacitor.	The **quantity** that decays is N, the number of unstable nuclei remaining.
3)	**Initially**, the charge on the plates is Q_0.	**Initially**, the number of nuclei is N_0.
4)	It takes RC seconds for the amount of charge remaining to fall to **37% of its initial value**.	It takes $1/\lambda$ seconds for the number of nuclei remaining to fall to **37% of the initial value**.
5)	The time taken for the amount of charge left to decay by half (the **half-life**) is $t_{1/2} = \ln 2 \times RC$.	The time taken for the number of nuclei to decay by half (the **half-life**) is $t_{1/2} = \ln 2 / \lambda$.

You Can Use a Logarithmic Graph to Find the Decay Constant and Half-life

1) If you plot a **graph** of the **number of undecayed nuclei** in a sample against **time**, you get an **exponential curve** like the one on page 48.
2) But, if you plot the **natural log** (ln) of the number of **undecayed nuclei** against **time**, you get a **straight line**. To find the **natural log** of a number, just use the **ln button** on your calculator.
3) You get a straight line because the **decay equation**, $N = N_0 e^{-\lambda t}$, can be **rearranged**, via the mystical wonder of **logs**, to the **general form** of a **straight line** — $y = mx + c$.
4) The **gradient** of the line is $-\lambda$, the **decay constant**. From this you can **calculate** the **half-life** of the sample.
5) This works for graphs of **activity** against **time** too — as long as you remember to **subtract** the **background activity** first.

$$N = N_0 e^{-\lambda t} \Longrightarrow \ln(N) = -\lambda t + \ln(N_0)$$
$$y = mx + c$$

If you understand logs you can work this out for yourself — if not, you'll just have to believe me. There's more stuff about logs on page 138.

Example The graphs below show how the number of undecayed nuclei of a radioactive isotope decreases over time. Calculate the half-life of the isotope using both graphs.

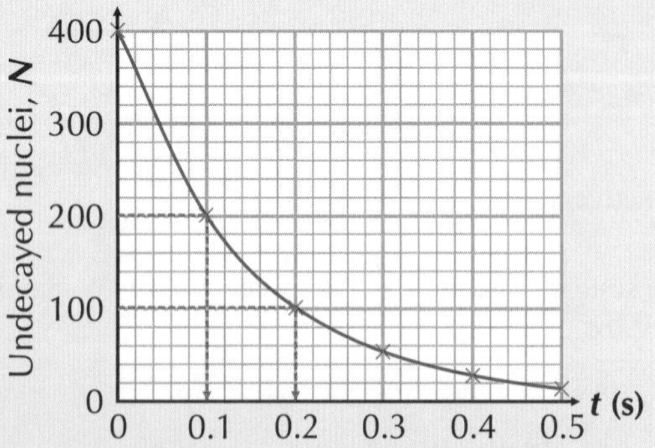

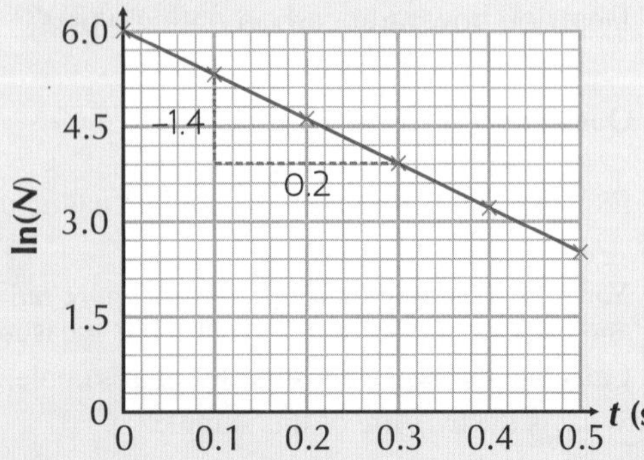

The first graph shows that it takes 0.1 s for the number of undecayed nuclei to fall from 200 to 100 (i.e. to halve). So, the **half-life** is **0.1 s**.

The **gradient** of this graph is $-1.4 \div 0.2 = -7$, so the **decay constant**, $\lambda = 7$. Substitute this into the equation for half-life: $t_{1/2} = \ln(2) \div 7 =$ **0.1 s**.

Modelling Decay

You Can Model Decay by Drawing a Graph

OCR B only

Check out page 39 for an alternative iterative method.

1) $N = N_0 e^{-\lambda t}$ is the **general solution** of the **differential equation** $dN/dt = -\lambda N$.
2) You can use an **iterative method** to find an **actual solution** if you know the value of *N* at any given time.
3) **Iterative methods** use a series of steps to **estimate** a solution — you've already seen one for **capacitor decay** on page 39. You can use the **same** method for **radioactive decay** — or use the **graphical method** below.

1) Start with the **initial value of *N*** (or use the value you have worked out in step 5).

2) **Substitute** the values of *N* and λ into the equation to work out the value of ***dN/dt***.

3) Increase the **time** by a small **interval** (the smaller the interval the more accurate your answer).

4) Starting at the **initial values** of *N* and *t* (or the **end** of the **previous line**), plot a **line** on the graph with the **gradient** you worked out in **step 2**. **Finish** the line at the end of the **time interval**.

5) Find the new value of *N* using the graph — it's the value at the **end of the line** you've plotted. Then go back to step 1 and **repeat the process** until you get to the time that you want.

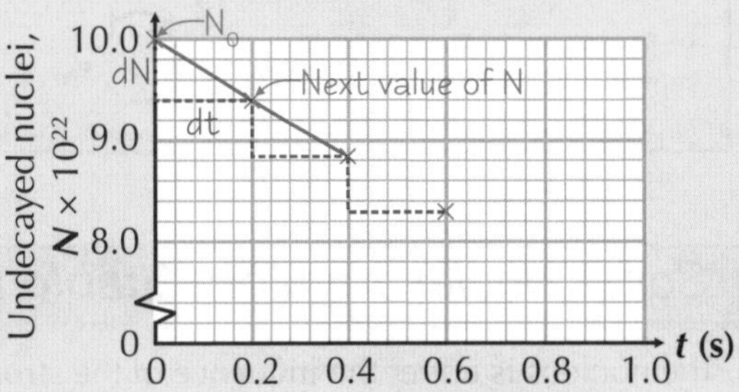

4) The great thing about this method and the one on page 39 is that you can use them for **any relationship** where the **rate of change** is **proportional** to the quantity changing — i.e. you can **extend the model** to other situations.

Practice Questions

Q1 What are the decay equations for the discharge of a capacitor and a radioactive isotope?

Q2 How can you use a logarithmic graph to find: a) the decay constant, b) the time constant?

Q3 Outline how you could estimate the solution of $dN/dt = -\lambda N$ using an iterative method.

Exam Questions

Q1 A teacher set up an R-C circuit to model the radioactive decay of a sample of radon gas. The values of R and C were chosen so that the charge on the capacitor decayed with the same half-life as the radon.

(a) Given that the capacitor decayed with the same half-life as the radon, write down an equation showing how the resistance and the capacitance are related to the decay constant. [2 marks]

(b) The capacitance of the capacitor was 500 μF and the resistance of the circuit was 144 kΩ. Find the value of the decay constant of the radon. [2 marks]

(c) What is the half-life of the radon? [2 marks]

Q2 The table shows the activity of a sample of protactinium. The values have been corrected for background radiation. Complete the table and draw a suitable logarithmic graph to find the half-life of the protactinium. [8 marks]

Time (s)	0	20	40	60
Activity (Bq)	60.0	52.6	46.1	40.4
ln(activity)	4.09			

Modelling decay — an ageing catwalk queen...

The point of these two pages is for you to learn how to solve decay equations (if you hadn't already worked that out). It's great if you understand why these methods work, but the main thing is to make sure you can do them — you could be asked to solve one in the exam. My top three tips for learning these methods are practice, practice and practice.

Nuclear Decay

These pages are for AQA A Unit 5 and OCR A Unit 5.

The stuff on these pages covers the most important facts about nuclear decay that you're just going to have to make sure you know inside out. I'd be very surprised if you didn't get a question about it in your exam...

Atomic Structure can be Represented Using Standard Notation

STANDARD NOTATION:

$$^{12}_{6}\mathrm{C}$$

The **nucleon number** or **mass number** (A) — there are a total of 12 protons and neutrons in a carbon-12 atom.

The **proton number** or **atomic number** (Z) — there are six protons in a carbon atom.

The symbol for the element carbon.

Atoms with the **same number of protons** but **different numbers of neutrons** are called **isotopes**. The following examples are all isotopes of carbon: $^{12}_{6}C$, $^{13}_{6}C$, $^{14}_{6}C$

Some Nuclei are More Stable than Others

The nucleus is under the **influence** of the **strong nuclear force holding** it **together** and the **electromagnetic force pushing** the **protons apart**. It's a very **delicate balance**, and it's easy for a nucleus to become **unstable**. You can get a stability graph by plotting **Z** (atomic number) against **N** (number of neutrons).

A nucleus will be **unstable** if it has:

1) **too many neutrons**
2) **too few neutrons**
3) **too many nucleons** altogether, i.e. it's **too heavy**
4) **too much energy**

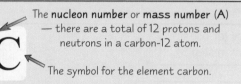

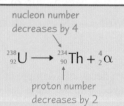

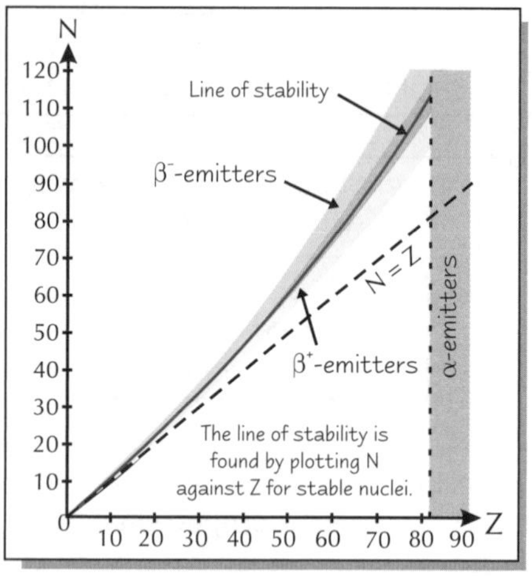

α Emission Happens in Heavy Nuclei

When an alpha particle is **emitted**:

The **proton number decreases** by **two**, and the **nucleon number decreases** by **four**.

$$^{238}_{92}U \longrightarrow {}^{234}_{90}Th + {}^{4}_{2}\alpha$$

nucleon number decreases by 4

proton number decreases by 2

1) **Alpha emission** only happens in **very heavy** atoms (with more than 82 protons), like **uranium** and **radium**.
2) The **nuclei** of these atoms are **too massive** to be stable.

β⁻ Emission Happens in Neutron Rich Nuclei

1) **Beta-minus** (usually just called beta) decay is the emission of an **electron** from the **nucleus** along with an **antineutrino**.
2) Beta decay happens in isotopes that are **"neutron rich"** (i.e. have many more **neutrons** than **protons** in their nucleus).
3) When a nucleus ejects a beta particle, one of the **neutrons** in the nucleus is **changed** into a **proton**.

When a **beta-minus** particle is **emitted**:

The **proton number increases** by **one**, and the **nucleon number stays the same.**

$$^{188}_{75}Re \longrightarrow {}^{188}_{76}Os + {}^{0}_{-1}\beta + {}^{0}_{0}\bar{\nu}_e$$

nucleon number stays the same

proton number increases by 1

In **beta-plus emission**, a **proton** gets **changed** into a **neutron**.
The **proton number decreases** by **one**, and the **nucleon number stays the same**.

Nuclear Decay

γ Radiation is Emitted from Nuclei with Too Much Energy

1) **After alpha** or **beta** decay, the **nucleus** often has **excess energy** — it's **excited**. This energy is **lost** by emitting a **gamma ray**.
2) **Another way** that gamma radiation is produced is when a nucleus **captures** one of its own orbiting **electrons**.

$$\mathbf{p} + \mathbf{e}^- \rightarrow \mathbf{n} + \nu_e$$

3) **Electron capture** causes a **proton** to **change** into a **neutron**. This makes the **nucleus unstable** and it **emits** gamma radiation.

The artificial isotope technetium-99^m is formed in an excited state from the decay of another element. It is used as a tracer in medical imaging (see p. 122).

During **gamma emission**, there is **no change** to the nuclear **constituents** — the nucleus just **loses excess energy**.

There are Conservation Rules in Nuclear Reactions

In every nuclear reaction **energy**, **momentum**, **proton number / charge** and **nucleon number** must be conserved.

238 = 234 + 4 — nucleon numbers balance

$${}^{238}_{92}\text{U} \longrightarrow {}^{234}_{90}\text{Th} + {}^{4}_{2}\alpha$$

92 = 90 + 2 — proton numbers balance

Mass is Not Conserved

1) The **mass** of the **alpha particle** is less than the **individual masses** of **two protons** and **two neutrons**. The difference is called the **mass defect**.
2) Mass **doesn't** have to be **conserved** because of **Einstein's equation**: $E = mc^2$
3) This says that **mass and energy** are **equivalent**.
The **energy released** when the nucleons **bonded together** accounts for the missing mass — so the **energy released** is the same as the **mass defect × c^2**.

Practice Questions

Q1 What makes a nucleus unstable? Describe the changes that happen in the nucleus during alpha, beta and gamma decay.

Q2 Explain the circumstances in which gamma radiation may be emitted.

Q3 Define the mass defect.

Exam Questions

Q1 (a) Radium-226 undergoes alpha decay to radon. Complete the balanced nuclear equation for this reaction.

$${}^{226}_{88}Ra \rightarrow \quad Rn +$$ [3 marks]

(b) Potassium-40 (Z = 19, A = 40) undergoes beta decay to calcium.
Write a balanced nuclear equation for this reaction. [3 marks]

Q2 Calculate the energy released during the formation of an alpha particle, given that the total mass of two protons and two neutrons is 6.695×10^{-27} kg, the mass of an alpha particle is 6.645×10^{-27} kg and the speed of light, c, is 3.00×10^8 ms^{-1}. [3 marks]

Nuclear decay — it can be enough to make you unstable...

$E = mc^2$ is an important equation that says mass and energy are equivalent. Remember it well, 'cos you're going to come across it a lot in questions about mass defect and the energy released in nuclear reactions over the next few pages...

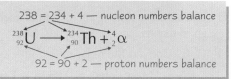

Binding Energy

These pages are for AQA A Unit 5, Edexcel Unit 5, OCR A Unit 5 and OCR B Unit 5.

Turn off the radio and close the door, 'cos you're going to need to concentrate hard on this stuff about binding energy...

The **Mass Defect** is **Equivalent** to the **Binding Energy**

1) The **mass** of a **nucleus** is **less than** the mass of its **constituent parts** — the difference is called the **mass defect** (see p. 53).
2) Einstein's equation, $E = mc^2$, says that mass and energy are **equivalent**.
3) So, as nucleons join together, the total mass **decreases** — the '**lost**' mass is **converted** into energy and **released**.
4) The amount of **energy released** is **equivalent** to the **mass defect**.
5) If you **pulled** the nucleus completely **apart**, the **energy** you'd have to use to do it would be the **same** as the energy **released** when the nucleus formed.

> The energy needed to **separate** all of the nucleons in a nucleus is called the **binding energy** (measured in **MeV**), and it is **equivalent** to the **mass defect**.

Example Calculate the binding energy of the nucleus of a lithium atom, ${}^{6}_{3}Li$, given that its mass defect is 0.0343 u.

1) Convert the mass defect into kg.

Mass defect = $0.0343 \times 1.66 \times 10^{-27} = 5.70 \times 10^{-29}$ kg

2) Use $E = mc^2$ to calculate the binding energy.

$E = 5.70 \times 10^{-29} \times (3 \times 10^8)^2 = 5.13 \times 10^{-12}$ J = 32 MeV

Atomic mass is usually given in atomic mass units (u), where 1 u = 1.66×10^{-27} kg.

1 MeV = 1.6×10^{-13} J

6) The **binding energy per unit of mass defect** can be calculated (using the example above):

$$\frac{\text{binding energy}}{\text{mass defect}} = \frac{32\ \text{MeV}}{0.0343\ \text{u}} \approx 931.3\ \text{MeV u}^{-1}$$

7) This means that a mass defect of **1 u** is equivalent to about **931.3 MeV** of binding energy.

Captain Skip didn't believe in ghosts, marmalade and that things could be bound without rope.

The **Binding Energy Per Nucleon** is at a **Maximum** around **N = 50**

A useful way of **comparing** the binding energies of different nuclei is to look at the **binding energy per nucleon**.

> Binding energy per nucleon (in MeV) = $\frac{\text{Binding energy (B)}}{\text{Nucleon number (A)}}$

So, the binding energy per nucleon for ${}^{6}_{3}Li$ (in the example above) is 32 ÷ 6 = 5.3 MeV.

If you're doing OCR B, you'll have seen this graph plotted the other way up (defining the binding energy as negative) to give you a 'nuclear valley'.

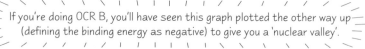

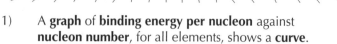

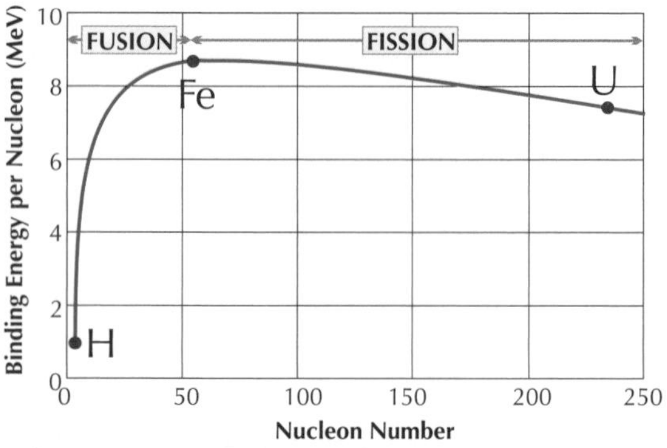

1) A **graph** of **binding energy per nucleon** against **nucleon number**, for all elements, shows a **curve**.
2) **High** binding energy per nucleon means that **more energy** is needed to **remove** nucleons from the nucleus.
3) In other words the **most stable** nuclei occur around the **maximum point** on the graph — which is at **nucleon number 56** (i.e. **iron**, Fe).
4) **Combining small nuclei** is called nuclear **fusion** (see p. 57) — this **increases** the **binding energy per nucleon** dramatically, which means a lot of **energy is released** during nuclear fusion.
5) **Fission** is when **large nuclei** are **split in two** (see p. 56) — the **nucleon numbers** of the two **new nuclei** are **smaller** than the original nucleus, which means there is an **increase** in the binding energy per nucleon. So, energy is also **released** during nuclear fission (but not as much energy per nucleon as in nuclear fusion).

Binding Energy

The Change in Binding Energy Gives the Energy Released...

The **binding energy per nucleon graph** can be used to **estimate** the **energy released** from nuclear reactions.

Energy released in nuclear fusion

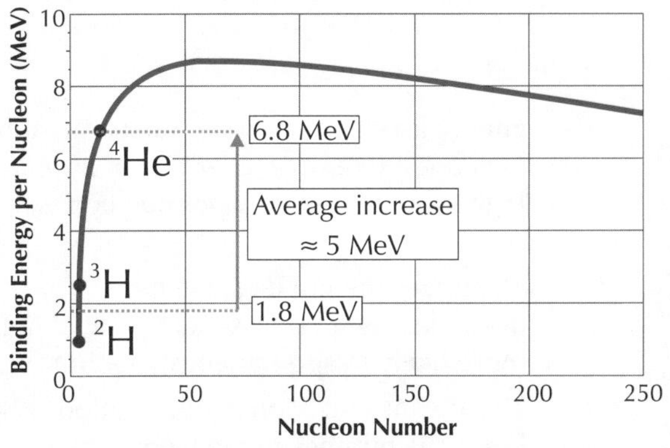

1) If ^{2}**H** and ^{3}**H** nuclei were **fused** together to form ^{4}He (and a neutron), the **average increase** in binding energy per ^{4}He nucleon would be about **5 MeV**.
2) There are **4 nucleons** in ^{4}He, so we can **estimate** the **energy released** as $4 \times 5 =$ **20 MeV**.

Energy released in nuclear fission

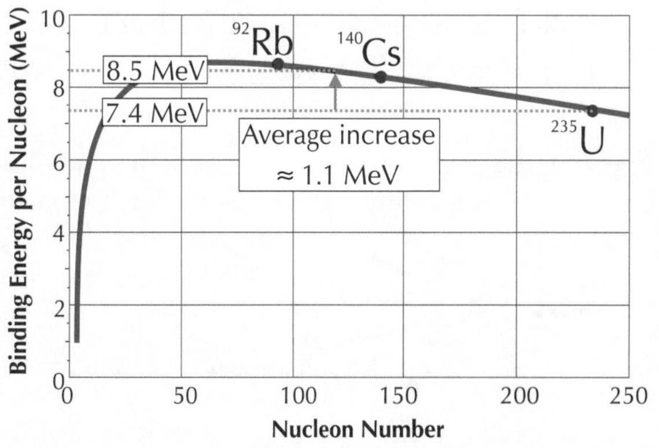

1) If a ^{235}**U** nucleus **splits** into ^{92}**Rb** and ^{140}**Cs** (plus a few neutrons) during nuclear **fission**, the **average increase** in **binding energy per nucleon** would be about 1.1 MeV.
2) There are **235 nucleons** in ^{235}U to begin with, so we can **estimate** the energy **released** as $235 \times 1.1 \approx$ **260 MeV**.

Practice Questions

Q1 What is the binding energy of a nucleus?

Q2 How can we calculate the binding energy for a particular nucleus?

Q3 What is the binding energy per nucleon?

Q4 Which element has the highest value of binding energy per nucleon?

Q5 Do nuclear fusion or fission reactions release the more energy per nucleon?

Exam Questions

Q1 The mass of a $^{14}_{6}$**C** nucleus is 13.999948 u. The mass of a proton is 1.007276 u, and a neutron is 1.008665 u.

(a) Calculate the mass defect of a $^{14}_{6}$**C** nucleus (given that $1\ u = 1.66 \times 10^{-27}$ kg). [3 marks]

(b) Use $E = mc^2$ to calculate the binding energy of the nucleus in MeV (given that $c = 3 \times 10^8\ ms^{-1}$ and $1\ MeV = 1.6 \times 10^{-13}$ J). [2 marks]

Q2 The following equation represents a nuclear reaction that takes place in the Sun:

$$^{1}_{1}p + ^{1}_{1}p \rightarrow ^{2}_{1}H + ^{0}_{+1}\beta + \text{energy released}$$

where p is a proton and β is a positron (opposite of an electron)

(a) State the type of nuclear reaction shown. [1 mark]

(b) Given that the binding energy per nucleon for a proton is 0 MeV and for a ^{2}H nucleus it is approximately 0.86 MeV, estimate the energy released by this reaction. [2 marks]

A mass defect of 1 u is equivalent to a binding energy of 931.3 MeV...

Remember this useful little fact, and it'll save loads of time in the exam — because you won't have to fiddle around with converting atomic mass from u → kg and binding energy from J → MeV. What more could you possibly want...

Nuclear Fission and Fusion

These pages are for AQA A Unit 5, Edexcel Unit 5, OCR A Unit 5 and OCR B Unit 5.

What did the nuclear scientist have for his tea? Fission chips... hohoho.

Fission Means Splitting Up Into Smaller Parts

1) **Large nuclei**, with at least 83 protons (e.g. uranium), are **unstable** and some can randomly **split** into two **smaller** nuclei — this is called **nuclear fission.**
2) This process is called **spontaneous** if it just happens **by itself**, or **induced** if we **encourage** it to happen.

Example

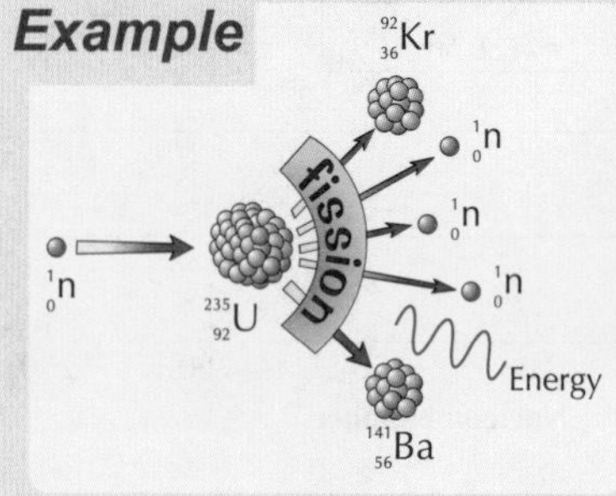

Fission can be induced by making a neutron enter a ^{235}U nucleus, causing it to become very unstable.

Only low energy neutrons can be captured in this way. A low energy neutron is called a **thermal neutron**.

3) **Energy is released** during nuclear fission because the new, smaller nuclei have a **higher binding energy per nucleon** (see p. 54).
4) The **larger** the nucleus, the more **unstable** it will be — so large nuclei are **more likely** to **spontaneously fission.**
5) This means that spontaneous fission **limits** the **number of nucleons** that a nucleus can contain — in other words, it **limits** the number of **possible elements**.

Controlled Nuclear Reactors Produce Useful Power

AQA A, OCR A and OCR B

We can **harness** the **energy** released during nuclear **fission reactions** in a **nuclear reactor**, but it's important that these reactions are very **carefully controlled**.

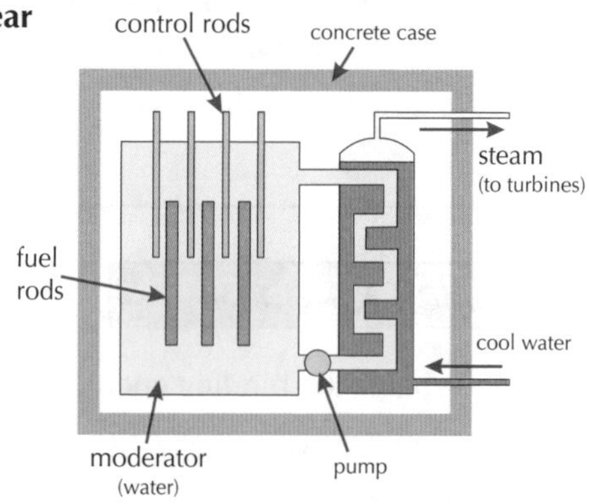

1) Nuclear reactors use **rods of uranium** that are rich in ^{235}**U** as '**fuel**' for fission reactions. (The rods also contain a lot of ^{238}**U**, but that doesn't undergo fission.)
2) These **fission** reactions produce more **neutrons** which then **induce** other nuclei to fission — this is called a **chain reaction**.
3) The **neutrons** will only cause a chain reaction if they are **slowed down**, which allows them to be **captured** by the uranium nuclei — these slowed down neutrons are called **thermal neutrons**.
4) ^{235}U **fuel rods** need to be placed in a **moderator** (for example, **water**) to **slow down** and/or absorb **neutrons**. You need to choose a moderator that will slow down some neutrons enough so they can cause **further fission**, keeping the reaction going at a steady rate. Choosing a moderator that absorbs **more neutrons the higher the temperature** will **decrease** the chance of **meltdown** if the reactor **overheats** — as it will naturally **slow down** the reaction.
5) You want the chain reaction to continue on its own at a **steady rate**, where **one** fission follows another. The amount of 'fuel' you need to do this is called the **critical mass** — any less than the critical mass (**sub-critical mass**) and the reaction will just peter out. Nuclear reactors use a **supercritical** mass of fuel (where several new fissions normally follow each fission) and **control the rate of fission** using **control rods**.
6) Control rods control the **chain reaction** by **limiting** the number of **neutrons** in the reactor. They **absorb neutrons** so that the **rate of fission** is controlled. **Control rods** are made up of a material that **absorbs neutrons** (e.g. boron), and they can be inserted by varying amounts to control the reaction rate.
In an **emergency**, the reactor will be **shut down** automatically by the **release of the control rods** into the reactor, which will stop the reaction as quickly as possible.
7) **Coolant** is sent around the reactor to **remove heat** produced by the fission — often the coolant is the **same water** that is being used in the reactor as a **moderator**. The **heat** from the reactor can then be used to make **steam** for powering **electricity-generating turbines**.

If the chain reaction in a nuclear reactor is **left to continue unchecked**, large amounts of **energy** are **released** in a very **short time**.

Many new fissions will follow each fission, causing a **runaway reaction** which could lead to an **explosion**. This is what happens in a **fission (atomic) bomb.**

Nuclear Fission and Fusion

Waste Products of Fission Must be Disposed of Carefully

1) The **waste products** of **nuclear fission** usually have a **larger proportion of neutrons** than stable nuclei of a similar atomic number — this makes them **unstable** and **radioactive**.
2) The products can be used for **practical applications** such as **tracers** in medical diagnosis (see p122).
3) However, they may be **highly radioactive** and so their **handling** and **disposal** needs **great care**.
4) When material is removed from the reactor, it is initially **very hot**, so is placed in **cooling ponds** until the **temperature falls** to a safe level.
5) The radioactive waste is then **stored** underground in **sealed containers** until its **activity has fallen** sufficiently.

Fusion Means Joining Nuclei Together

1) **Two light nuclei** can **combine** to create a larger nucleus — this is called **nuclear fusion**.
2) Nuclei can **only fuse** if they have enough energy to overcome the **electrostatic repulsive** force between them, and get close enough for the **strong interaction** to bind them.
3) Typically they need about **1 MeV** of kinetic energy — and that's **a lot of energy**.

Example

In the Sun, **hydrogen nuclei** fuse in a series of reactions to form **helium**.

$$^{2}_{1}H + ^{1}_{1}H \rightarrow ^{3}_{2}He + \text{energy}$$

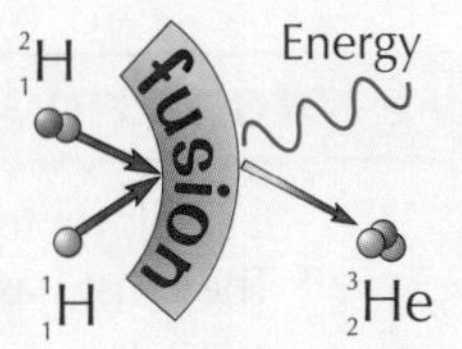

Fusion Happens in the Core of Stars

1) The **energy** emitted by the **Sun** and other stars comes from nuclear **fusion** reactions.
2) Fusion can happen because the **temperature** in the **core of stars** is so **high** — the core of the Sun is about 10^7 K.
3) At these temperatures, **atoms don't exist** — the negatively charged electrons are **stripped away**, leaving **positively charged nuclei** and **free electrons**. The resulting mixture is called a **plasma**.
4) A lot of **energy** is released during nuclear fusion because the new, heavier nuclei have a **much higher binding energy per nucleon** (see p. 54). This helps to **maintain the temperature** for further fusion reactions to happen.
5) Experimental **fusion reactors** like JET (the Joint European Torus) are trying to **recreate** these conditions to generate **electricity** (without all the nasty waste you get from fission reactors). Unfortunately, the electricity generated at the moment is **less** than the amount needed to get the reactor up to temperature. But watch this space...

Practice Questions

Q1 What is spontaneous fission?

Q2 How can fission be induced in ^{235}U?

Q3 Why must the waste products of nuclear fission be disposed of very carefully?

Q4 Describe the conditions in the core of a star.

Exam Questions

Q1 Nuclear reactors use carefully controlled chain reactions to produce energy.

(a) Explain what is meant by the expression 'chain reaction' in terms of nuclear fission. [2 marks]

(b) Describe and explain one feature of a nuclear reactor whose role is to control the rate of fission. Include an example of a suitable material for the feature you have chosen. [3 marks]

(c) Explain what happens in a nuclear reactor during an emergency shut-down. [2 marks]

Q2 Discuss two advantages and two disadvantages of using nuclear fission to produce electricity. [4 marks]

Q3 This equation shows the fusion reaction between deuterium (^2H) and tritium (^3H): $^{2}_{1}H + ^{3}_{1}H \rightarrow ^{4}_{2}He + ^{1}_{0}n + \text{energy}$

Masses: Deuterium nucleus = 2.013553 u, tritium nucleus = 3.015501 u, helium nucleus = 4.001505 u and neutron = 1.008665 u.

(a) Calculate the total mass defect for this reaction. [2 marks]

(b) How much energy is released in this reaction, if a mass defect of 1 u releases 931 MeV of energy? [1 mark]

If anyone asks, I've gone fission... that joke never gets old...

So, controlled nuclear fission reactions can provide a shedload of energy to generate electricity. There are pros and cons to using fission reactors... But then, you already knew that — now you need to learn all the grisly details.

Classification of Particles

These pages are for Edexcel Unit 4, OCR A Unit 5 and OCR B Unit 5.

There are loads of different types of particle apart from the ones you get in normal matter (protons, neutrons, etc.). They only appear in cosmic rays and in particle accelerators, and they often decay very quickly, so they're difficult to get a handle on. Nonetheless, you need to learn about a load of them and their properties.

Don't expect to really understand this (I don't) — you only need to learn it. Stick with it — you'll get there.

Hadrons are Particles that Feel the Strong Interaction (e.g. Protons and Neutrons)

1) The **nucleus** of an atom is made up from **protons** and **neutrons** held together by the strong interaction (déjà vu).
2) **Not all particles** can **feel** the **strong interaction** — the ones that **can** are called **hadrons**.
3) Hadrons aren't **fundamental** particles. They're made up of **smaller particles** called **quarks** (see page 62).
4) There are **two** types of **hadron** — **baryons** and **mesons**.

Protons and Neutrons are Baryons

1) It's helpful to think of **protons** and **neutrons** as **two versions** of the **same particle** — the **nucleon**. They just have **different electric charges**.
2) As well as **protons** and **neutrons**, there are **other baryons** that you don't get in normal matter — like **sigmas** (Σ) — they're **short-lived** and you **don't** need to **know about them** for A2 (woohoo!).

The Proton is the Only Stable Baryon

All baryons except protons decay to a **proton**.
Most physicists think that protons don't **decay**.

Some theories predict that protons should decay with a very long half-life of about 10^{32} years — but there's no experimental evidence for it at the moment.

Baryon and Meson felt the strong interaction.

The Number of Baryons in a reaction is called the Baryon Number

The **baryon number** is the number of baryons. (A bit like **nucleon number** but including unusual baryons like Σ too.)
The **proton** and the **neutron** each have a baryon number **B = +1**.
The **total baryon number** in **any** particle reaction **never changes**.

The Mesons You Need to Know About are Pions and Kaons

Edexcel and OCR A

1) **All mesons** are **unstable** and have **baryon number B = 0** (because they're not baryons).
2) **Pions** (π-mesons) are the **lightest mesons**. You get **three versions** with different **electric charges** — π^+, π^0 and π^-. Pions were **discovered** in **cosmic rays**. You get **loads** of them in **high energy particle collisions** like those studied at the **CERN** particle accelerator.
3) **Kaons** (**K**-mesons) are **heavier** and more **unstable** than **pions**. You get different ones like K^+, K^- and K^0.
4) Mesons **interact** with **baryons** via the **strong interaction**.

Pion interactions swap p's with n's and n's with p's, but leave the overall baryon number unchanged.

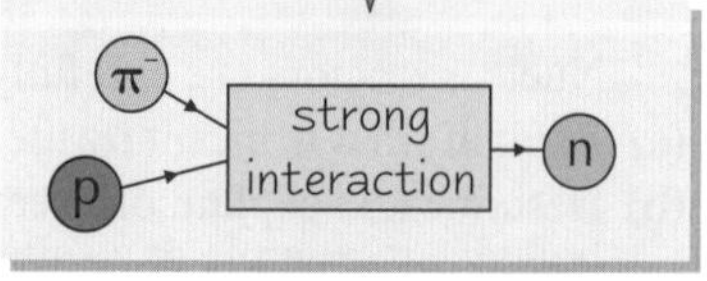

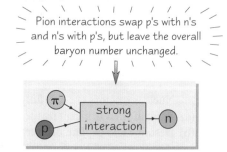

Summary of Hadron Properties

DON'T PANIC if you don't understand all this yet. For now, just **learn** these properties. You'll need to work through to the end of page 64 to see how it **all fits in**.

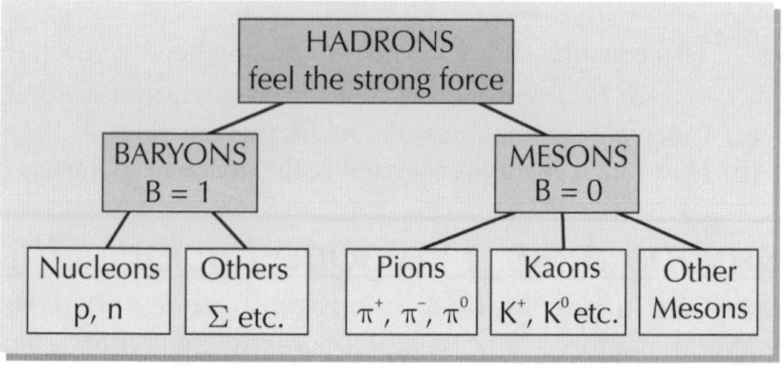

Classification of Particles

Leptons Don't feel the Strong Interaction (e.g. Electrons and Neutrinos)

1) **Leptons** are **fundamental particles** and they **don't** feel the **strong interaction**. The only way they can **interact** with other particles is via the **weak interaction** and gravity (and the electromagnetic force as well if they're charged).
2) **Electrons** (e^-) are **stable** and very **familiar** but — you guessed it — there are also **two more leptons** called the **muon** (μ^-) and the **tau** (τ^-) that are just like **heavy electrons**.
3) **Muons** and **taus** are **unstable**, and **decay** eventually into **ordinary electrons**.
4) The **electron**, **muon** and **tau** each come with their **own neutrino**: ν_e, ν_μ and ν_τ.
5) **Neutrinos** have **zero** or **almost zero mass** and **zero electric charge** — so they don't do much. **Neutrinos** only take part in **weak interactions** (see p. 63). In fact, a neutrino can **pass right through the Earth** without **anything** happening to it.

ν is the Greek letter "nu".

You Have to Count the Three Types of Lepton Separately

Each lepton is given a **lepton number** of **+1**, but the **electron**, **muon** and **tau** types of lepton have to be **counted separately**.

You get **three different** lepton numbers: L_e, L_μ and L_τ.

Name	Symbol	Charge	L_e	L_μ	L_τ
electron	e^-	−1	+1	0	0
electron neutrino	ν_e	0	+1	0	0
muon	μ^-	−1	0	+1	0
muon neutrino	ν_μ	0	0	+1	0
tau	τ^-	−1	0	0	+1
tau neutrino	ν_τ	0	0	0	+1

Like the baryon number, the lepton number is just the number of leptons.

Neutrons Decay into Protons

The **neutron** is an **unstable particle** that **decays** into a **proton**. (But it's much more stable when it's part of a nucleus.) It's really just an **example** of β^- decay, which is caused by the **weak interaction**.

$$n \rightarrow p + e^- + \bar{\nu}_e$$

The antineutrino has $L_e = -1$ so the total lepton number is zero. Antineutrino? Yes, well I haven't mentioned antiparticles yet. Just wait for the next page ...

Free neutrons (i.e. ones not held in a nucleus) have a half-life of about 15 minutes.

Practice Questions

Q1 List the differences between a hadron and a lepton.

Q2 Which is the only stable baryon?

Q3 A particle collision at CERN produces 2 protons, 3 pions and 1 neutron. What is the total baryon number of these particles?

Q4 Which two particles have lepton number $L_\tau = +1$?

Exam Questions

Q1 List all the decay products of the neutron. Explain why this decay cannot be due to the strong interaction. [3 marks]

Q2 Initially the muon was incorrectly identified as a meson. Explain why the muon is not a meson. [3 marks]

Go back to the top of page 58 — do not pass GO, do not collect £200...

Do it. Go back and read it again. I promise — read these pages about 3 or 4 times and you'll start to see a pattern. There are hadrons that feel the force, leptons that don't. Hadrons are either baryons or mesons, and they're all weird except for those well-known baryons: protons and neutrons. There are loads of leptons, including good old electrons.

Antiparticles

These pages are for Edexcel Unit 4, OCR A Unit 5 and OCR B Unit 5.

More stuff that seems to laugh in the face of common sense — but actually, antiparticles help to explain a lot in particle physics... (Oh, and if you haven't read pages 58 and 59 yet then go back and read them now — no excuses, off you go...)

Antiparticles were Predicted Before they were Discovered

When **Paul Dirac** wrote down an equation obeyed by **electrons**, he found a kind of **mirror image** solution.

1) It predicted the existence of a particle like the **electron** but with **opposite electric charge** — the **positron**.
2) The **positron** turned up later in a cosmic ray experiment. Positrons are **antileptons** so $\mathbf{L_e = -1}$ for them. They have **identical mass** to electrons but they carry a **positive** charge.

Nice one Paul. Now we've got twice as many things to worry about.

Every Particle has an Antiparticle

Each particle type has a **corresponding antiparticle** with the **same mass** but with **opposite charge**. For instance, an **antiproton** is a **negatively charged** particle with the same mass as the **proton**.

Even the shadowy **neutrino** has an antiparticle version called the **antineutrino** — it doesn't do much either.

Particle	Symbol	Charge	B	L_e	Antiparticle	Symbol	Charge	B	L_e
proton	p	+1	+1	0	antiproton	$\bar{p}$	–1	–1	0
neutron	n	0	+1	0	antineutron	$\bar{n}$	0	–1	0
electron	e	–1	0	+1	positron	e^+	+1	0	–1
electron neutrino	ν_e	0	0	+1	electron antineutrino	$\bar{\nu}_e$	0	0	–1

You can Create Matter and Antimatter from Energy

You've probably heard about the **equivalence** of energy and mass. It all comes out of Einstein's special theory of relativity. **Energy** can turn into **mass** and **mass** can turn into **energy** if you know how — all you need is one fantastic and rather famous formula. →

$$E = mc^2$$

It's a good thing this doesn't randomly happen all the time or else you could end up with cute bunny rabbits popping up and exploding unexpectedly all over the place. Oh, the horror...

As you've probably guessed, there's a bit **more to it** than that:

When **energy** is converted into **mass** you have to make **equal amounts** of **matter** and **antimatter**.

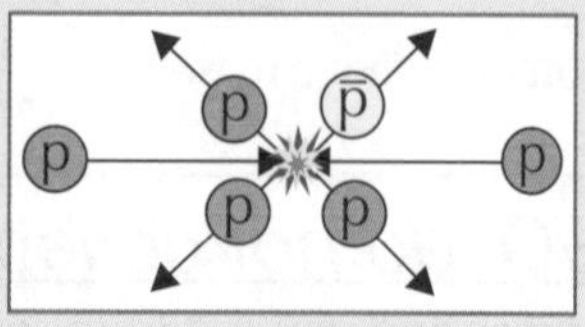

Fire **two protons** at each other at high speed and you'll end up with a lot of **energy** at the point of impact. This energy can form **more particles**.

If an extra **proton** is created, there has to be an **antiproton** made to go with it. It's called **pair production**.

Antiparticles

Each Particle-Antiparticle Pair is Produced from a Single Photon

Pair production only happens if **one gamma ray photon** has enough energy to produce that much mass. It also tends to happen near a **nucleus**, which helps conserve momentum.

You usually get **electron-positron** pairs produced (rather than any other pair) — because they have a relatively **low mass**.

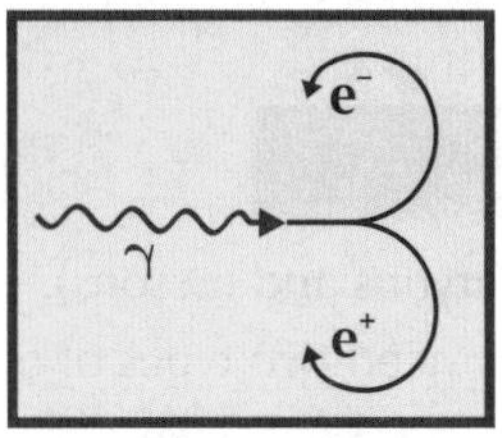

The particle tracks are curved because there's usually a magnetic field present in particle physics experiments (see p. 65). They curve in opposite directions because of the opposite charges on the electron and positron.

Example An electron and a positron are produced from a single photon. Find the minimum energy of the photon. (The rest mass of an electron $m_e = 9.11\times10^{-31}$ kg.)

The minimum energy the photon must have is enough energy to produce the particles' mass alone (the particles will have no kinetic energy).
Energy before = Energy after.
So the energy of the photon $\geq 2m_ec^2 = 2 \times 9.11\times10^{-31} \times (3\times10^8)^2 = 1.64 \times10^{-13}$ J = **1.0 MeV**

The Opposite of Pair Production is Annihilation

When a **particle** meets its **antiparticle** the result is **annihilation**. All the **mass** of the particle and antiparticle gets converted to **energy**. In ordinary matter antiparticles can only exist for a fraction of a second before this happens, so you won't see many of them.

The electron and positron annihilate and their mass is converted into the energy of a pair of gamma ray photons.

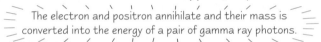

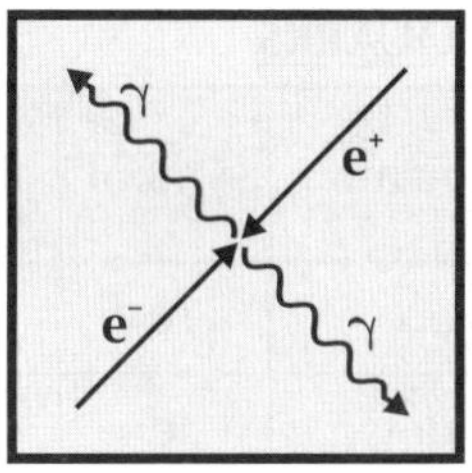

Mesons are Their Own Antiparticles

Edexcel and OCR A

Just before you leave this bit it's worth mentioning that the π^- meson is just the **antiparticle** of the π^+ meson, and the **antiparticle** of a π^0 meson is **itself**. You'll see why on p. 62. So we don't need any more particles here... Phew.

(If you don't know what a meson is, look back at page 58.)

Practice Questions

Q1 Which antiparticle has zero charge and a baryon number of –1?

Q2 Describe the properties of an electron antineutrino.

Q3 What is pair production? What happens when a proton collides with an antiproton?

Exam Questions

Q1 Write down an equation for the reaction between a positron and an electron and give the name for this type of reaction. [2 marks]

Q2 According to Einstein, mass and energy are equivalent. Explain why the mass of a block of iron cannot be converted directly into energy. [2 marks]

Q3 Give a reason why the reaction $\mathbf{p + p \rightarrow p + p + n}$ is not possible. [1 mark]

Q4 An electron and a positron each have a kinetic energy of 300 MeV and a rest mass of 9.11×10^{-31} kg. They annihilate to produce two photons. Find the energy of one of the photons produced. [3 marks]

Now stop meson around and do some work...

The idea of every particle having an antiparticle might seem a bit strange, but just make sure you know the main points — a) if energy is converted into a particle, you also get an antiparticle, b) an antiparticle won't last long before it bumps into the right particle and annihilates it with a big ba-da-boom, c) this releases the energy it took to make them to start with...

Quarks

These pages are for Edexcel Unit 4, OCR A Unit 5 and OCR B Unit 5.

*If you haven't read pages 58 to 61, do it now! For the rest of you — here are the **juicy bits** you've been waiting for. Particle physics makes **a lot more sense** when you look at quarks. More sense than it did before anyway.*

Quarks are Fundamental Particles

Quarks are the **building blocks** for **hadrons** (baryons and mesons).

If that first sentence doesn't make much sense to you, read pages 58-61 — you have been warned... twice.

1) To make **protons** and **neutrons** you only need two types of quark — the **up** quark (**u**) and the **down** quark (**d**).
2) An extra one called the **strange** quark (**s**) lets you make more particles with a property called **strangeness**.
3) There are another three types of quark called **top**, **bottom** and **charm** (tut... physicists) that were predicted from the symmetry of the quark model. But luckily you don't have to know much about them...

The antiparticles of hadrons are made from **antiquarks**.

Quarks and Antiquarks have Opposite Properties

The **antiquarks** have **opposite properties** to the quarks — as you'd expect.

QUARKS

name	symbol	charge	baryon number	strangeness
up	u	$+\frac{2}{3}$	$+\frac{1}{3}$	0
down	d	$-\frac{1}{3}$	$+\frac{1}{3}$	0
strange	s	$-\frac{1}{3}$	$+\frac{1}{3}$	–1

ANTIQUARKS

name	symbol	charge	baryon number	strangeness
anti-up	$\bar{u}$	$-\frac{2}{3}$	$-\frac{1}{3}$	0
anti-down	$\bar{d}$	$+\frac{1}{3}$	$-\frac{1}{3}$	0
anti-strange	$\bar{s}$	$+\frac{1}{3}$	$-\frac{1}{3}$	+1

Baryons are Made from Three Quarks

Evidence for quarks came from **hitting protons** with **high energy electrons**.
The way the **electrons scattered** showed that there were **three concentrations of charge** (quarks) **inside** the proton.

Proton = **uud**

Total charge = 2/3 + 2/3 – 1/3 = 1

Baryon number = 1/3 + 1/3 + 1/3 = 1

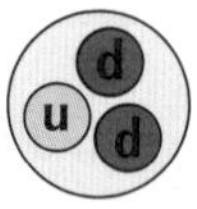

Neutron = **udd**

Total charge = 2/3 – 1/3 – 1/3 = 0

Baryon number = 1/3 + 1/3 + 1/3 = 1

Antiprotons are $\bar{u}\bar{u}\bar{d}$ and antineutrons are $\bar{u}\bar{d}\bar{d}$ — so no surprises there then.

Mesons are a Quark and an Antiquark

Edexcel and OCR A

Pions are just made from **up** and **down** quarks and their **antiquarks**.
Kaons have **strangeness** so you need to put in **s** quarks as well (remember that the **s** quark has a strangeness of S = –1).

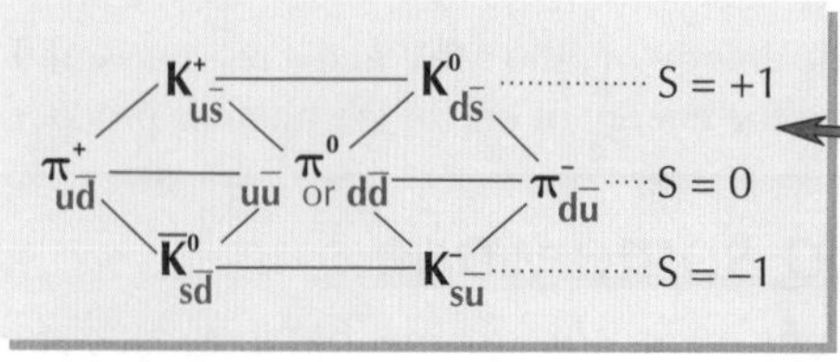

Physicists love patterns. Gaps in patterns like this predicted the existence of particles that were actually found later in experiments. Great stuff.

Quarks

There's no Such Thing as a Free Quark

What if you **blasted** a **proton** with **enough energy** — could you **separate out** the quarks? Nope. The energy just gets changed into more **quarks and antiquarks** — it's **pair production** again and you just make **mesons**. This is called **quark confinement**.

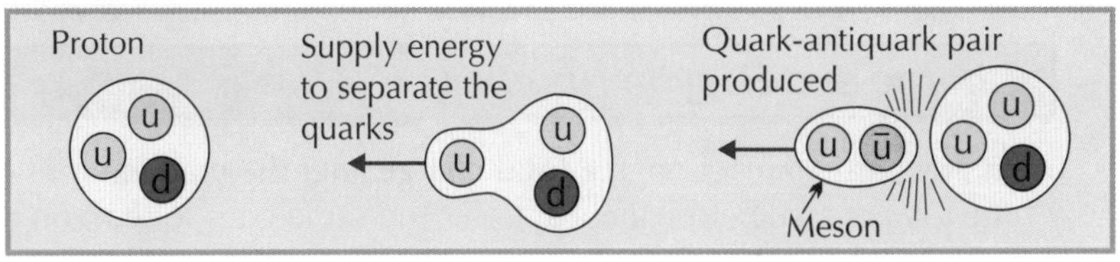

Gluons Provide Force Between Quarks

OCR B only

1) When two particles **interact**, something must **happen** to let one particle know that the other one's there. That's the idea behind **exchange particles**. You can picture them if you think about **balls** and **boomerangs**:

Repulsion — Each time the ball is thrown or caught the people get **pushed apart**. It happens because the ball carries **momentum**.

Attraction — Each time the boomerang is thrown or caught the people **get pushed together**. (In real life, you'd probably fall in first.)

The particles don't actually loop round like that, though.

The exchange particles are called **gauge bosons** — they're virtual particles that only last for a very short time.

2) **All forces in nature** are caused by four **fundamental** forces. Each one has its **own gauge boson**:

Type of Interaction	Gauge Boson	Particles Affected
strong	gluon	hadrons only
electromagnetic	photon	charged particles only
weak	W^+, W^-, Z^0	all types
gravity	graviton?	all types

Particle physicists never bother about gravity because it's so incredibly feeble compared with the other types of interaction. Gravity only really matters when you've got big masses like stars and planets. The graviton may exist but there's no evidence for it.

3) The exchange particle that causes the **strong force** that 'glues' hadrons like protons and neutrons together is imaginatively called the **gluon**.
4) Because they cause a force, you can think of them as **fields** as well as particles. It's just the same as thinking of a **gravitational force** as being caused by a **gravitational field**.
5) As you try to **separate** quarks, you actually **increase** the **energy** of the gluon field, **increasing** the **attraction** between them.
6) If you keep pulling, eventually the energy in the gluon field will be enough that it produces a **quark-antiquark pair**. This is why you can **never** detect a quark on its own.

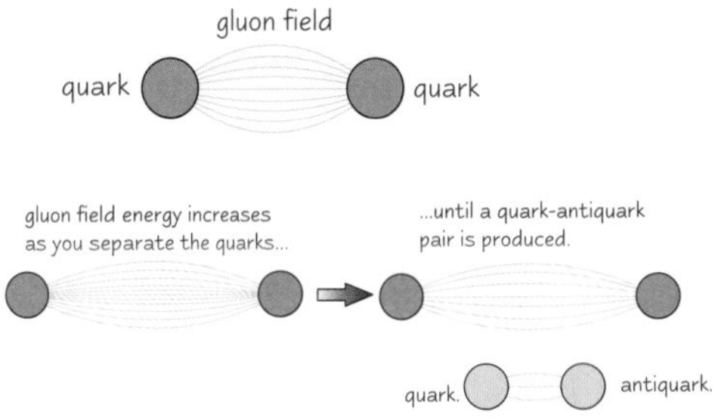

The Weak Interaction is something that Changes the Quark Type

OCR A only

In β^- decay a **neutron** is changed into a **proton** — in other words **udd** changes into **uud**. It means turning a **d** quark into a **u** quark. Only the weak interaction can do this.

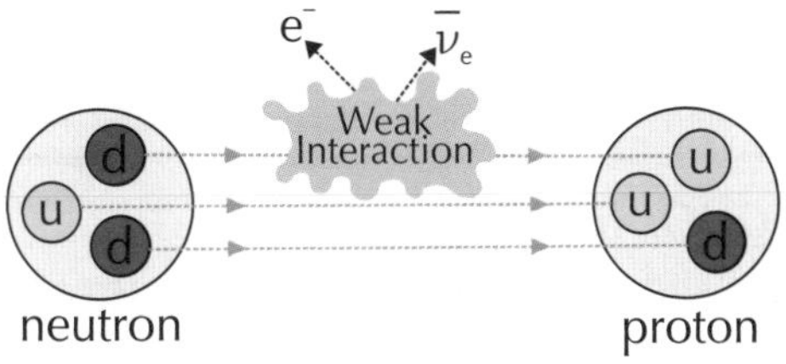

Some unstable isotopes like **carbon-11** decay by β^+ emission. In this case a **proton** changes to a **neutron**, so a **u** quark changes to a **d** quark and we get:

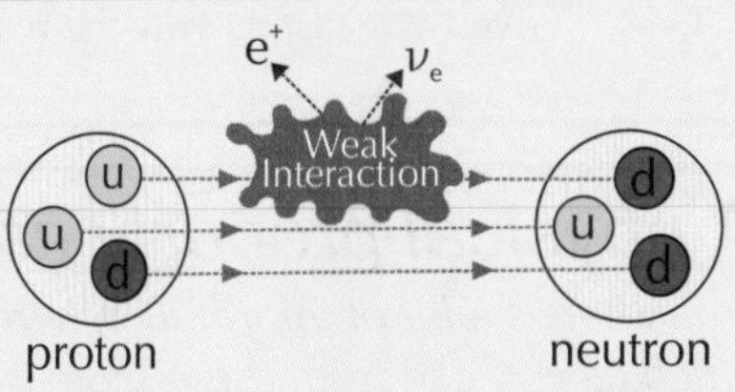

Quarks

More conservation? This is starting to sound like biology...

Four Properties are Conserved in Particle Reactions

Edexcel and OCR A

Charge and Baryon Number are Always Conserved

In **any** particle reaction, the **total charge** after the reaction must equal the total charge before the reaction. The same goes for **baryon number**.

Strangeness is Conserved in Strong Interactions

The **only** way to change the **type** of quark is with the **weak interaction**, so in strong interactions there has to be the same number of strange quarks at the beginning as at the end.

The reaction $K^- + p \rightarrow n + \pi^0$ is fine for **charge** and **baryon number** but not for **strangeness** — so it won't happen. The negative kaon has an **s** quark in it.

Conservation of Lepton Number is a Bit More Complicated

The **three types** of lepton number have to be conserved **separately**.

1) For example, the reaction $\pi^- \rightarrow \mu^- + \bar{\nu}_\mu$ has $L_\mu = 0$ at the start and $L_\mu = 1 - 1 = 0$ at the end, so it's OK.

2) On the other hand, the reaction $\nu_\mu + \mu^- \rightarrow e^- + \nu_e$ can't happen. At the start $L_\mu = 2$ and $L_e = 0$ but at the end $L_\mu = 0$ and $L_e = 2$.

Sid had been conserving his strangeness for years...

Practice Questions

Q1 What is a quark?

Q2 Which type of particle is made from a quark and an antiquark?

Q3 Describe how a neutron is made up from quarks.

Q4 Name the exchange particle for the strong force felt between two quarks.

Q5 Explain why quarks are never observed on their own.

Q6 List four quantities that are conserved in particle reactions.

Exam Questions

Q1 State the combination of three quarks that make up a proton. [1 mark]

Q2 Give the quark composition of the π^- and explain how the charges of the quarks give rise to its charge. [2 marks]

Q3 Explain how the quark composition is changed in the β^- decay of the neutron. [2 marks]

Q4 Give two reasons why the reaction $p + p \rightarrow p + K^+$ does not happen. [2 marks]

A physical property called strangeness — how cool is that...

True, there's a lot of information here, but this page really does tie up a lot of the stuff on the last few pages. Learn as much as you can from these three pages, then go back to page 58, and work back through to here. Don't expect to understand it all — but you will definitely find it much easier to learn when you can see how all the bits fit together.

Detecting Particles

These pages are for Edexcel Unit 4 only.

Luckily for us, charged particles affect atoms as they pass by — which means we can see what's going on...

Charged Particles Leave Tracks

When a charged particle passes through a substance it causes **ionisation** — electrons are knocked out of atoms. The particle leaves a **trail of ions** as it goes.

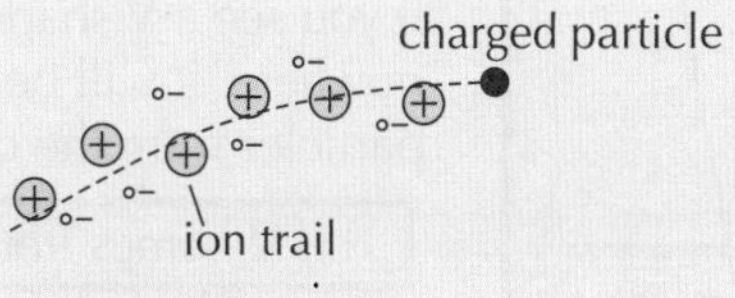

The easiest way to **detect** the particle is if you somehow make the **trail of ions show up** and then take a **photo**.

Ion tracks Cindy, not iron tracks...

Cloud Chambers and Bubble Chambers detect Charged Particles

1) **Cloud chambers** work using a **supercooled vapour** — that's something that's still a gas below its usual condensation temperature. The ions left by particles make the vapour **condense** and you get "**vapour trails**" (a bit like the ones left by jet planes). Heavy, **short** tracks mean lots of ionisation, so those will be the **α-particles**. Fainter, **long** tracks are **β-particles**.

A cloud chamber photograph from an alpha source would look like this:

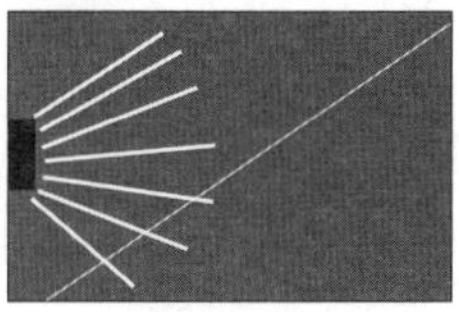

The thin line is a cosmic ray particle.

2) **Bubble chambers** are a bit like cloud chambers in reverse. Hydrogen is kept as a **liquid** above its normal **boiling point** by putting it under **pressure**. If the pressure is suddenly **reduced**, **bubbles of gas** will start to form in the places where there is a trail of ions. You have to take the photo **quickly** before the bubbles grow too big.
3) Both chambers only show up **charged particles**.

Charged Particles are Affected by a Magnetic Field

1) A **charged particle** in a **magnetic field** will experience a **force** — making the particle follow a **curved track**. (See Section Two.)

The radius of a charged particle's curved track, ***r***, is given by the equation:
The **larger** the curve **radius**, the **greater** the particle's **momentum**.

$$r = \frac{p}{BQ}$$

where p is the particle's momentum, B is the strength of the magnetic field and Q is the charge on the particle.

2) Positive and negative particles curve **opposite** ways — you can find out which is which using **Fleming's** left-hand rule (see p24).
3) You don't see neat circular patterns, but instead see **spirals**, as interactions with the detector decrease the energy (and so the momentum) of the particle.
4) You can also use this equation to find the magnetic field you need to keep a charge in a particular radius of circular path — very handy when you're dealing with **particle accelerators** (see p 68).

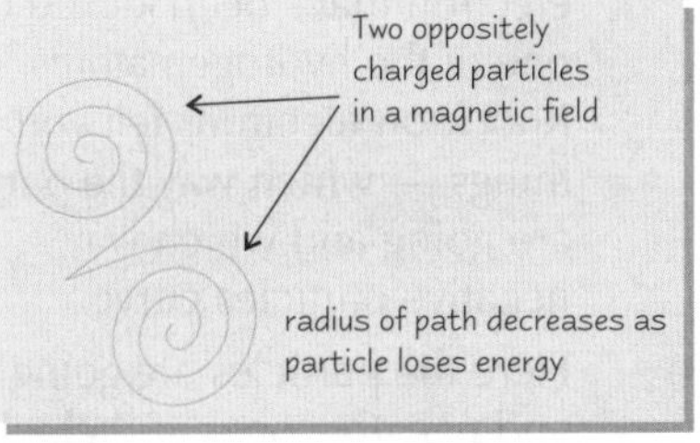

Charge, Energy and Momentum are Always Conserved

1) When you're looking at particle interactions and trying to work out what the blazes is going on, remember that **charge**, **momentum** and **energy** are always conserved.
2) If they're not conserved for the reaction you think you're looking at, you know you've got it wrong — it can't have happened.

Detecting Particles

And now for the best bit — the pretty pictures...

Neutral Particles Only Show Up When They Decay

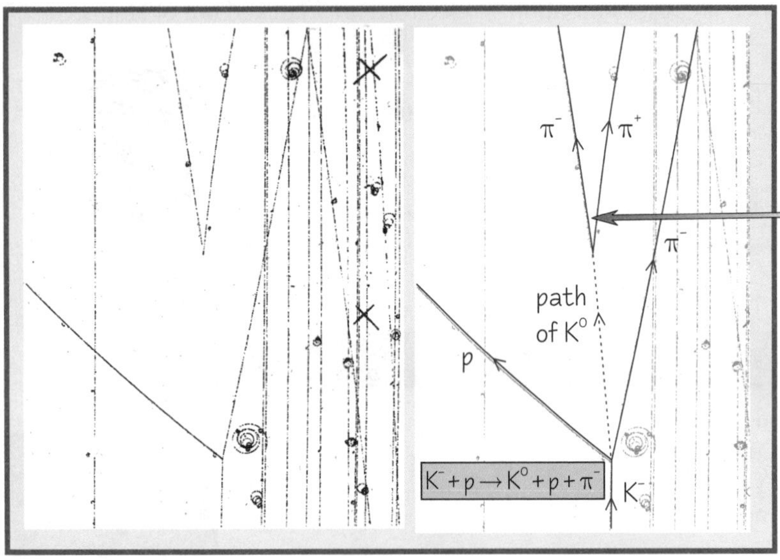

Here the particles have so much momentum that the tracks are almost straight.

Remember that **neutral** particles **don't** make tracks. You can only see them when they **decay** or **interact**.

If you see a **V** shape starting in the middle of nowhere, it will be two oppositely charged particles from the decay of a neutral particle.

This V comes from the decay $K^0 \rightarrow \pi^+ + \pi^-$

The **distance** from the **interaction point** to the V depends on the **half-life** of the neutral particle. Longer-lived particles travel **further** on average before they decay — but you have to be careful.

The particles are travelling **close to the speed of light** so relativistic **time dilation** (aaarghhh — see p. 136) makes them survive for much longer than normal.

Real Bubble Chamber Photographs can be a bit Intimidating

At first sight the photo might look a bit of a mess with tracks everywhere.
Don't panic — start by finding the incoming beam...

1) The **straight** lines are from the incoming beam. Several particles will go straight through without doing anything — you can just ignore them.
2) Look for a little spiral coming from one of the straight tracks. It shows a **knock-on electron** — an electron that's been kicked out of one of the hydrogen atoms. Knock-on electrons tell you **two** things — **which way** the particles are going and which way negative particles **curve**.
3) Here the particles are going **up** and **negative** ones curl **clockwise**.
4) Find a **point** with **several** curved tracks coming from it — that's a reaction. You can identify positively and negatively charged particles from the **way they curve**.

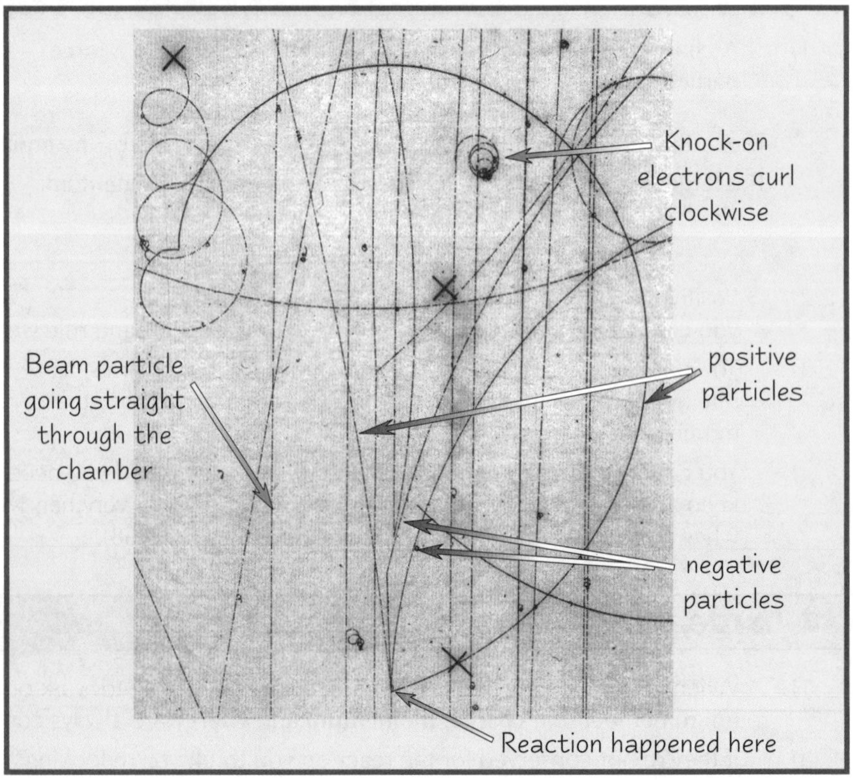

Detecting Particles

You can Calculate the Particle's **Momentum**

From the **radius** of the track, you can find the **momentum** of a particle.

Example

Particle X is an unstable neutral particle that quickly decays into a positron and an electron while in a bubble chamber. Both the electron and positron follow circular tracks in a 1.2×10^{-4} T magnetic field with an initial radius of 260 m.

Find the initial momentum of the electron ($e = 1.6 \times 10^{-19}$ C).

Using $r = \frac{p}{BQ}$, so $p = rBQ = 260 \times 1.2 \times 10^{-4} \times 1.6 \times 10^{-19}$ = **5.0×10^{-21} kgms^{-1}**

Cloud Chambers and **Bubble Chambers aren't used** Any More

Nowadays, particle physicists use detectors that give out **electrical signals** that are sent **straight** to a **computer**. It's a bit easier than having a whole team of scientists squinting over thousands of photos. Modern detectors include **drift chambers**, **scintillation counters** and **solid state detectors**. You don't need to know any details about these for the exam.

Practice Questions

Q1 Describe how a cloud chamber works.

Q2 Explain the operation of a bubble chamber.

Q3 Which particles don't show up in bubble chamber photos?

Q4 How does the track of an electron show that the electron is losing energy?

Q5 Explain why a positron and an electron will move in opposite directions in a magnetic field.

Q6 Write down the equation used to relate the radius of a circular path taken by a charged particle in a magnetic field to the particle's momentum.

Exam Questions

Q1 Explain how the charges of particles can be found from their tracks in bubble chamber photographs. [3 marks]

Q2 Suggest one reason why antineutrinos are harder to detect than beta particles. [1 mark]

Q3 The reaction $\mathbf{p} + \mathbf{p} \rightarrow \mathbf{p} + \mathbf{n} + \pi^+ + \pi^0$ occurs in a bubble chamber.
Which products of this reaction will form tracks? [1 mark]

Q4 A photon, travelling through a bubble chamber, is converted into an $\mathbf{e^-}\,\mathbf{e^+}$ pair.
Draw a sketch showing the tracks that would be formed by this reaction. [3 marks]

Q5 Particle Y decays to form an electron and a positron in a cloud chamber. The electron leaves a track with an initial radius of 3.2 m in a magnetic field of 1.8×10^{-6} T. Find the momentum of the electron. [2 marks]

Look, there's one... →·

*Typical. They now have an easy way of detecting particles — but you have to learn the methods that are a) harder, and b) now completely obsolete. *sigh* I suppose it's quite nice to actually see the pictures though.*

Particle Accelerators

These pages are for Edexcel Unit 4 and OCR B Unit 5.

Particle accelerators are devices that (surprisingly) accelerate particles, using electric and magnetic fields. Accelerated particles can be used to investigate the fundamental particles that make up matter...

Particle Accelerators Cause High-Energy Collisions

There are lots of different types of accelerator out there smashing particles together. One of the main types is the linear accelerator (a **linac**)...

1) A **linear accelerator** is a long **straight** tube containing a series of **electrodes**.
2) **Alternating current** is applied to the electrodes so that their **charge** continuously **changes** between + and –.
3) The alternating current is **timed** so that the particles are always **attracted** to the **next electrode** in the accelerator and **repelled** from the **previous** one.
4) A particle's **speed** will **increase** each time it **passes** an electrode — so if the accelerator is long enough particles can be made to approach the **speed of light**.
5) The **high-energy particles** leaving a linear accelerator **collide** with a **fixed target** at the end of the tube.

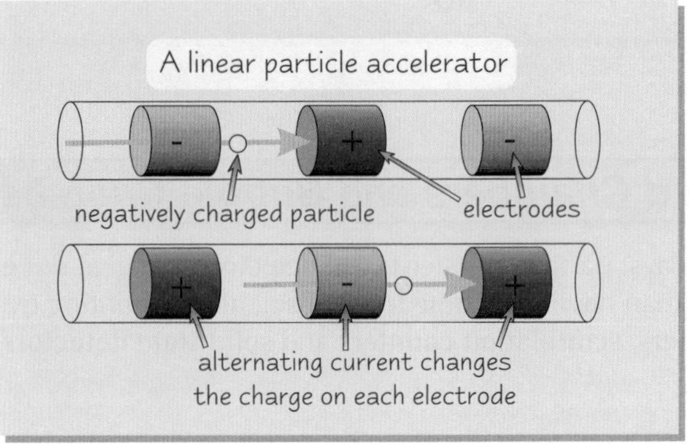

A Cyclotron is a Circular Particle Accelerator

Edexcel only

1) A cyclotron uses **two semicircular electrodes** to accelerate protons or other charged particles across a gap.
2) Since it is **circular**, a cyclotron can take up **much less room** than a linear accelerator.
3) An **alternating potential difference** is applied between the electrodes — as the **particles** are **attracted** from one side to the other their **energy increases** (i.e. they are **accelerated**).
4) A **magnetic field** is used to keep the particles moving in a **circular motion** (in the diagram on the right, the magnetic field would be perpendicular to the page).
5) The combination of the **electric** and **magnetic fields** makes the particles **spiral outwards** as their energy increases.

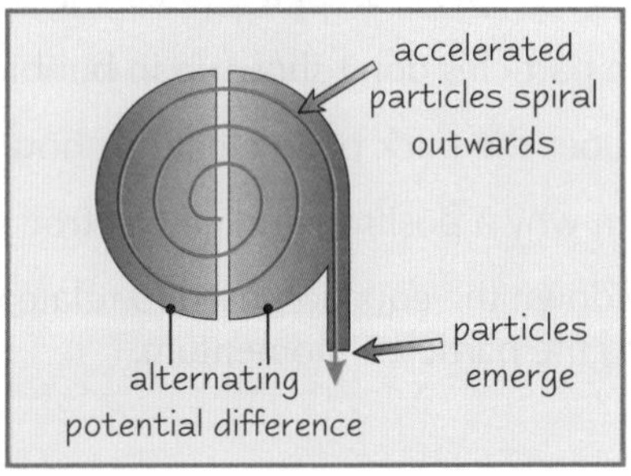

Energies in Particle Accelerators are Measured in Electronvolts

1) The **kinetic energies** of individual particles are so small that it makes sense to use a more appropriate unit than the joule.
2) The **electronvolt** (**eV**) (defined on p.124) is used instead.
3) Here are some handy **conversion factors**:

1 **eV**		$= 1.6 \times 10^{-19}$ J
1 **keV**	$= 10^3$ eV	$= 1.6 \times 10^{-16}$ J
1 **MeV**	$= 10^6$ eV	$= 1.6 \times 10^{-13}$ J
1 **GeV**	$= 10^9$ eV	$= 1.6 \times 10^{-10}$ J
1 **TeV**	$= 10^{12}$ eV	$= 1.6 \times 10^{-7}$ J

Particle Accelerators

The Mass of Particles Increases with Speed

1) According to **special relativity** (see p.136), as you **accelerate** an object you **increase** its **mass**.
2) The increase in mass **isn't usually noticeable**, it's only when you get close to the **speed of light** that it starts to have a **big effect**.
3) This means that as an object, like a **particle** in an **accelerator**, **travels faster and faster** its **mass gets greater and greater**. As the mass of the particle increases, it gets **harder** to accelerate it.
4) This effect **limits** how much you can accelerate a particle in a cyclotron. Protons can be accelerated to energies of around **20 MeV**. If you want higher energies than that, you have to use a different type of accelerator called a **synchrotron**.

Kim knew that slowing down wouldn't decrease her mass — but it was a good excuse.

Synchrotrons Produce Very High Energy Beams

1) A **synchrotron** can produce particle collisions with much **higher energies** than either a linear accelerator or a cyclotron.
2) **Electromagnets** keeps the particles in a **circular path** by increasing the **magnetic field** strength to compensate for increases in **mass**.
3) Magnets are also used to keep the particles in **focused beams**.
4) In this way, **synchrotrons** can produce particles with energies reaching from **500 GeV to several TeV**.

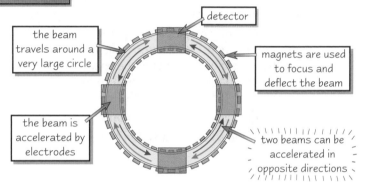

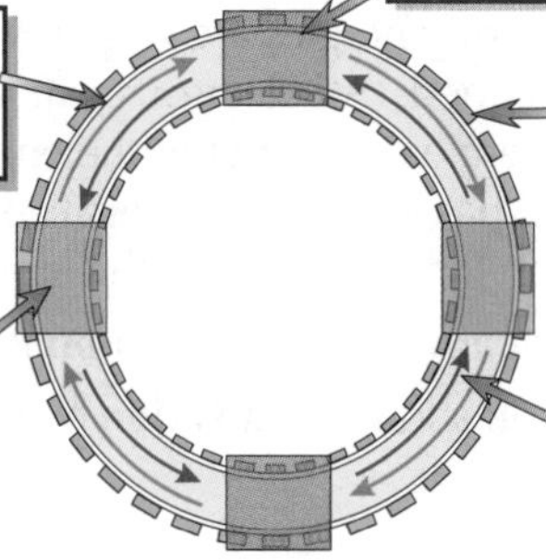
detector
the beam travels around a very large circle
magnets are used to focus and deflect the beam
the beam is accelerated by electrodes
two beams can be accelerated in opposite directions

The Relativistic Factor — $E_{tot} \div E_{rest}$

OCR B only

The **relativistic factor**, γ, is the total energy of a particle travelling with $v \gg c$ divided by the rest energy of the particle.

$$\gamma = \frac{E_{tot}}{E_{rest}}$$

$$E_{rest} = mc^2$$

Example An electron is accelerated to almost the speed of light. It has a rest energy of 5.1×10^5 eV. If $\gamma = 235$, find the total energy of the accelerated electron in MeV.

$$E_{tot} = \gamma \times E_{rest} = 235 \times 5.1 \times 10^5$$
$$= 1.2 \times 10^8 \text{ eV} = \mathbf{120\ MeV}$$

Practice Questions

Q1 Explain how particles are accelerated in a linear accelerator.

Q2 What forces act on a particle in a cyclotron?

Q3 Which type of accelerator is able to produce the highest energy particles?

Exam Questions

Q1 A cyclotron is used to accelerate particles to very high speeds.
Outline the function of the electric and magnetic fields in a cyclotron. [2 marks]

Q2 A proton with a rest mass of 1.7×10^{-27} kg is accelerated by a synchrotron to a total energy of 500 GeV.
Show that the relativistic factor for a proton of this energy is about 500. [4 marks]

Smash high-energy particles together to see what they're made of...

So, the three types of particle accelerator all have their advantages, but the synchrotron wins hands down on making very high energy particles for investigating fundamental particles. A famous synchrotron (in the physics world) is the Large Hadron Collider (LHC) found at CERN on the Swiss-French border — this accelerator is a whopping 27 km loop...

Electron Energy Levels

These pages are for OCR B Unit 5 only.

Electrons only exist in set energy levels. They leap into higher energy levels when they get excited.

Electrons in Atoms Exist in Discrete Energy Levels

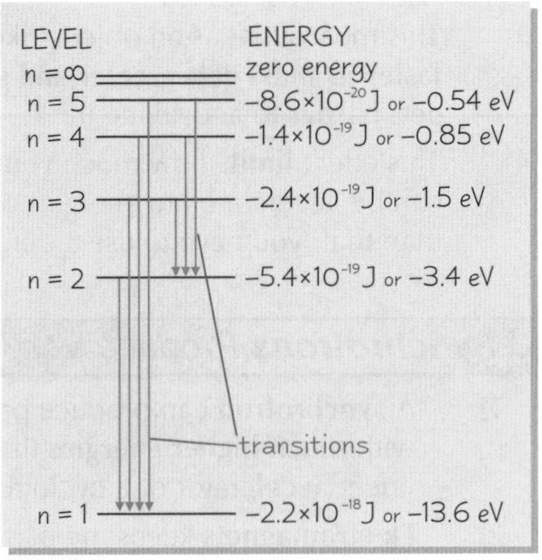

1) **Electrons** in an **atom** can **only exist** in certain **well-defined energy levels**. Each level is given a **number** (called the **principal quantum number** of the electron in that state), with ***n* = 1** representing the electron's lowest possible energy — its **ground state**.
2) Electrons can **move down** an energy level by **emitting** a **photon**.
3) Since these **transitions** are between **definite energy levels**, the **energy** of **each photon** emitted can **only** take **certain values**.
4) The diagram on the right shows the **energy levels** for **atomic hydrogen**.
5) On the diagram, energies are labelled in **both eV** (see p. 68) and **joules** for **comparison**.
6) All the electron energies are negative because of the way the zero energy is defined. All electrons that are **bound** to the atom have **negative** energies. The higher the energy level, the more energy the electron has and the less negative the energy. An electron is 'free' and no longer bound to the atom when it has a **potential energy** of **zero** — the atom becomes **ionised**.
7) The **energy** carried by each **photon** is **equal** to the **difference in energies** between the **two levels**. This equation shows a **transition** between levels ***n* = 2** and ***n* = 1**:

$$\Delta E = E_2 - E_1 = hf = \frac{hc}{\lambda}$$

(You should recognise these equations for photon energy from AS, but take a look at page 130 if you need a quick recap.)

8) In the same way, atoms can only **absorb** allowed photon energies. This **quantisation** of electron energies in atoms produces **line emission** and **absorption spectra** (see below).

Electrons (as well as protons and neutrons) are **fermions**. That means they obey the **Pauli exclusion principle**. This states that **no two fermions** can be in **exactly** the same **quantum state** at the same time. In the context of energy levels, that means **no more than two** electrons can be in the same **energy level** at the same time.

The Evidence — Line Spectra

1) The **spectrum** of **white light** is **continuous**.
2) If you **split** the **light** up with a **prism**, the **colours** all **merge** into each other — there **aren't** any **gaps** in the spectrum.

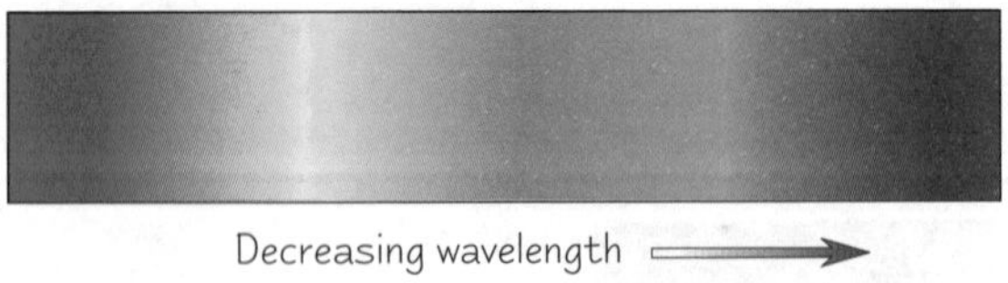

3) You get a **line absorption spectrum** when **light** with a **continuous spectrum** passes through a cool gas.
4) At **low temperatures**, **most** of the **electrons** in the **gas atoms** will be in their **ground states**.
5) **Photons** of the **correct wavelength** are **absorbed** by the **electrons** to **excite** them to **higher energy levels**.
6) These **wavelengths** are then **missing** from the **continuous spectrum** when it **comes out** the other side of the gas.
7) You see a **continuous spectrum** with **black lines** in it corresponding to the **absorbed wavelengths**.
8) When an electron falls into a **lower** energy level, it **emits** a photon. **Emission spectra** show the wavelengths of photons emitted. They are made up of a series of **bright lines** corresponding to the **wavelengths emitted**.
9) If you **compare** the **absorption** and **emission spectra** of a **particular gas**, the **black lines** in the **absorption spectrum match up** to the **bright lines** in the **emission spectrum**.

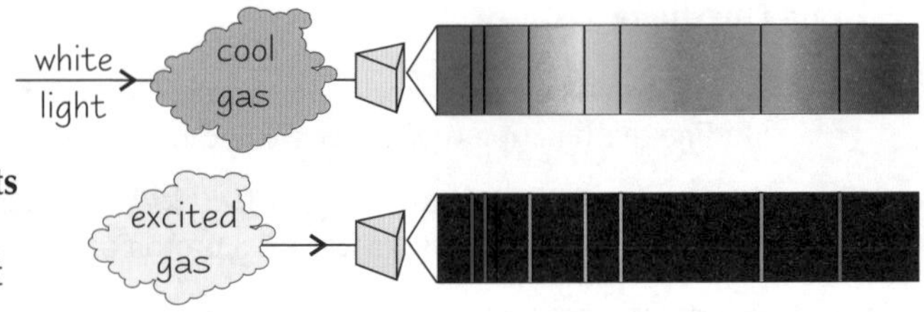

Electron Energy Levels

The *Wave Model* of the *Atom* can Help you Understand *Energy Levels*

1) Since light has both **particle** and **wave** characteristics (see p. 132), de Broglie suggested that **electrons** should have a **wave-like character**.
2) Specifically, when they're in orbit **around a nucleus** they ought to behave like the **standing waves** that are formed on a guitar string when it's plucked.
3) Just as standing waves on the guitar string only exist at certain **well-defined frequencies**, only certain standing waves are possible in an atom.
4) The **wavelength** of the electron waves should fit the **circumference** of the orbit a **whole number** of times.
5) The **principal quantum number** (corresponding to the number of the energy level) is equal to the number of **complete waves** that fit the circumference.

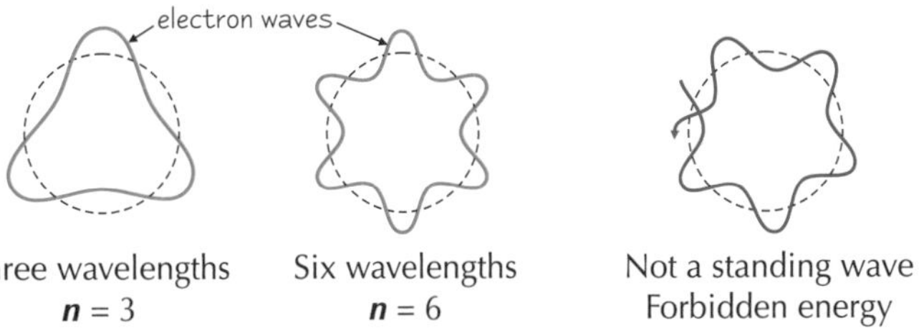

6) You can think of the electrons as being trapped by a **potential well** made by the nucleus. That way you can think of them as being standing waves between **two fixed walls**... so it's even more like a guitar string.
7) Erwin Schrödinger used the standing wave model and found that the **energy levels** in a **hydrogen atom** are given by:

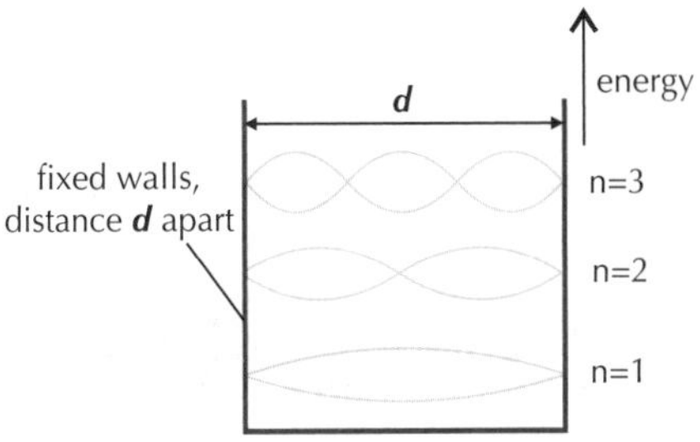

$$E_n = \frac{-13.6\ \text{eV}}{n^2}$$

Practice Questions

Q1 Write down the equation you would use to find the difference in energy between two energy levels in an atom.

Q2 Describe the standing-wave model of electrons in an atom.

Q3 Describe how line spectra show the existence of discrete energy levels in atoms.

Exam Questions

Q1 The Balmer series is a series of spectral lines emitted by excited hydrogen atoms. One Balmer line is caused by photons with a frequency of 4.57×10^{14} Hz.

(a) Find the energy of the photons that make up this line ($h = 6.6 \times 10^{-34}$ Js). [2 marks]

(b) The diagram shows some of the energy levels in a hydrogen atom. Draw an arrow to show the energy level transition that causes this spectral line. [1 mark]

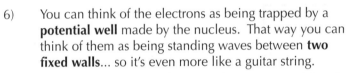

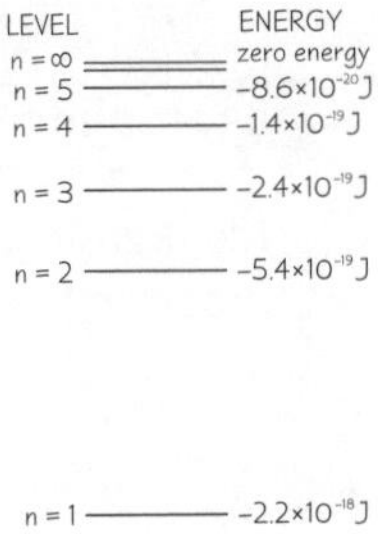

Q2 The second is defined using the radiation from a particular quantum jump in the caesium-133 atom. The difference in energy levels is 3.8×10^{-5} eV.

(a) Calculate the frequency of this radiation ($h = 6.6 \times 10^{-34}$ Js). [2 marks]

(b) How many oscillations occur in 1 second, as used in the definition of the second? [1 mark]

My energy level's about n = 1 after that — I need chocolate...

I always find this the trickiest stuff to get — I mean, it's not like you can see an electron skipping about inside an atom every day, and the whole quarks and leptons stuff sounds like the cast list for a cheap sci-fi film. Once you've been through it all a few times though it does start to click, so stick with it and soon it'll be as easy as an electron transition from n = 2 to n = 1.

Ideal Gases

These pages are for AQA A Unit 5, Edexcel Unit 5, OCR A Unit 4 and OCR B Unit 4.

*Aaahh... great... another one of those 'our equation doesn't work properly with **real gases**, so we'll invent an **ideal** gas that it **does work** for and they'll think we're dead clever' situations. Hmm. Physicists, eh...*

There's an Absolute Scale of Temperature

There is a **lowest possible temperature** called **absolute zero***. Absolute zero is given a value of **zero kelvin**, written **0 K**, on the absolute temperature scale.

At **0 K** all particles have the **minimum** possible **kinetic energy** — everything pretty much stops — at higher temperatures, particles have more energy. In fact, with the **Kelvin scale**, a particle's **energy** is **proportional** to its **temperature** (see page 77).

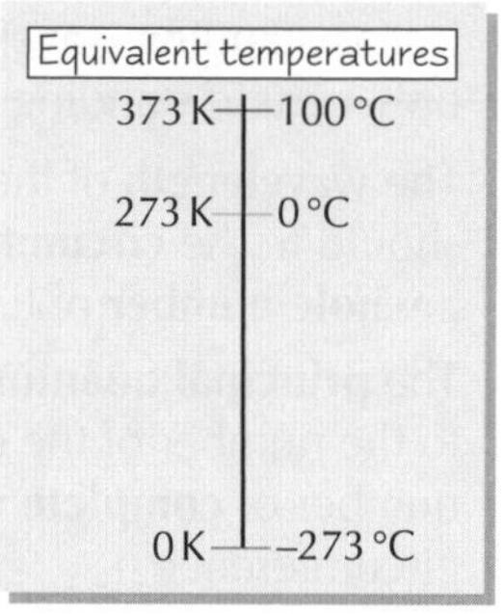

1) The Kelvin scale is named after Lord Kelvin who first suggested it.
2) A change of **1 K** equals a change of **1 °C**.
3) To change from degrees Celsius into kelvin you **add 273** (or 273.15 if you need to be really precise).

$$K = C + 273$$

All equations in **thermal physics** use temperatures measured in kelvin.

It's true. –273.15 °C is the lowest temperature theoretically possible. Weird, huh. You'd kinda think there wouldn't be a minimum, but there is.

There are Three Gas Laws

The three gas laws were each worked out **independently** by **careful experiment**. Each of the gas laws applies to a **fixed mass** of gas.

Boyle's Law

At a **constant temperature** the **pressure *p*** and **volume *V*** of a gas are **inversely proportional**.

A (theoretical) gas that obeys Boyle's law at all temperatures is called an **ideal gas**.

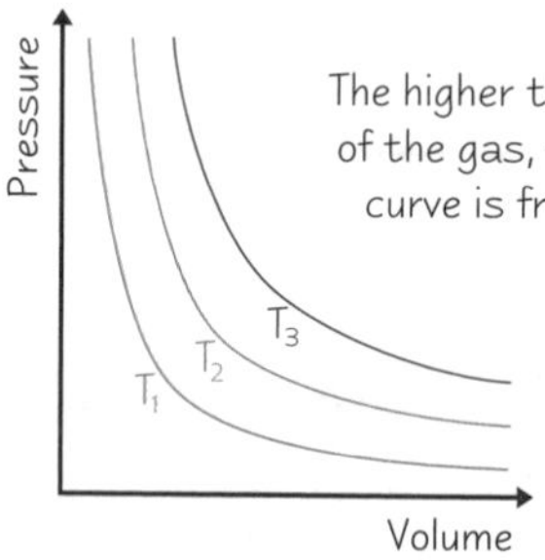

The higher the temperature of the gas, the further the curve is from the origin.

$$pV = \text{constant}$$

Charles' Law

At constant **pressure**, the **volume *V*** of a gas is **directly proportional** to its **absolute temperature *T***.

Ideal gases obey this law and the pressure law as well.

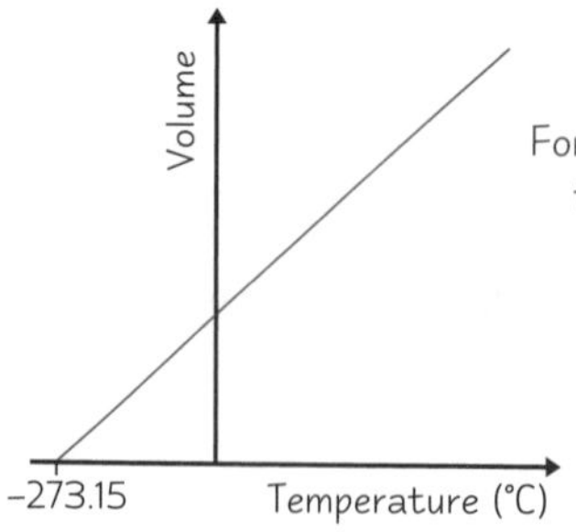

For any ideal gas, the line meets the temperature axis at –273.15 °C — that is, absolute zero.

$$V/T = \text{constant}$$

'Ello, 'ello...

If you'd plotted these graphs in kelvin, they'd both have gone through the origin.

The Pressure Law

At constant **volume**, the **pressure *p*** of a gas is **directly proportional** to its **absolute temperature *T***.

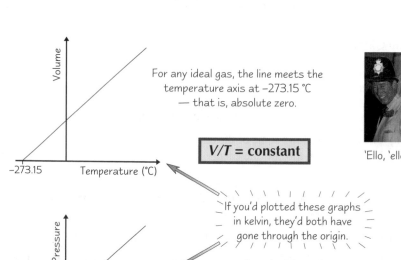

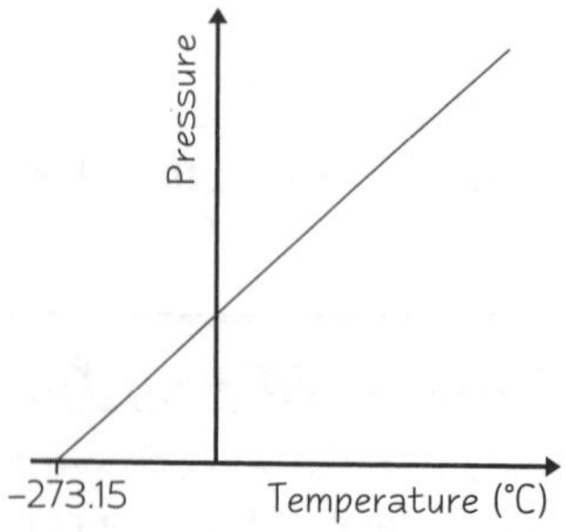

$$p/T = \text{constant}$$

Ideal Gases

If you Combine All Three you get the Ideal Gas Equation

Combining all three gas laws gives the equation: $\frac{pV}{T} = $ **constant**

1) The constant in the equation depends on the amount of gas used. ← (Pretty obvious... if you have more gas it takes up more space.)
   The amount of **gas** can be **measured** in **moles**, ***n***.
2) The constant then becomes ***nR***, where ***R*** is called the **molar gas constant**.
   Its value is 8.31 J mol^{-1} K^{-1}.
3) Plugging this into the equation gives: $\frac{pV}{T} = nR$ or rearranging, $pV = nRT$ — ***the ideal gas equation***

You don't need to learn this equation if you're doing Edexcel.

This equation works well (i.e., a real gas approximates to an ideal gas) for gases at **low pressure** and fairly **high temperatures**.

Boltzmann's Constant k is like a Gas Constant for One Particle of Gas

One mole of any **gas** contains the same number of particles.
This number is called **Avogadro's constant** and has the symbol N_A. The value of N_A is **6.02 × 10^{23} particles per mole**.

1) The **number of particles** in a **mass of gas** is given by the **number of moles**, ***n***, multiplied by **Avogadro's constant**.
   So the number of particles, $N = nN_A$
2) **Boltzmann's constant, *k***, is equivalent to R/N_A — you can think of Boltzmann's constant as the **gas constant** for **one particle of gas**, while ***R*** is the gas constant for **one mole of gas**.
3) The value of Boltzmann's constant is **1.38 × 10^{-23} JK^{-1}**.
4) If you combine $N = nN_A$ and $k = R/N_A$ you'll see that $Nk = nR$
   — which can be substituted into the ideal gas equation: → $pV = NkT$ — ***the equation of state***

   The equation $pV = NkT$ is called the equation of state of an ideal gas.

Practice Questions

Q1 State Boyle's law, Charles' law and the pressure law.

Q2 What is the ideal gas equation?

Q3 The pressure of a gas is 100 000 Pa and its temperature is 27 °C. The gas is heated — its volume stays fixed but the pressure rises to 150 000 Pa. Show that its new temperature is 177 °C.

Q4 What is the equation of state of an ideal gas?

Exam Questions

Q1 The mass of one mole of nitrogen gas is 0.028 kg. R = 8.31 J mol^{-1} K^{-1}.

(a) A flask contains 0.014 kg of nitrogen gas.

i) How many moles of nitrogen gas are in the flask? [1 mark]

ii) How many nitrogen molecules are in the flask? [1 mark]

(b) The flask has a volume of 0.01 m^3 and is at a temperature of 27 °C. What is the pressure inside it? [2 marks]

(c) What would happen to the pressure if the number of molecules of nitrogen in the flask was halved? [2 marks]

Q2 A large helium balloon has a volume of 10 m^3 at ground level.
The temperature of the gas in the balloon is 293 K and the pressure is 1 × 10^5 Pa.
The balloon is released and rises to a height where its volume becomes 25 m^3 and its temperature is 260 K.
Calculate the pressure inside the balloon at its new height. [3 marks]

Ideal revision equation — marks = (pages read × questions answered)^2...

All this might sound a bit theoretical, but most gases you'll meet in the everyday world come fairly close to being 'ideal'. They only stop obeying these laws when the pressure's too high or they're getting close to their boiling point.

The Pressure of an Ideal Gas

These pages are for AQA A Unit 5, OCR A Unit 4 and OCR B Unit 4 only.

Kinetic theory *tries to* ***explain*** *the* ***gas laws****. It basically models a gas as a series of hard balls that obey Newton's laws.*

*You Need to be Able to **Derive** the **Pressure** of an **Ideal Gas***

...unless you're doing OCR B.

Start by **Deriving** the **Pressure** on **One Wall** of a Box — in the x direction

This isn't an easy page. Work through it properly and make sure you understand it.

Imagine a cubic box with sides of length l containing N particles each of mass m.

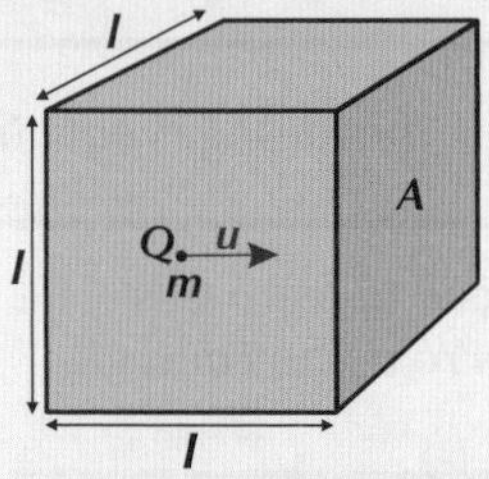

1) Say particle **Q** moves directly towards **wall A** with velocity u. Its **momentum** approaching the wall is mu. It strikes wall **A**. Assuming the **collisions** are perfectly **elastic**, it rebounds and heads back in the opposite direction with momentum $-mu$. So the **change in momentum** is $mu - (-mu) = 2mu$.
2) Assuming **Q** suffers no collisions with other particles, the **time between collisions** of **Q** and wall **A** is $2l/u$. The number of **collisions per second** is therefore $u/2l$.
3) This gives the **rate of change of momentum** as $2mu \times u/2l$.
4) Force equals the rate of change of momentum (Newton's second law), so the **force exerted on the wall** by this one particle = $2mu^2/2l = mu^2/l$.
5) Particle **Q** is only one of many in the cube. Each particle will have a different velocity u_1, u_2 etc. towards **A**. The total force, **F**, of all these particles on wall **A** is:

$$F = \frac{m(u_1^2 + u_2^2 + \text{etc.})}{l}$$

6) You can define a quantity called the **mean square speed**, $\overline{u^2}$ as:

$$\overline{u^2} = \frac{u_1^2 + u_2^2 + \text{etc.}}{N}$$

7) If you put that into the equation above, you get:

$$F = \frac{Nm\overline{u^2}}{l}$$

8) So, the pressure of the gas on end **A** is given by: where V = volume of the cube

$$\text{pressure}, p = \frac{\text{force}}{\text{area}} = \frac{Nm\overline{u^2}/l}{l^2} = \frac{Nm\overline{u^2}}{V}$$

*...Then for the **General Equation** you need to think about **All 3 Directions** — **x, y** and **z***

A gas particle can move in **three dimensions** (i.e. the x, y and z directions).

1) You can calculate its **velocity**, **c**, from Pythagoras' theorem:
   $c^2 = u^2 + v^2 + w^2$ where u, v and w are the components of the particle's velocity in the x, y and z directions.
2) If you treat all N particles in the same way, this gives an **overall** mean square speed of: $\overline{c^2} = \overline{u^2} + \overline{v^2} + \overline{w^2}$
3) Since the particles move **randomly**: $\overline{u^2} = \overline{v^2} = \overline{w^2}$ and so $\overline{c^2} = 3\overline{u^2}$
4) You can substitute this into the equation for pressure that you derived above to give:

$$pV = \frac{1}{3}Nm\overline{c^2}$$

*A Useful Quantity is the **Root Mean Square Speed** $\sqrt{\overline{c^2}}$*

$\overline{c^2}$ is the **mean square speed** and has **units** m^2s^{-2}.

In kinetic theory, it helps to think about the motion of a typical particle.

1) $\overline{c^2}$ is the **square** of the **speed** of an **average particle**, so the square root of it gives you the typical speed.
2) This is called the **root mean square speed** or, usually, the **r.m.s. speed**.

$$\text{r.m.s. speed} = \sqrt{\text{mean square speed}} = \sqrt{\overline{c^2}}$$

The Pressure of an Ideal Gas

Lots of *Simplifying Assumptions* are Used in *Kinetic Theory*

In **kinetic theory**, physicists picture gas particles moving at **high speed** in **random directions**.
To get **equations** like the one you just derived though, some **simplifying assumptions** are needed:

1) The gas contains a **large number of particles**.
2) The particles **move rapidly** and **randomly**.
3) The motion of the particles follows **Newton's laws**.
4) **Collisions** between particles themselves or at the walls of a container are **perfectly elastic**.
5) There are **no attractive forces** between particles.
6) Any **forces** that act during collisions are **instantaneous**.
7) Particles have a **negligible volume** compared with the volume of the container.

A **gas obeying** these **assumptions** is called an **ideal** gas. Real gases behave like ideal gases as long as the **pressure isn't too big** and the **temperature** is **reasonably high** (compared with their boiling points).

Brownian Motion Supports Kinetic Theory

This experiment is just for people doing OCR A.

In 1827, the botanist **Robert Brown** noticed that pollen grains in water constantly moved with a zigzag, **random motion**.

Brownian Motion Experiment

You can **observe** Brownian motion in the lab.

Put some **smoke** in a **brightly illuminated** glass jar and observe the particles using a **microscope**.

The smoke particles appear as **bright specks** moving **haphazardly** from side to side, and up and down.

Brown couldn't explain this, but nearly 80 years later Einstein showed that this provided evidence for the existence of atoms or **molecules** in the air. The **randomly moving** air particles were hitting the smoke particles unevenly, causing this motion.

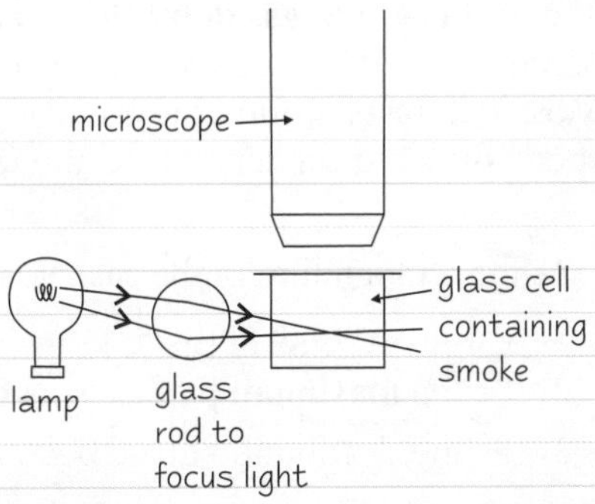

OCR B only — There's no way you can **record** the **random motion** of all the particles in a **gas** (without going cross-eyed in the process, of course) — instead you can **model** the movement of the molecules by a **random walk**.
A **random walk** assumes that each **molecule** starts in one place, **moves N steps** in random directions and ends up **somewhere else** — what's really useful is that the average **distance moved** in those N steps is proportional to $\sqrt{N}$.

Practice Questions

Q1 What is the definition of the mean square speed for N particles?

Q2 What are the seven assumptions made about ideal gas behaviour?

Q3 What did Robert Brown observe?

Q4 Why do smoke particles show Brownian motion?

Exam Question

Q1 Some helium gas is contained in a flask of volume 7×10^{-5} m³. Each helium atom has a mass of 6.6×10^{-27} kg, and there are 2×10^{22} atoms present. The pressure of the gas is 1×10^{5} Pa.

(a) What is the mean square speed of the atoms? [2 marks]

(b) What is the r.m.s. speed of the atoms? [1 mark]

(c) If the absolute temperature of the gas is doubled, what will the r.m.s. speed of the atoms become? [2 marks]

Brownian motion — Girl Guide in a tumble-drier...

***Mean square speed** is the average (mean) of the squared speeds. To find its value **square all the speeds** and then **find the average**. Don't make the mistake of finding the average speed first and then squaring. Cos that would be, like, soooo stupid.*

Internal Energy and Temperature

***These pages are for** AQA A Unit 5, Edexcel Unit 5, OCR A Unit 4 **and** OCR B Unit 4.*

*The energy of a particle depends on its temperature on the **thermodynamic scale** (that's Kelvin to you and me).*

If A and B are in Thermal Equilibrium with C, A is in Equilibrium with B

If **body A** and **body B** are both in **thermal equilibrium** with **body C**, then **body A** and **body B** must be in thermal equilibrium with **each other**.

This is linked with the idea of **temperature**.

1) Suppose A, B and C are three identical metal blocks. A has been in a **warm oven**, B has come from a **refrigerator** and C is at **room temperature**.
2) **Thermal energy** flows from A to C and C to B until they all reach **thermal equilibrium** and the net flow of energy stops. This happens when the three blocks are at the **same temperature**.

Thermal energy is **always** transferred from regions of **higher temperature** to regions of **lower temperature**.

The Speed Distribution of Gas Particles Depends on Temperature

The **particles** in a **gas don't** all **travel** at the **same speed**. Some particles will be moving fast but others much more slowly. Most will travel around the average speed. The shape of the **speed distribution** depends on the **temperature** of the gas.

As the temperature of the gas increases:
1) the **average** particle speed increases.
2) the **maximum** particle speed increases.
3) the distribution curve becomes more **spread out**.

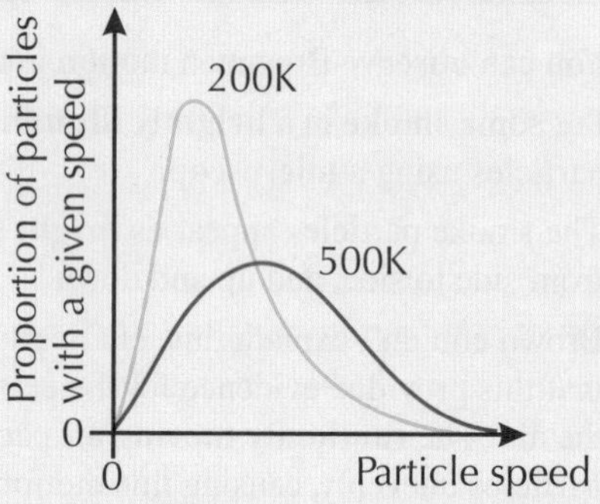

Energy Changes Happen Between Particles

The particles of a gas **collide** with each other **all the time**. Some of these collisions will be '**head-on**' (particles moving in **opposite directions**) while others will be '**shunts from behind**' (particles moving in the **same direction**).

1) As a result of the collisions, **energy** will be **transferred** between particles.
2) Some particles will **gain speed** in a collision and others will **slow down**.
3) **Between collisions**, the particles will travel at **constant speed**.
4) Although the energy of an individual particle changes at each collision, the collisions **don't alter** the **total energy** of the **system**.
5) So, the **average** speed of the particles will stay the same provided the **temperature** of the gas **stays the same**.

Internal Energy is the Sum of Kinetic and Potential Energy

All things (solids, liquids, gases) have **energy** contained within them. The amount of **energy** contained in a system is called its **internal energy** — it's found by **summing** the **kinetic** and **potential energy** of all the **particles** within it.

Internal energy is the **sum** of the **kinetic** and **potential energy** of the **particles** within a system.

For example, the **internal energy** of an **ideal gas** is due to the **kinetic energy** of the **particles** within it. But, how do you **sum** the **individual energies** when the particles all move at **different speeds**, so have **different kinetic energies**? The answer is to find the **average kinetic energy** of a particle (page 77), then **multiply** by the number of particles.

Internal Energy and Temperature

Average Kinetic Energy is Proportional to Absolute Temperature

There are **two equations** for the **product** pV of a gas — the ideal gas equation (page 73), and the equation involving the mean square speed of the particles (page 74). You can **equate these** to get an expression for the **average kinetic energy**.

1) The **ideal gas equation:** $pV = nRT$

2) The **pressure** of an **ideal gas** given by kinetic theory: $pV = \frac{1}{3}Nm\overline{c^2}$

c is the velocity of a particle. $\overline{c^2}$ is the average of the squared speeds of the particles, called the mean square speed.

N is the number of particles in the gas.

m is the mass of one particle in the gas.

3) **Equating** these two gives: $\frac{1}{3}Nm\overline{c^2} = nRT$

4) **Multiplying** by **3/2** gives: $\frac{3}{2} \times \frac{1}{3}Nm\overline{c^2} = \frac{3nRT}{2}$

so: $$\frac{1}{2}m\overline{c^2} = \frac{3}{2}\frac{nRT}{N}$$

5) $\frac{1}{2}m\overline{c^2}$ is the **average kinetic energy** of a **particle**.

6) What's more, you can substitute Nk for nR, where k is the **Boltzmann constant** (see page 73), to show that the **average kinetic energy** of a particle is $\frac{3}{2}kT$ — i.e. **directly proportional** to T (**absolute temperature**). You can use kT as an **approximation** for the **average kinetic energy** of the particles in **any substance**.

The **internal energy** of an ideal gas is the **product** of the **average kinetic energy** of its particles and the **number of particles** within it. **Average kinetic energy** is directly proportional to the **absolute temperature** (see above), so **internal energy** must also be **dependent** on **temperature** — a **rise** in the **absolute temperature** will cause an **increase** in the kinetic energy of each particle, meaning a rise in **internal energy**.

Practice Questions

Q1 Describe the changes in the distribution of gas particle speeds as the temperature of a gas increases.

Q2 What is internal energy? What would cause a rise in internal energy?

Q3 What happens to the average kinetic energy of a particle if the temperature of a gas doubles?

Exam Questions

Q1 The mass of one mole of nitrogen molecules is 2.8×10^{-2} kg. There are 6.02×10^{23} molecules in one mole.

(a) What is the mass of one molecule? [1 mark]

(b) Calculate the typical speed of a nitrogen molecule at 300 K. ($k = 1.38 \times 10^{-23}$ JK^{-1}) [3 marks]

(c) Explain why all the nitrogen molecules will not be moving at this speed. [2 marks]

Q2 Some air freshener is sprayed at one end of a room. The room is 8.0 m long and the temperature is 20 °C.

(a) Assuming the average freshener molecule moves at 400 ms^{-1}, how long would it take for a particle to travel directly to the other end of the room? [1 mark]

(b) The perfume from the air freshener only slowly diffuses from one end of the room to the other. Explain why this takes much longer than suggested by your answer to part (a). [2 marks]

(c) How would the speed of diffusion be different if the temperature was 30 °C? Explain your answer. [3 marks]

Positivise your internal energy, man...

Phew... there's a lot to take in on these pages. Go back over it, step by step, and make sure you understand it all: the distribution of particle speeds, the average kinetic energy of the particles in a gas, Boltzmann's constant and the r.m.s. speed.

Specific Heat Capacity & Specific Latent Heat

***This page is for** AQA A Unit 5, **Edexcel Unit 5,** OCR A Unit 4 **and** OCR B Unit 4.*

You need energy to heat something up, and to change its state. Everything comes down to energy. Pretty much always.

Specific Heat Capacity is how much Energy it Takes to Heat Something

When you heat something, its particles get more **kinetic energy** and its **temperature** rises.

The **specific heat capacity** (*c*) of a substance is the amount of **energy** needed to **raise** the **temperature** of **1 kg** of the substance by **1 K** (or 1 °C).

or put another way: **energy change = mass × specific heat capacity × change in temperature**

in symbols: $\Delta E = mc\Delta\theta$ ← ΔQ is sometimes used instead of ΔE for the change in thermal energy.

ΔE is the energy change in J, m is the mass in kg and $\Delta\theta$ is the temperature change in K or °C. Units of **c** are J kg^{-1} K^{-1} or J kg^{-1} °C^{-1}.

You can Measure Specific Heat Capacity in the Laboratory

The **method**'s the same for **solids** and **liquids**, but the **set-up**'s a little bit different:

Specific Heat Capacity of a Solid

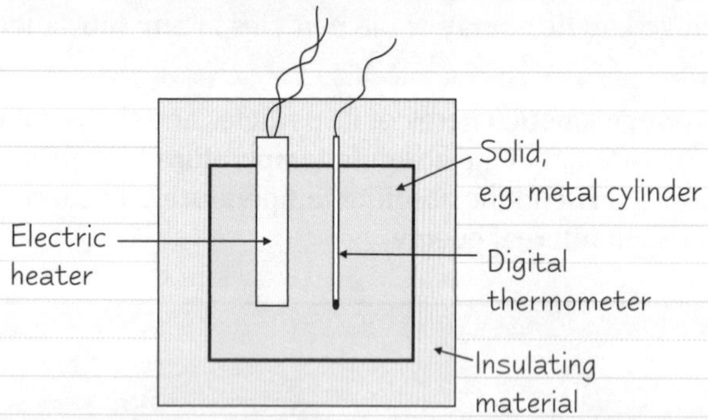

Specific Heat Capacity of a Liquid

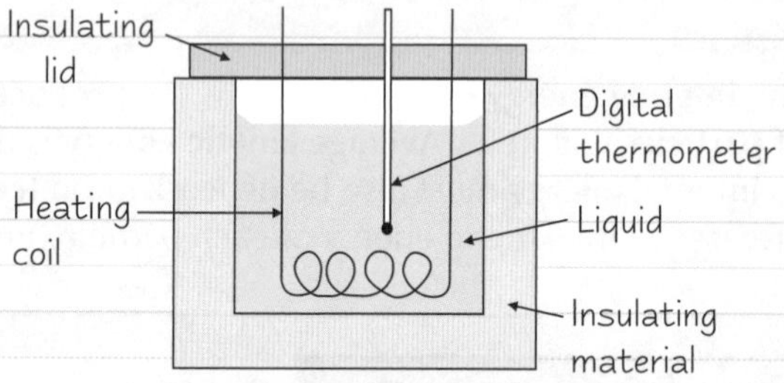

Method for Both

1) **Heat** the substance with the heater. You need a **temperature rise** of about 10 K to get an **accurate** value of **c**. [NB The insulation **reduces** the heat loss, but it's far from perfect. If you're really keen, start **below** and finish **above** room temperature to **cancel out** gains and losses.]

2) With an ammeter and voltmeter attached to your **electric heater** you can work out the energy supplied. Here's the circuit:

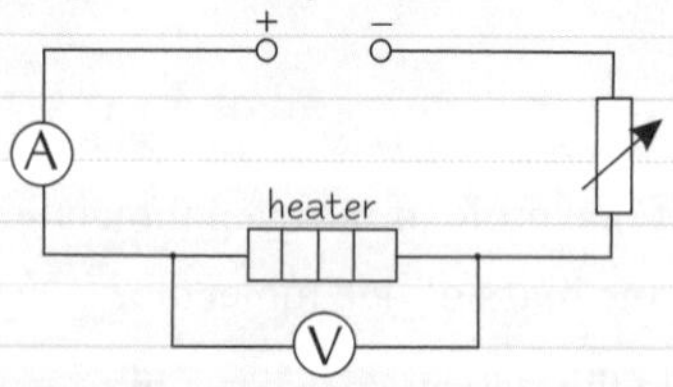

Calculate the energy (ΔE) using: $\Delta E = VI\Delta t$
where V is the heater voltage, I is the current and Δt is the time in seconds (you should know this from AS).

3) Plug your data into: $\Delta E = mc\Delta\theta$ to calculate **c**.

The value you end up with for c will probably be too high by quite a long way. That's because some of the energy from the heater gets transferred to the air and the container.

Example You heat 0.25 kg of water from 12.1 °C to 22.9 °C with an electric immersion heater. The heater has a voltage of 11.2 V and a current of 5.3 A, and is switched on for 205 s.

Electrical energy supplied = $VI\Delta t$ = 11.2 × 5.3 × 205 = 12 170 J

Temperature rise = 22.9 – 12.1 = 10.8 °C = 10.8 K

So $c = \dfrac{12170}{0.25 \times 10.8} = 4510$ Jkg^{-1}K^{-1}

The actual value for water is 4180 J kg^{-1} K^{-1}. This result's too big, because ΔE is bigger than it should be (like I said before).

Specific Heat Capacity & Specific Latent Heat

***This page is for** AQA A Unit 5, OCR A Unit 4 **and** OCR B Unit 4.*

*It takes **Energy** to **Change State***

You'll remember the **three states of matter** (**solid**, **liquid** and **gas**) from GCSE — but here's a quick recap just in case.

Particles vibrate about fixed positions in a regular lattice. They're held in position by strong forces of attraction.

Particles are constantly moving around and are free to move past one another, but are attracted to each other.

Particles are free to move around with constant random motion. There are no forces of attraction between particles in an ideal gas.

To **melt** a **solid**, you need to **break the bonds** that hold the particles in place. The **energy** needed for this is called the **latent heat of fusion**. Similarly, when you **boil or evaporate a liquid**, **energy is needed** to **pull the particles apart** completely. This is the **latent heat of vaporisation**.

Specific Latent Heat** is Defined as the Latent Heat **per kg

You wouldn't be laughing if it was your bum stuck to the ice. I need some latent heat energy, pronto.

The **larger** the **mass** of the substance, the **more energy** it takes to **change** its **state**. That's why the **specific latent heat** is defined per kg:

> The **specific latent heat** (*l*) of **fusion** or **vaporisation** is the quantity of **thermal energy** required to **change the state** of **1 kg** of a substance.

which gives: **energy change = specific latent heat × mass of substance changed**

or in symbols: $\Delta E = ml$

You'll usually see the latent heat of vaporisation written l_v and the latent heat of fusion written l_f.

Where ΔE is the energy change in J and m is the mass in kg. The units of l are J kg^{-1}.

*A **Change of State** Means a **Change of Internal Energy***

When you **heat** a substance, you **increase** the **kinetic energy** of the particles within it, thereby **increasing** its **internal energy** (page 76). When a substance **changes state**, its **internal energy** changes, but its **temperature doesn't**. This is because the **change of state** alters the **potential energy** of the particles — not their kinetic energy.

For example, each **molecule** of **steam** leaving a saucepan of boiling water has **more potential energy** than each molecule **in the pan**, even though **all** the molecules are at **100 °C** and have the **same** amount of **kinetic energy**.

Practice Questions

Q1 Define specific heat capacity.

Q2 Describe how you would measure the specific heat capacity of olive oil.

Q3 Show that the thermal energy needed to heat 2 kg of water from 20 °C to 50 °C is ~250 kJ (c_{water} = 4180 Jkg^{-1}K^{-1}).

Q4 Explain why energy is needed to evaporate a liquid and define the specific latent heat of vaporisation.

Exam Questions

Q1 A 2 kg metal cylinder is heated uniformly from 4.5 °C to 12.7 °C in 3 minutes.
The electric heater used is rated at 12 V, 7.5 A.
Assuming that heat losses were negligible, calculate the specific heat capacity of the metal. [3 marks]

Q2 A 3 kW electric kettle contains 0.5 kg of water already at its boiling point.
(a) Explain how two molecules of the water can have different energies. [3 marks]
(b) Neglecting heat losses, how long will it take to boil dry? (l_v (water) = 2.26 × 10^6 J kg^{-1}) [3 marks]

My specific eat capacity — 24 pies...

*This stuff's a bit dull, but hey... make sure you're comfortable using those equations. Interesting(ish) fact for the day — it's the **huge** difference in specific heat capacity between the land and the sea that causes the monsoon in Asia. So there.*

The Boltzmann Factor

These pages are for OCR B Unit 4 only.

Welcome to the big bad world of statistical physics — Ludwig Boltzmann's got a lot to answer for...

The Average Thermal **Energy** of a Particle is Proportional to the **Temperature**

1) Any particle above absolute zero has some **thermal energy**.

The **average thermal energy per particle** is (very roughly) kT.

k is Boltzmann's constant, $k = 1.38 \times 10^{-23}$ JK^{-1}.
T is the temperature in kelvin. See page 77 for more.

2) This table gives you an idea of the magnitude of the thermal energy at various temperatures:

Temperature (K)	average thermal energy (approx.) — kT		
	J (per particle)	J mol^{-1}	eV (per particle)
1	1×10^{-23}	8	9×10^{-5}
300 (room temp)	4×10^{-21}	2000	0.03
6000 (Sun's surface)	8×10^{-20}	5×10^{4}	0.5

To convert kT to J mol^{-1}, multiply by Avogadro's constant (6.02×10^{23} particles per mole).

To convert kT to eV (electron-volts), divide by the charge on the electron (1.6×10^{-19} C).

3) Particles in matter are **held together** by **bonds**. The **energy** needed to break these bonds in a given substance is the **activation energy** ε (the Greek "epsilon").

4) The ratio ε/kT is really important. When kT is **big enough** compared with ε, the bonds are broken and the matter comes apart.

Lots of Processes have an **Activation Energy**

1) For a process like a change of state to happen, particles need to **'climb'** an **energy barrier**.

2) The **activation energy**, ε, is the **energy needed** to climb that barrier (so, for a change of state, this activation energy corresponds to the latent heat — see page 79).

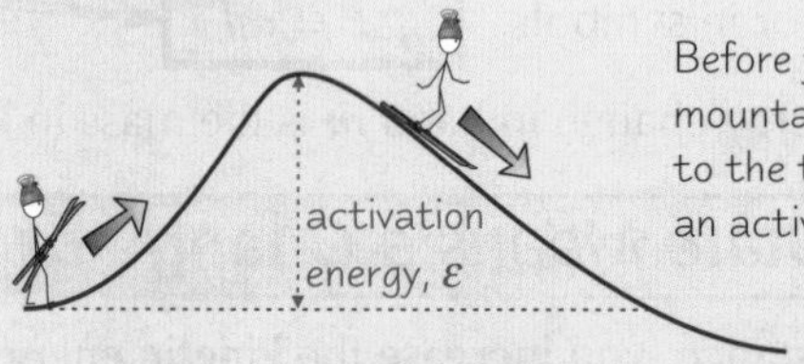

Before you can ski down a mountain, you need to climb to the top of it. So skiing is an activation process.

3) Lots of processes involving **particles** have activation energies — for example:

a) **A change of state**: the particles need enough energy to break the intermolecular forces.
b) **Thermionic emission**: if you heat up a conductor, electrons are released from the surface. These electrons need enough energy to escape from the attraction of the positive nuclei.
c) **Ionisation in a candle flame**: the molecules in the air need enough energy to split up into individual atoms and ions. This is a similar process to thermionic emission.
d) **Conduction in a semiconductor**: semiconductors will only start to conduct once there are electrons in a high-energy state called the "conduction band", so electrons need enough energy to jump from the ground state to this higher-energy state.

4) In each of these examples, the **activation energy**, ε, comes from the **random thermal energy** of the particles. You might think, then, that these processes wouldn't happen unless $kT \geq \varepsilon$... but it's not that simple...

Getting **Extra Energy** is all about **Probabilities**

1) If the **ratio** between the activation energy and the average energy of the particles (ε/kT) is too high, nothing happens. But as ε/kT gets down to somewhere around **15–30**, the process starts to happen at a **fair rate**.

2) So some particles must have energies of **15–30 times** the **average energy**.

3) Every time particles **collide**, there's a **chance** that one of them will gain **extra energy** — above and beyond the average kT. If that happens to the **same particle** several times in a row (unlikely but possible), it can gain energies **much, much higher** than the average.

4) To end up with an energy of $15kT$ to $30kT$, a particle would have to get **very lucky**, so there will only be a tiny proportion of particles with this energy.

The Boltzmann Factor

The **Boltzmann Factor** tells you the **Ratio** of Particles in two Energy States

The **Boltzmann factor, $e^{-\frac{\varepsilon}{kT}}$**, gives the **ratio** of the **numbers of particles** in energy states ε joules apart.

1) Processes start happening **quickly** when ε/kT is between 15 and 30, so try these values in the **Boltzmann factor**.
2) For $\varepsilon/kT = 15$, the Boltzmann factor is $\sim 10^{-7}$, and for $\varepsilon/kT = 30$ it's only $\sim 10^{-13}$.
3) That means that only **one in 10^{13}** to **one in 10^{7}** particles have **enough energy** to overcome the activation energy.
4) That might sound like a **tiny** proportion, but you have to remember how **fast** these particles are moving. Think about a reaction between two gases: gas particles collide about **10^9 times every second**. Every time there's a collision, there's an 'attempt' at the reaction, so even with **so few** particles having enough energy, the reaction can happen in a matter of **seconds**.

The **Boltzmann Factor** varies with **Temperature**

For any particular **reaction**, the values of ε (activation energy) and k (Boltzmann's constant) are **fixed**.
This means that the **only** thing that will change the **Boltzmann factor** is the **temperature**.

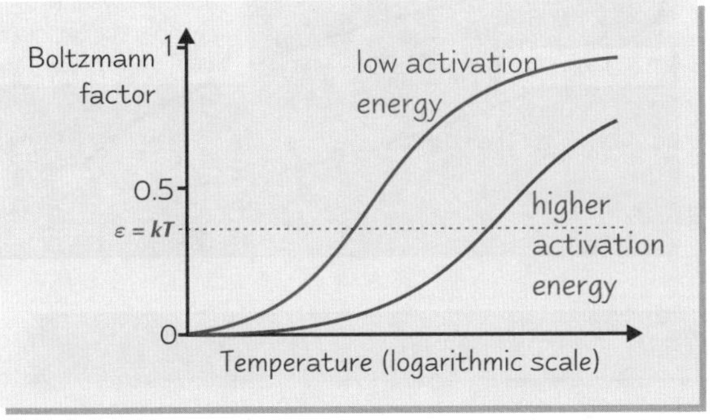

If you plot a **graph** of the **Boltzmann factor** against **temperature** you get an s-shaped curve like the ones on the **left**.

This **shape** shows that at **low temperatures**, the **Boltzmann factor** is also very **low**, so **very few** (if any) particles will have sufficient **energy** to **react** and the reaction will be really **slow**.

At **high temperatures**, the **Boltzmann factor approaches 1**, so nearly **all** the **particles** will have enough **energy** to **react** and the **reaction** will be really **fast**. In between, the Boltzmann factor **increases rapidly** with **temperature**. So a **small increase** in **temperature** can make a **big difference** to the rate.

The Boltzmann factor and **rate** of a reaction both vary with **temperature**, and it is a **reasonable approximation** to say:

The **rate** of a reaction with **activation energy** ε is proportional to the **Boltzmann factor, $e^{-\frac{\varepsilon}{kT}}$**.

Practice Questions

Q1 Give an expression for the approximate energy per particle at a given temperature.

Q2 What range of values must the ratio ε/kT have for a process to occur at a reasonable speed?

Q3 What is activation energy?

Q4 What is the Boltzmann factor? How is it related to the rate of a reaction?

Exam Question

Q1 A fish tank is in a room at a temperature of 300 K [$k = 1.38 \times 10^{-23}$ JK^{-1}].

(a) Calculate the approximate average energy of one of the water molecules in the tank. [1 mark]

(b) Water molecules are joined together by two hydrogen bonds. The energy needed to break each bond is 3.2×10^{-20} J. Calculate the energy, ε, that a water molecule needs in order to evaporate. [1 mark]

(c) Use your answers to parts (a) and (b) to find the ratio ε/kT. [1 mark]

(d) Explain why the water in the tank must be topped up regularly. [3 marks]

The Boltzmann Factor — not as much fun as the X Factor...

*You can think of the Boltzmann factor as the **probability** of a particle having a certain energy, or the fraction of particles that **do** have that energy. **Or** you could think of it as a big pair of grandma pants with pink polka dots — up to you...*

The Solar System & Astronomical Distances

This page is for AQA A Unit 5 Option A (just the two sections at the bottom on distances), OCR A Unit 5 (you need the whole page) and OCR B Unit 4 (everything except the first section on the Solar System).

The Meaning of Life, Part 6: A2 Physics...

Our **Solar System** Contains the **Sun**, **Planets**, **Satellites**, **Asteroids** and **Comets**

1) Our **Solar System** consists of the **Sun** and all of the objects that **orbit** it:

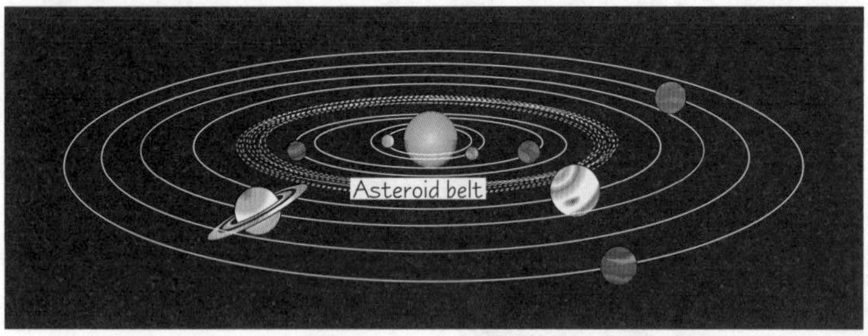
Asteroid belt

The planets (in order): **Mercury**, **Venus**, **Earth**, **Mars**, **Jupiter**, **Saturn**, **Uranus** and **Neptune** (as well as the asteroid belt) all have nearly **circular** orbits. We used to call Pluto a planet too, but it's been reclassified now.

Remember — planets, moons and comets don't emit light; they just reflect it.

2) The orbits of the **comets** we see are **highly elliptical**. Comets are "**dirty snowballs**" that we think usually orbit the Sun about **1000 times further away** than **Pluto** does (in the "Oort cloud"). Occasionally one gets **dislodged** and heads towards the Sun. It follows a new elliptical orbit, which can take **millions of years** to complete. Some comets (from closer in than the Oort cloud) follow a **smaller orbit** and they return to swing round the Sun more regularly. The most famous is **Halley's comet**, which orbits in **76 years**.

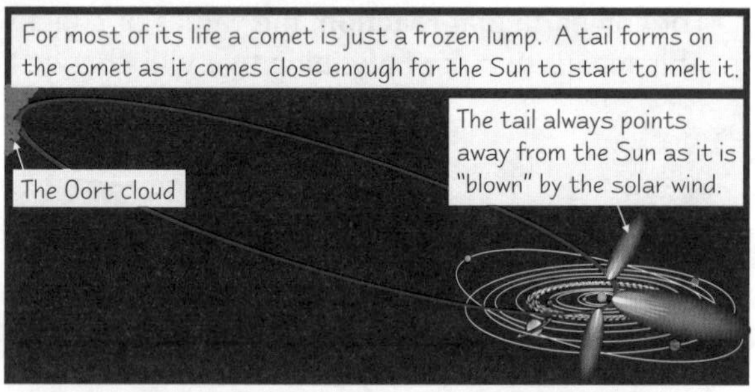
For most of its life a comet is just a frozen lump. A tail forms on the comet as it comes close enough for the Sun to start to melt it.
The tail always points away from the Sun as it is "blown" by the solar wind.
The Oort cloud

Distances and **Velocities** in the Solar System can be Measured using **Radar**

1) **Radio telescopes** (see p. 87) can be used to send **short pulses** of **radio waves** towards a planet or asteroid (a rock flying about the Solar System), which **reflect** off the surface and bounce back.
2) The telescope picks up the reflected radio waves, and the **time taken** (***t***) for them to return is measured.
3) Since we know the **speed** of radio waves (**speed of light, *c***) we can work out the **distance, *d***, to the object using:

$$2d = ct$$

It's 2d, not just d, because the pulse travels twice the distance to the object — there and back again.

4) If **two** short pulses are sent a certain **time interval** apart, you can measure the **distance** an object has moved in that time. From this time and distance, you can calculate the **average speed** of the object **relative** to Earth. More accurate measurements can be made using Doppler shifts (see p. 98).

Distances in the Solar System are Often Measured in **Astronomical Units (AU)**

1) From **Copernicus** onwards, astronomers were able to work out the **distance** the **planets** are from the Sun **relative** to the Earth, using **astronomical units** (AU). But they could not work out the **actual distances**.

One **astronomical unit** (**AU**) is defined as the **mean distance** between the **Earth** and the **Sun**.

2) The **size** of the AU wasn't accurately known until 1769 — when it was carefully **measured** during a **transit of Venus** (when Venus passed between the Earth and the Sun).

Another Measure of Distance is the **Light-Year (ly)**

1) All **electromagnetic waves** travel at the **speed of light**, **c**, in a vacuum ($c = 3.00 \times 10^8$ ms^{-1}).

The **distance** that electromagnetic waves travel through a vacuum in **one year** is called a **light-year** (**ly**).

2) If we see the light from a star that is, say, **10 light-years away** then we are actually seeing it as it was **10 years ago**. The further away the object is, the further **back in time** we are actually seeing it.
3) **1 ly** is equivalent to about **63 000 AU**.

The Solar System & Astronomical Distances

***This page is for** AQA A Unit 5 Option A, Edexcel Unit 5, OCR A Unit 5 **and** OCR B Unit 4.*

The Distance to **Nearby Stars** can be Measured by **Parallax**

You all need to know about parsecs, but only** Edexcel **people need to know the details of parallax.

1) You experience parallax every day. Imagine you're in a **moving car**. You see that (stationary) objects in the **foreground** seem to be **moving faster** than objects in the **distance**.
2) This **apparent change in position** is called **parallax** and is measured in terms of the **angle of parallax**. The **greater** the **angle**, the **nearer** the object is to you.

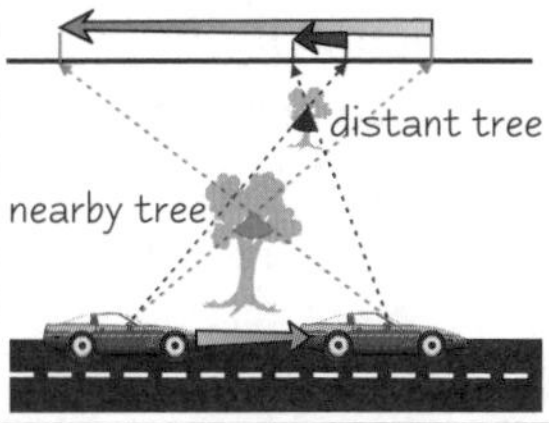

The nearby tree seems to have moved much further relative to the horizon than the more distant tree. The angles marked are called angles of parallax.

3) The distance to **nearby stars** can be calculated by observing how they **move relative** to **very distant stars** when the Earth is in **different parts** of its **orbit**. This gives a **unit** of distance called a **parsec** (**pc**).

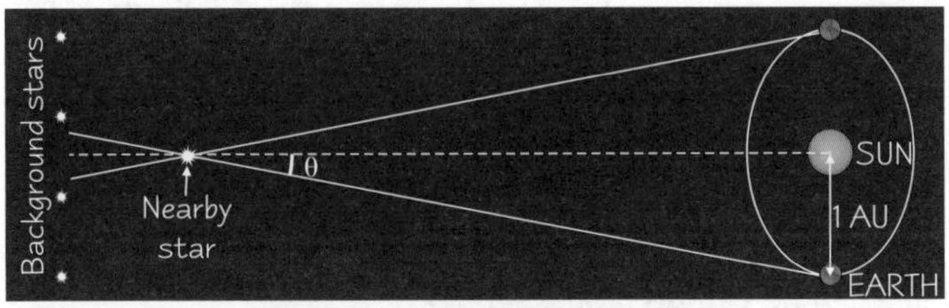

A star is exactly **one parsec** (**pc**) away from Earth if the **angle of parallax**,

$$\theta = \textbf{1 arcsecond} = \left(\frac{1}{3600}\right)^{\circ}$$

Important **Sizes and Conversions**

Unit of Distance	Astronomical Unit (AU)	Light Year (ly)	Parsec (pc)
Approximate Length in metres	1.50×10^{11}	9.46×10^{15}	3.09×10^{16}

For OCR A, you need to be able to state the length of a light year and a parsec.

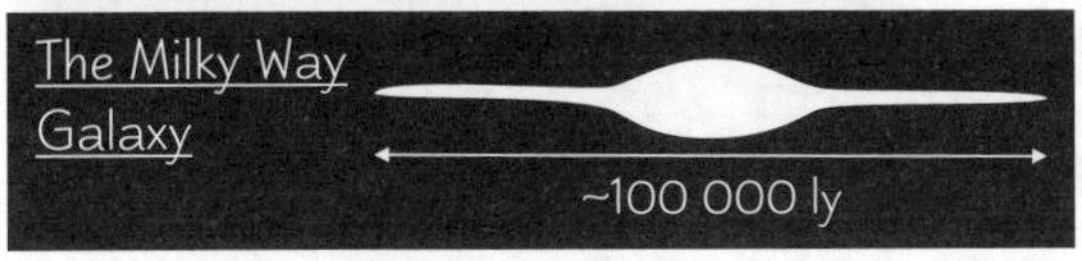

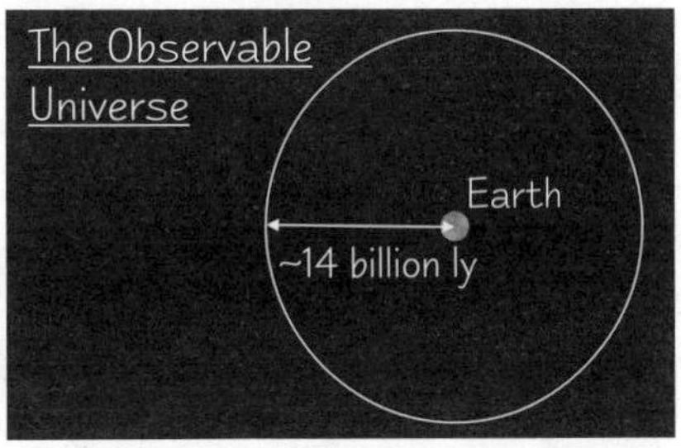

When we look at the stars we're looking **back in time**, and we can only see as far back as the **beginning of the Universe**.
So the **size** of the **observable Universe** is the **age** of the Universe multiplied by the **speed of light**.

Practice Questions

Q1 What are the principal contents of our Solar System?

Q2 What is meant by: a) an astronomical unit, b) a parsec and c) a light-year?

Q3 How do we measure the distance to objects in the Solar System using radar?

Exam Questions

Q1 (a) Outline the main differences between planets and comets. [5 marks]

(b) Explain why a comet has a tail which always points away from the Sun. [2 marks]

Q2 (a) Give the definition of a *light-year*. [1 mark]

(b) Calculate the distance of a light-year in metres. [2 marks]

(c) Why is the size of the observable universe limited by the speed of light? [2 marks]

So — using a ruler's out of the question then...

Don't bother trying to get your head round these distances — they're just too big to imagine. Just learn the powers of ten and you'll be fine. Make sure you understand the definition of a parsec — it's a bit of a weird one.

Optical Telescopes

These pages are for AQA A Unit 5 Option A only.

Some optical telescopes use lenses (no, really), so first, here's a bit of lens theory...

Converging Lenses Bring Light Rays *Together*

1) **Lenses** change the **direction** of light rays by **refraction**.
2) Rays **parallel** to the **principal axis** of the lens converge onto a point called the **principal focus**. Parallel rays that **aren't** parallel to the principal axis converge somewhere else on the **focal plane** (see diagram).
3) The **focal length**, ***f***, is the distance between the **lens axis** and the **principal focus**.

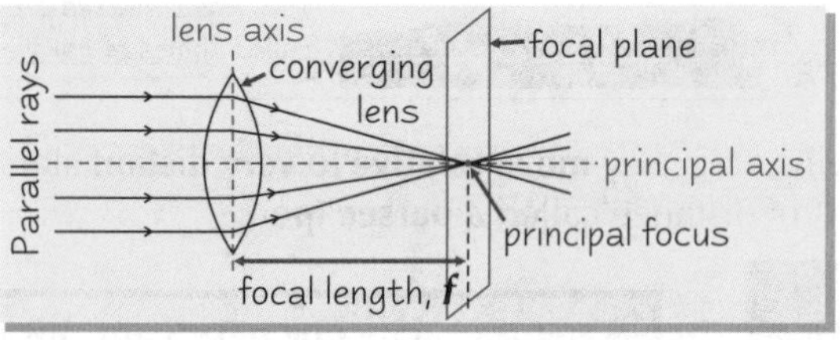

4) A **more powerful** (thicker) lens converges the rays more **strongly** and will have a **shorter focal length**.
5) The power of a lens with focal length ***f*** m is:

$$P = \frac{1}{f}$$

where lens power is measured in **dioptres, D**.

Images can be *Real* or *Virtual*

1) A **real image** is formed when light rays from an object are made to **pass through** another point in space. The light rays are **actually there**, and the image can be **captured** on a **screen**.
2) A **virtual image** is formed when light rays from an object **appear** to have come from another point in space. The light rays **aren't really where the image appears to be**, so the image **can't** be captured on a screen.
3) Converging lenses can form both **real** and **virtual** images, depending on where the object is. If the object is **further** than the **focal length** away from the lens, the image is **real**. If the object's **closer**, the image is **virtual**.
4) To work out where an image will appear, you can draw a **ray diagram**. You only need to draw **two rays** on a ray diagram: one **parallel** to the principal axis that passes through the **principal focus**, and one passing through the **centre** of the lens that **doesn't get bent**.

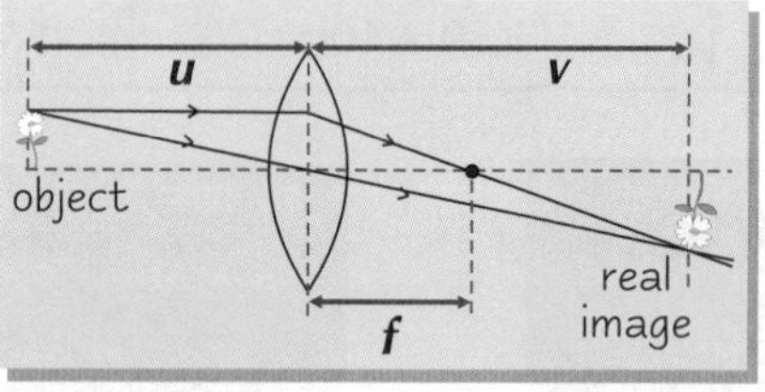

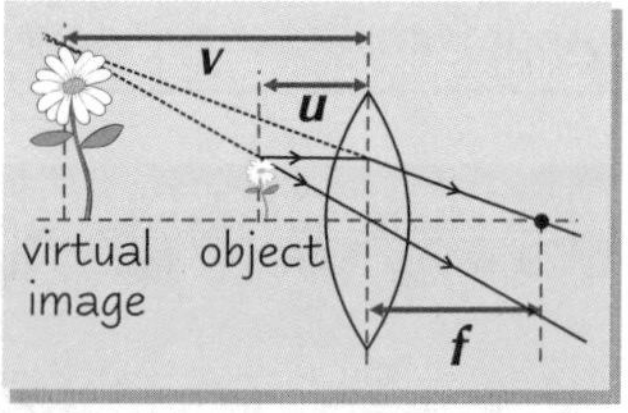

In the diagram, ***u*** = distance between object and lens axis, ***v*** = distance between image and lens axis (**positive** if image is **real**, **negative** if image is **virtual**), ***f*** = focal length.

5) The values ***u***, ***v*** and ***f*** are related by the **lens equation**: ⟶

$$\frac{1}{f} = \frac{1}{u} + \frac{1}{v}$$

A *Refracting Telescope* uses *Two* Converging Lenses

1) The **objective lens** converges the rays from the object to form a **real image**.
2) The **eye lens** acts as a **magnifying glass** on this real image to form a **magnified virtual image**.

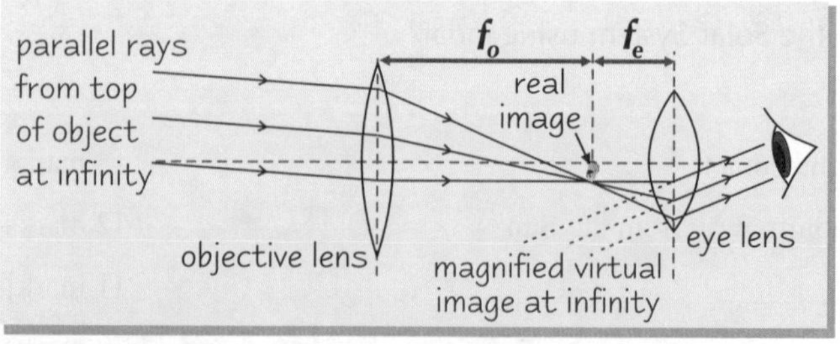

3) If you assume the object is at infinity, then the rays from it are **parallel**, and the real image is formed on the **focal plane**.
4) A **telescope** (in normal adjustment) is set up so that the **principal focus** of the **objective** lens is in the **same position** as the principal focus of the **eye** lens, so the **final magnified image** appears to be at **infinity**.
5) The **magnification**, ***M***, of the telescope can be calculated in terms of angles, or the focal length. The **angular magnification** is the **angle** subtended by the **image** θ_i over the **angle** subtended by the **object** θ_o at the eye:

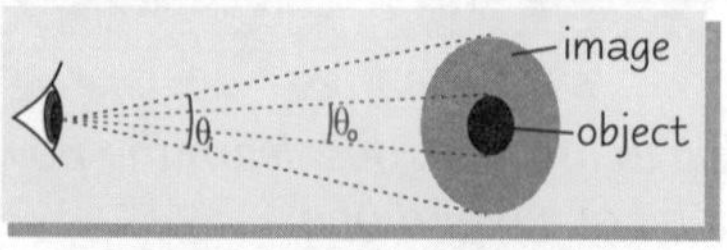

$$M = \frac{\theta_i}{\theta_o}$$

or in terms of **focal length** (with the telescope in normal adjustment as shown above):

$$M = \frac{f_o}{f_e}$$

Optical Telescopes

A Reflecting Telescope uses a Concave Mirror and a Converging Lens

1) A **parabolic concave mirror** (the **primary mirror**) converges parallel rays from an object, forming a **real image**.
2) An **eye lens magnifies** the image as before.
3) The focal point of the mirror (where the image is formed) is **in front** of the mirror, so an arrangement needs to be devised where the observer doesn't **block out** the light. A set-up called the **Cassegrain arrangement**, which uses a **convex secondary mirror**, is a common solution to this problem.

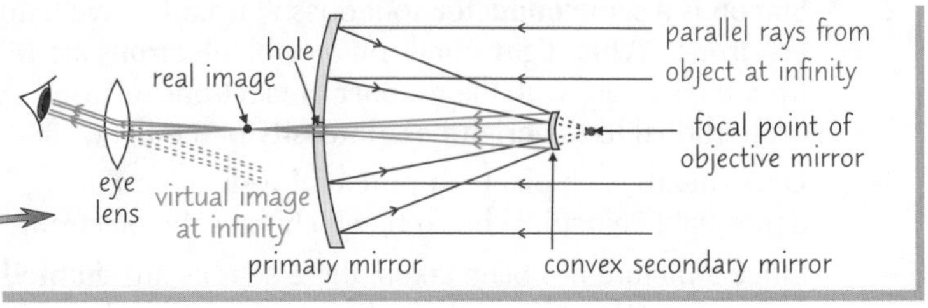

The Resolving Power of a Telescope — how much Detail you can See

1) The **resolving power** of an instrument is the **smallest angle** at which it can **distinguish** two points.

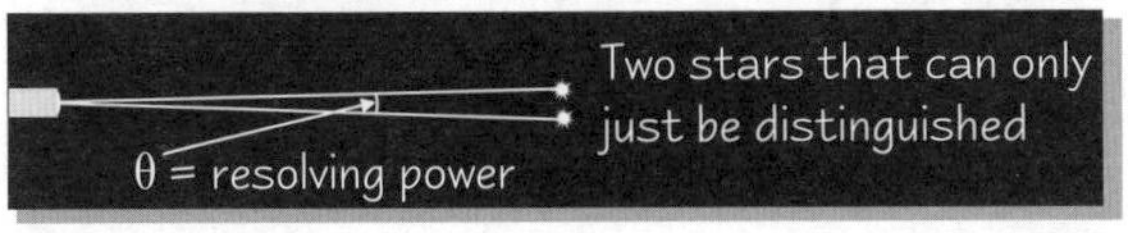

About half of the stars that we see in the night sky are actually collections of two or more stars. Our eyes see them as a single star since the angle between them is too small to resolve.

2) Resolution is limited by diffraction. If a beam of light passes through a circular **aperture**, then a **diffraction pattern** is formed. The central circle is called the **Airy disc** (see p.132 for an example of the pattern).
3) **Two** light sources can **just** be distinguished if the **centre** of the **Airy disc** from one source is **at least as far away** as the **first minimum** of the other source. This led to the **Rayleigh criterion**:

$$\theta \approx \frac{\lambda}{D}$$

where θ is the **minimum angle** that can be resolved in **radians**, λ is the **wavelength** of the light in **metres** and D is the **diameter** of the **aperture** in **metres**.

4) For **telescopes**, D is the diameter of the **objective lens** or the **objective mirror**. So **very large** lenses or mirrors are needed to see **fine detail**.

There are Big Problems with Refracting Telescopes

1) Glass refracts **different colours** of light by **different amounts** and so the image for each colour is in a slightly **different position**. This **blurs** the image and is called **chromatic aberration**.

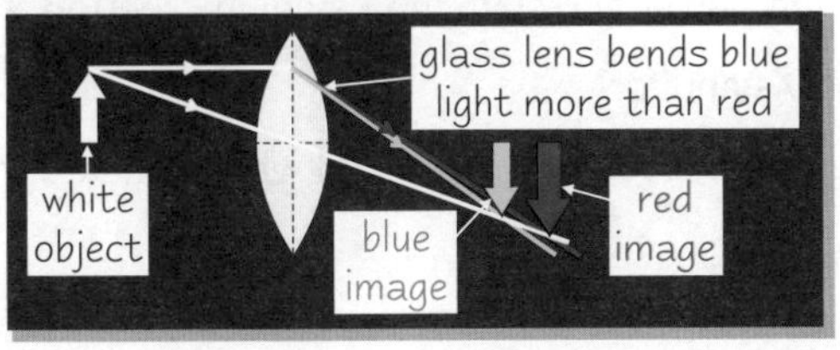

2) Any **bubbles** and **impurities** in the glass **absorb** some of the light, which means that **very faint** objects **aren't seen**. Building large lenses that are of a **sufficiently good quality** is **difficult** and **expensive**.
3) **Large lenses** are very **heavy** and can only be **supported** from their **edges**, so their **shape** can become **distorted**.
4) For a **large magnification**, the **objective lens** needs to have a **very long focal length**. This means that refracting telescopes have to be **very long**, leading to very **large** and **expensive buildings** needed to house them.

Reflecting Telescopes are Better than Refractors but they have Problems too

1) **Large mirrors** of **good quality** are much **cheaper** to build than large lenses. They can also be **supported** from **underneath** so they don't **distort** as much as lenses.
2) Mirrors don't suffer from **chromatic aberration** (see above) but can have **spherical aberration**:

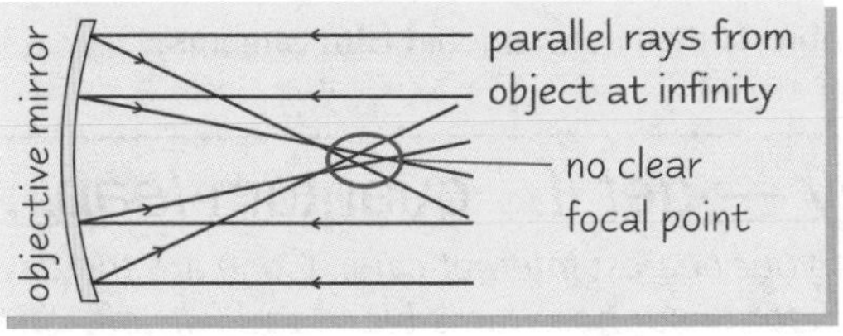

If the **shape** of the mirror isn't quite **parabolic**, parallel rays reflecting off different parts of the mirror do not all **converge** onto the same point.

When the **Hubble Space Telescope** was first launched it suffered from **spherical aberration**. They had to find a way round the problem before it could be used.

Optical Telescopes

Charge-Coupled Devices (CCDs) are Very Sensitive Light Detectors

1) CCDs are **silicon chips** about the size of a postage stamp, divided up into a grid of millions of **identical pixels**.
2) Silicon is a **semiconductor** so it doesn't usually have many **free electrons**. When **light** shines on a pixel, **electrons** are released from the silicon, with the **number** of electrons released being proportional to the **brightness/intensity** of the light.
3) **Underneath** each **pixel** is a **potential well** (a kind of controllable electrical bucket), which traps the electrons.
4) Once a picture has been taken, the electrons are **shunted** from **one potential well** to **another** so that they all come out **in sequence** from **one corner** of the CCD. (This is called an 'electrical bucket brigade', to use the lingo.)
5) This sequence can be converted into a **digital signal** and sent to computers **anywhere in the world**.

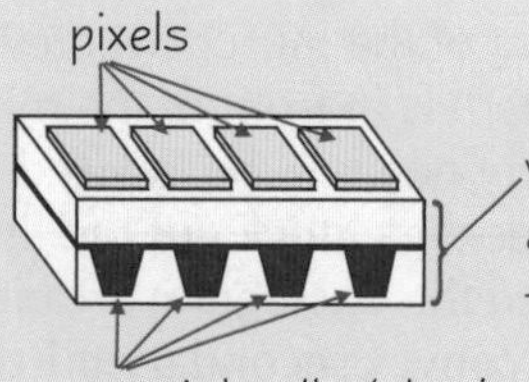

CCDs use Quantum Effects

1) **Quantum physics** tells us that EM radiation is formed in **discrete packets** of energy called **photons**.
2) The incoming photons release electrons in the silicon due to the **photoelectric effect**. (See p. 130.)
3) Electrons are released by **more than 70%** of the photons that hit a pixel, so the **quantum efficiency** of a CCD is greater than 70%. On average, a cell in the **eye** needs about **100 photons** before it responds and so has a quantum efficiency of about **1%**. The quantum efficiency of a **photographic emulsion** is about **4%**.

Practice Questions

Q1 Define the focal length and the power of a converging lens.

Q2 Draw ray diagrams to show how an image is formed in a refracting and a reflecting (Cassegrain) telescope.

Q3 Explain resolving power and state the Rayleigh criterion.

Q4 What does CCD stand for?

Q5 What does quantum efficiency mean and what is the quantum efficiency of a CCD?

Exam Questions

Q1 (a) Define the *principal focus* and the *focal length* of a converging lens. [2 marks]

(b) An object was placed 0.20 m in front of a converging lens with a focal length of 0.15 m. How far behind the lens was the image formed? [3 marks]

(c) The object was placed 0.10 m in front of the same lens. Where was the image formed? [2 marks]

Q2 An objective lens with a focal length of 5.0 m and an eye lens with a focal length of 0.10 m are used in a refracting telescope.

(a) How far apart should the lenses be placed for the telescope to be in normal adjustment? [1 mark]

(b) Define angular magnification and calculate the angular magnification of this telescope. [2 marks]

Q3 (a) Outline the basic function of a CCD. [3 marks]

(b) Why are CCDs much better at taking pictures of very faint objects than conventional film cameras? [3 marks]

CCDs were a quantum leap for astronomy — get it... quantum leap... *sigh*

With CCDs, you can get all the images you want from the comfort of your nearest internet café. Gone are the days of standing on a hill with a telescope and a flask hoping the sky clears before your nose turns black and falls off. Shame.

Non-Optical Telescopes

These pages are for AQA A Unit 5 Option A only.

Some telescopes don't use visible light — they use radio waves, IR, UV or X-rays instead — read on to learn more...

Radio Telescopes are Similar to Optical Telescopes in Some Ways

1) The most obvious feature of a radio telescope is its **parabolic dish**. This works in exactly the same way as the **objective mirror** of an **optical reflecting** telescope.
2) An **antenna** is used as a detector at the **focal point** instead of an eye or camera in an optical telescope, but there is **no equivalent** to the **eye lens**.

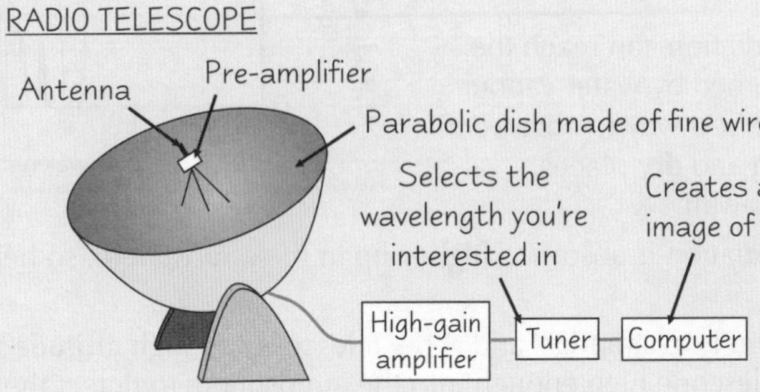

3) Most radio telescopes are **manoeuvrable**, allowing the source of the waves to be **tracked** (in the same way as optical telescopes). The telescope moves with the source, stopping it 'slipping out of view' as the Earth rotates.

Radio Waves have a Much Longer Wavelength than Light...

1) The **wavelengths** of **radio waves** are about a **million times longer** than the wavelengths of **light**.
2) The **Rayleigh criterion** (see p. 85) gives the **resolving power** of a telescope as $\boldsymbol{\theta \approx \lambda/D}$.
3) So for a radio telescope to have the **same resolving power** as an optical telescope, its dish would need to be a **million times bigger** (about the size of the UK for a decent one). The **resolving power** of a radio telescope is **worse** than the **unaided eye**.

Radio astronomers get around this by **linking** lots of telescopes together.

Using some nifty computer programming, their data can be combined to form a **single image**. This is equivalent to one **huge dish** the size of the **separation** of the telescopes.

Resolutions **thousands** of times better than optical telescopes can be achieved this way.

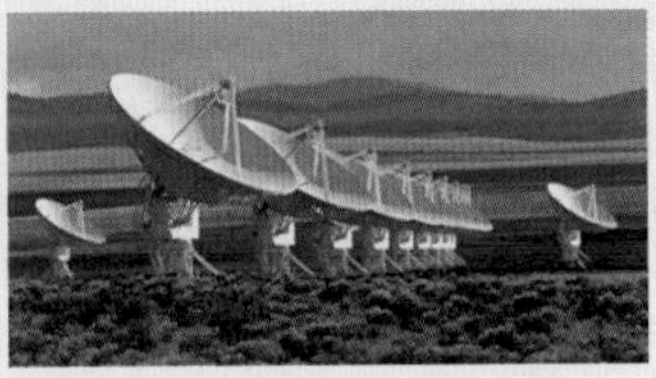

...so Radio Telescopes aren't as Fiddly to Make as Optical Reflectors

1) Instead of a **polished mirror**, a **wire mesh** can be used since the long wavelength radio waves don't notice the gaps. This makes their **construction** much **easier** and **cheaper** than optical reflectors.
2) The **shape** of the dish has to have a **precision** of about **λ/20** to avoid **spherical aberration** (see page 85). So the dish does not have to be **anywhere near as perfect** as a mirror.
3) Unlike an optical telescope, a radio telescope has to **scan across** the radio source to **build up** the **image**.

Non-Optical Telescopes

The **Atmosphere Blocks** Certain **EM Wavelengths**

1) One of the big problems with doing astronomy on Earth is trying to look through the atmosphere.
2) Our atmosphere only lets **certain wavelengths** of **electromagnetic radiation** through and is **opaque** to all the others. The graph shows how the **transparency** of the atmosphere varies with **wavelength**.

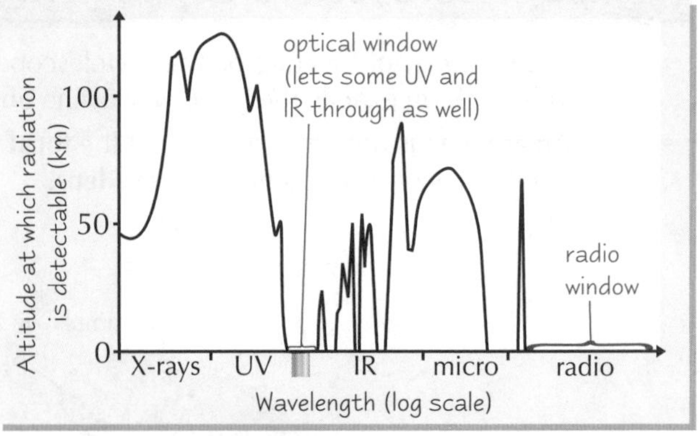

3) We can use **optical** and **radio** telescopes on the surface of the Earth because the atmosphere is **transparent** to these wavelengths. Observing other wavelengths can be a bit more tricky.
4) A few wavelengths of **infrared** radiation can reach the Earth's surface, but most are absorbed by water vapour in the atmosphere. On Earth, the best way to observe IR radiation is to set up shop in **high** and **dry** places, like the Mauna Kea volcano in Hawaii.
5) But most **ultraviolet** and **X-ray** radiation is absorbed **higher up** in the atmosphere, so being on a mountain doesn't help.
6) One way to get round this problem is to strap UV and X-ray telescopes to **high altitude weather balloons** or **aeroplanes**. They can take the telescope high enough into the atmosphere to detect the radiation.
7) The ideal situation is to get your telescope **above the atmosphere** altogether, by launching it into **space** and setting it in orbit around the Earth.

IR and **UV** Telescopes have a **Very Similar Structure** to **Optical** Telescopes

1) Infrared and ultraviolet telescopes are very similar to optical reflecting telescopes. They use the same **parabolic mirror** set-up to focus the radiation onto a detector.
2) In both cases, **CCDs** (see p 86) or **special photographic paper** are used as the radiation detectors, just as in optical telescopes.
3) The **longer** the **wavelength** of the radiation, the **less** it's affected by imperfections in the mirror (see previous page). So the mirrors in **infrared** telescopes **don't** need to be as perfectly shaped as in optical telescopes. But the mirrors in **UV** telescopes have to be even **more** precisely made.

IR telescopes have the added problem that they produce their **own** infrared radiation due to their **temperature**. They need to be **cooled** to very low temperatures using liquid helium, or refrigeration units.

X-ray Telescopes have a **Different Structure** from Other Telescopes

1) X-rays don't reflect off surfaces in the same way as most other EM radiation. Usually X-ray radiation is either **absorbed** by a material or it **passes straight through** it.

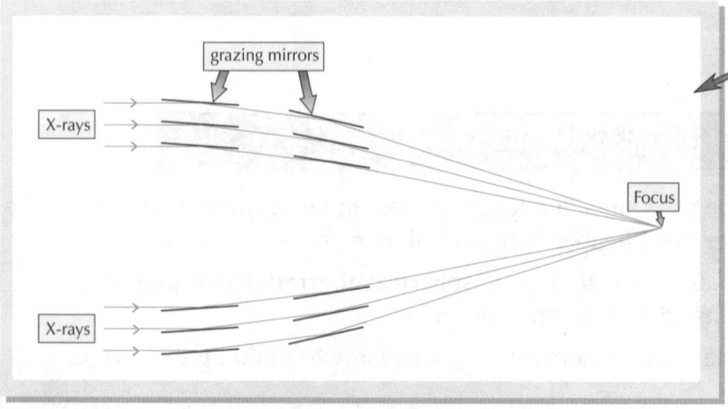

2) X-rays **do** reflect if they just **graze** a mirror's surface though. By having a series of **nested mirrors**, you can gradually alter the direction of X-rays enough to bring them to a **focus** on a detector. This type of telescope is called a **grazing telescope**.
3) The X-rays can be detected using a modified **Geiger counter** or a **fine wire mesh**. Modern X-ray telescopes such as the XMM-Newton telescope use highly sensitive X-ray **CCD** cameras.

Non-Optical Telescopes

Different Telescopes have Different **Resolving** and **Collecting Powers**

The **RESOLVING POWER** of a telescope is limited by two main factors:

1) The **Rayleigh criterion** (see page 85):
This depends on the **wavelength** of the radiation and the **diameter** of the objective mirror or dish.
So, for the **same size** of dish, a UV telescope has a much better resolving power than a radio telescope.

2) The quality of the **detector**:
Just like in digital cameras, the resolving power of a telescope is limited by the resolving power of the detector. That can be how many **pixels** there are on a CCD, or for a wire mesh X-ray detector, how **fine** the wire mesh is.

The **COLLECTING POWER** of a telescope is proportional to its **collecting area.**

1) A **bigger dish** or **mirror** collects **more energy** from an object in a given time.
This gives a **more intense image**, so the telescope can observe **fainter** objects.

2) The **collecting power** (energy collected per second) is proportional to the area:

$$\text{Power} \propto \text{Diameter}^2$$

3) For a **radio**, **optical**, **UV** or **IR** telescope, this is the area of the objective mirror or dish.

4) For **X-ray** telescopes, it's the size of the **opening** through which X-rays can enter the telescope.
In general, X-ray telescopes have a much **smaller collecting power** than other types of telescope.

The bigger the dish, the greater the collecting power. Mmm....

Practice Questions

Q1 Why do radio telescopes tend to have poor resolving powers?

Q2 Why is it easier to make a parabolic dish for a radio telescope than it is to make a mirror for an optical telescope?

Q3 Why don't astronomers install UV and X-ray telescopes on the top of mountains?

Exam Questions

Q1 Describe and explain the differences in resolving and collecting powers between radio and UV telescopes. [4 marks]

Q2 In 1983, the IRAS satellite observed the entire sky in infrared wavelengths. The satellite was kept at a temperature of 2 K by a reservoir of liquid helium which cooled the satellite by evaporation.

(a) Why did the satellite need to be kept at such a low temperature? [2 marks]

(b) Some infrared telescopes are on the surface of the Earth. What is special about their location? [1 mark]

Q3 (a) Many X-ray and UV telescopes are housed on satellites that orbit high above the Earth's atmosphere. Where else are X-ray and UV telescopes positioned? Explain why this is necessary. [2 marks]

(b) Describe and explain the major differences between the mirrors in X-ray and UV telescopes. [3 marks]

Q4 (a) How is the collecting power of a telescope related to its objective diameter? [1 mark]

(b) The Arecibo radio telescope has a dish diameter of 300 m. The Lovell radio telescope has a dish diameter of 76 m. Calculate the ratio of their collecting powers. [2 marks]

Power is proportional to diameter^2? Bring on the cakes...

If you can't observe the radiation you want to from Earth, just strap your telescope to a rocket and blast it into space. Sounds easy enough till you remember it's going to be reeeally hard to repair if anything goes wrong.

Luminosity and Magnitude

This page is for AQA A Unit 5 Option A, Edexcel Unit 5 (just the luminosity bit) and OCR B Unit 4 only.

There are a couple of ways to classify stars — the first is by luminosity, using the magnitude scale.

The **Luminosity** of a Star is the **Total Energy** Emitted **per Second**

1) Stars can be **classified** according to their luminosity — that is, the **total** amount of energy emitted in the form of electromagnetic radiation **each second** (see p.92).
2) The **Sun's** luminosity is about 4×10^{26} W (luminosity is measured in watts, since it's a sort of power). The **most luminous** stars have a luminosity about a **million** times that of the Sun.
3) The **intensity**, I, of an object that we observe is the power **received** from it per unit area **at Earth**. This is the effective **brightness** of an object.

Apparent Magnitude, m, is based on how **Bright** things **Appear** from **Earth**

1) The **brightness** of a star in the night sky depends on **two** things — its **luminosity** and its **distance from us** (if you ignore weather and light pollution, etc.). So the **brightest** stars will be **close** to us and have a **high luminosity**.
2) About 2000 years ago, a Greek called Hipparchus invented a way of **classifying** the **brightness** of stars (as seen from the Earth). The very **brightest** stars were given an **apparent magnitude** of **1** and the **dimmest** stars were given an apparent magnitude of **6**, with the other levels catering for the stars in between.
3) In the 19th century, the scale was redefined using a strict **logarithmic** scale:

   A **magnitude 1** star has an **intensity 100 times** greater than a **magnitude 6** star.

   This means a difference of **one magnitude** corresponds to a difference in **intensity** of $\mathbf{100^{1/5}}$ **times**. So a magnitude 1 star is about **2.5 times brighter** than a magnitude 2 star.
4) At the same time, the range was **extended** in **both directions** with the very brightest objects in the sky having **negative apparent magnitude**.

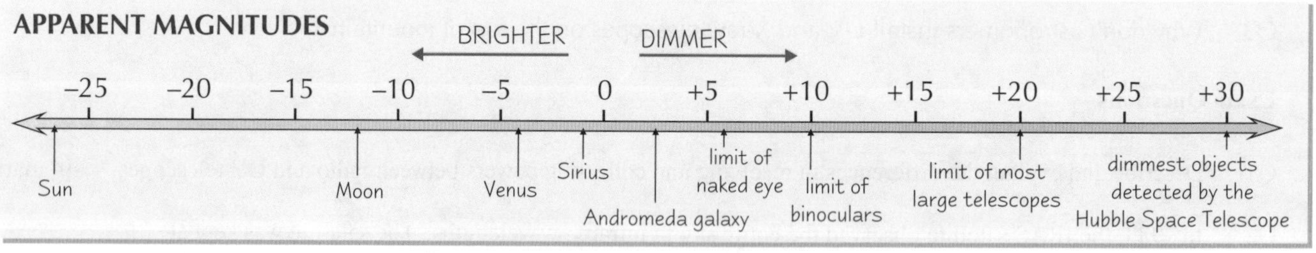

5) The **apparent magnitude**, m, is related to the **intensity**, I, by the following formula:

$$m = -2.5 \log I + \text{constant}$$

Note that log is $\log_{10}$, not the natural logarithm ln. And that 2.5 is exactly 2.5 — not $100^{1/5}$.

Absolute Magnitude, M, is based only on the **Luminosity** of the Star

1) The **absolute magnitude** of a star or galaxy, M, does not depend on its distance from Earth. It is defined as what its apparent magnitude **would be** if it were **10 parsecs** away from Earth.
2) The relationship between M and m is given by the following formula:

$$m - M = 5\log\left(\frac{d}{10}\right)$$

where d is the distance in parsecs

Luminosity and Magnitude

You Can Use **Standard Candles** to Find **Distances** to Galaxies

If you know the absolute magnitude of a star, you can use the equation from the previous page to calculate its **distance** from Earth. This is really handy, since the distance to most stars is **too big** to measure using parallax (see p. 83).

This method uses objects, such as **supernovae** and **Cepheid variable stars**, known as **standard candles**. Standard candles are objects that you can calculate the luminosity of **directly**. So, if you find a cepheid variable within a galaxy, you can work out how far that galaxy is from us. This is how the **Hubble constant** was worked out (see p. 100).

Example Eta Aquilae is a cepheid variable star in the constellation Aquila. It has an apparent magnitude of 3.87 and an absolute magnitude of –3.91. Calculate the distance of Eta Aquilae from Earth.

A star's distance from Earth can be found using the formula: $m - M = 5\log\left(\frac{d}{10}\right)$.

Remember in this case 'log' means '$\log_{10}$'.

Rearrange the formula to find d: $m - M = 5\log_{10}\left(\frac{d}{10}\right)$

$$\frac{m-M}{5} = \log_{10}\left(\frac{d}{10}\right)$$

$$\frac{d}{10} = 10^{\left(\frac{m-M}{5}\right)}$$

The rule of logs is that if $n = \log_b(x)$ then $x = b^n$.

$$d = 10 \times 10^{\left(\frac{m-M}{5}\right)} = 10^{\left(\frac{m-M}{5}+1\right)}$$

The rule of powers is $n^a \times n^b = n^{(a+b)}$.

Then substitute the values $m = 3.87$ and $M = -3.91$: $d = 10^{\left(\frac{3.87-(-3.91)}{5}+1\right)}$

Subtracting a negative is the same as adding a positive.

$$d = 10^{(2.556)} = 359.75 \text{ pc}$$

So, Eta Aquilae is approximately **360 pc** from Earth.

Practice Questions

Q1 What is the relationship between apparent magnitude and intensity?

Q2 What is the equation that links apparent magnitude, absolute magnitude and distance?

Q3 What are standard candles?

Exam Questions

Q1 Define the *absolute magnitude* of a star. [2 marks]

Q2 Calculate the absolute magnitude of the Sun given that the Sun's apparent magnitude is –27.
[1 pc = 2 × 10^5 AU] [4 marks]

Q3 The star Sirius has an apparent magnitude of –1.46 and an absolute magnitude of +1.4.
The star Canopus has an apparent magnitude of –0.72 and an absolute magnitude of –5.5.

(a) Which of the two stars appears brighter from Earth? [1 mark]

(b) Calculate the distance of Canopus from Earth. [3 marks]

Logs — the cheap and easy alternative pet...*

The magnitude scale is a pretty weird system, but like with a lot of astronomy, the old ways have stuck. Remember — the lower the number, the brighter the object. The definition of absolute magnitude is a bit random as well — I mean, why ten parsecs? Ours not to reason why, ours but to... erm... learn it. (Doesn't have quite the same ring does it.)

* Too young to remember Twin Peaks...? Ah well, never mind.

Stars as Black Bodies

This page is for AQA A Unit 5 Option A and Edexcel Unit 5 only.

Now they're telling us the Sun's black. Who writes this stuff?

A **Black Body** is a **Perfect Absorber** and **Emitter**

1) Objects emit **electromagnetic radiation** due to their **temperature**. At everyday temperatures this radiation lies mostly in the **infrared** part of the spectrum (which we can't see) — but heat something up enough and it will start to **glow**.
2) **Pure black** surfaces emit radiation **strongly** and in a **well-defined way**. We call it **black body radiation**.
3) A black body is defined as:

> A body that **absorbs all wavelengths** of electromagnetic radiation (that's why it's called a **black** body) and can **emit all wavelengths** of electromagnetic radiation.

4) To a reasonably good approximation **stars** behave as **black bodies** and their black body radiation produces their **continuous spectrum**.
5) The graph of **intensity** against **wavelength** for black body radiation varies with **temperature**, as shown in the graph:

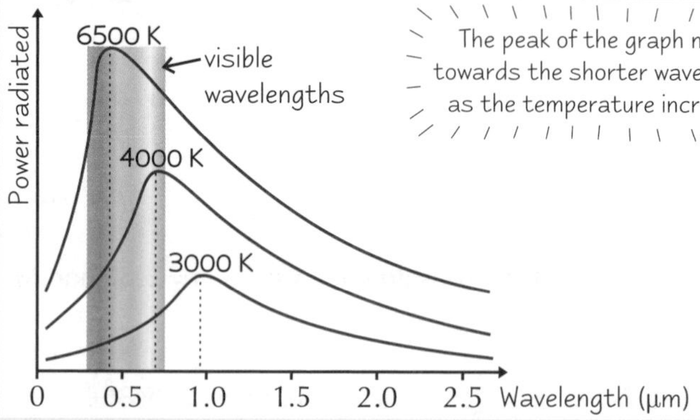

The peak of the graph moves towards the shorter wavelengths as the temperature increases.

The **Peak Wavelength** gives the **Temperature**

1) For each temperature, there is a **peak** in the black body curve at a wavelength called the **peak wavelength**, λ_{max}.
2) λ_{max} is related to the **temperature** by **Wien's displacement law**:

$$\lambda_{max}T = 0.0029 \text{ m·K}$$

where T is the temperature in kelvin and m·K is a metre-kelvin.

The **Luminosity** of a Star Depends on its **Temperature** and **Surface Area**

1) The **luminosity** of a star is the **total energy** it emits **per second** and is related to the **temperature** of the star and its **surface area**.
2) The luminosity is proportional to the **fourth power** of the star's **temperature** and is **directly proportional** to the **surface area**. This is **Stefan's law**:

$$L = \sigma A T^4$$

where L is the luminosity of the star (in W), A is its surface area (in m^2), T is its surface temperature (in K) and σ (a little Greek "sigma") is Stefan's constant.

3) Measurements give Stefan's constant as $\sigma = 5.67 \times 10^{-8}$ **Wm^{-2}K^{-4}**.
4) From **Earth**, we can measure the **intensity** of the star. The intensity is the **power** of radiation **per square metre**, so as the radiation spreads out and becomes **diluted**, the intensity **decreases**. If the energy has been emitted from a **point** or a **sphere** (like a star, for example) then it obeys the **inverse square law**:

$$I = \frac{L}{4\pi d^2}$$

where L is the luminosity of the star (in W), and d is the distance from the star.

Stars as Black Bodies

You Can Put the **Equations Together** to **Solve Problems**

Example The star Sirius B has a surface area of 4.1×10^{13} m^2 and produces a black body spectrum with a peak wavelength of 115 nm. The intensity of the light from Sirius B when it reaches Earth is 1.12×10^{-11} Wm^{-2}. How long does the light from Sirius B take to reach Earth? *($\sigma = 5.67 \times 10^{-8}$ Wm^{-2}K^{-4}, **c** $= 3.0 \times 10^8$ ms^{-1})*

First, find the temperature of Sirius B:

$\lambda_{max}T = 0.0029$ m·K, so $T = 0.0029 \div \lambda_{max} = 0.0029 \div 115 \times 10^{-9} = 25\,217$ K.

Now, you can use Stefan's law to find the luminosity:

$L = \sigma AT^4 = (5.67 \times 10^{-8}) \times (4.1 \times 10^{13}) \times 25\,217^4 = 9.4 \times 10^{23}$ W

Then use $I = \frac{L}{4\pi d^2}$ to find the distance of Sirius B from Earth:

$$d = \sqrt{\frac{L}{4\pi I}} = \sqrt{\frac{9.4\times10^{23}}{4\times\pi\times1.12\times10^{-11}}} = \sqrt{6.68\times10^{23}} = 8.2\times10^{16}\text{m}$$

Finally, use $c = d \div t$ to find the time taken $t = d \div c = 8.2 \times 10^{16} \div 3 \times 10^8 = 273\,333\,333$ s $\approx$ **8.7 years**

It's Hard to get **Accurate** Measurements

1) **Wien's displacement law**, **Stefan's law** and the **inverse square law** can all be used to work out various **properties** of stars. This needs very **careful measurements**, but our **atmosphere** mucks up the results.
2) It only lets through **certain wavelengths** of **electromagnetic radiation** — **visible** light, most **radio** waves, **very near infrared** and a bit of **UV**. It's **opaque** to the rest.
3) And then there are things like **dust** and **man-made light pollution** to contend with. Observatories are placed at **high altitudes**, well away from **cities**, and in **low-humidity** climates to minimise the problem. The best solution, though, is to send up **satellites** that can take measurements **above** the atmosphere.
4) Our **detectors** don't do us any favours either. The **measuring devices** that astronomers use aren't perfect since their **sensitivity** depends on the **wavelength** of the radiation. For example, **glass absorbs UV** light but is **transparent** to **visible light**, so any instruments that use glass affect UV readings straight off.
5) All you can do about this is choose the best materials for what you want to measure, and then **calibrate** your instruments really carefully.

Practice Questions

Q1 What is Wien's displacement law and what is it used for?

Q2 What is the relationship between luminosity, surface area and temperature?

Q3 Why are accurate measurements of black body radiation difficult on the Earth's surface?

Exam Questions

Q1 A star has a surface temperature of 4000 K and the same luminosity as the Sun (3.9×10^{26} W).

(a) Which radiation curve represents this star — X, Y or Z? Explain your answer. [2 marks]

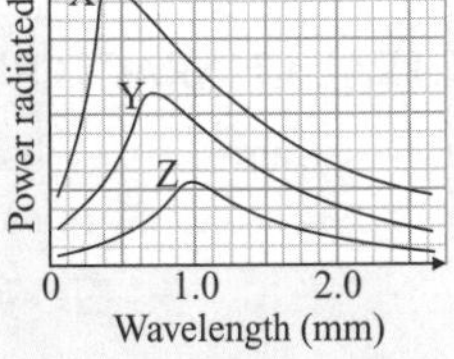

(b) Calculate the star's surface area. [2 marks]

Q2 The star Procyon A, which has a luminosity of 2.3×10^{27} W, produces a black body spectrum with a peak wavelength of 436 nm.

Calculate the surface area of Procyon A. [4 marks]

Astronomy — theories, a bit of guesswork and a whole load of calibration...

Astronomy isn't the most exact of sciences, I'm afraid. The Hubble Space Telescope's improved things a lot, but try and get a look at some actual observational data. Then look at the error bars — they'll generally be about the size of a house.

Spectral Classes and the H-R Diagram

This page is for AQA A Unit 5 Option A only.

As well as classifying stars by luminosity (the magnitude scale, p.90), they can be classified by colour.

The **Visible** Part of **Hydrogen's Spectrum** is called the **Balmer Series**

1) The lines in **emission** and **absorption spectra** occur because electrons in an atom can only exist at certain well-defined **energy levels**.
2) In **atomic hydrogen**, the electron is usually in the **ground state** (**n** = 1), but there are lots of energy levels (**n** = 2 to **n** = ∞ — called excitation levels) that the electron **could** exist in if it was given more energy.

> The wavelengths corresponding to the **visible bit** of hydrogen's spectrum are caused by electrons moving from **higher energy levels** to the **first excitation level** (**n = 2**).
> This leads to a series of **lines** called the **Balmer series**.

The **Strengths** of the **Spectral Lines** Show the **Temperature** of a Star

1) For a **hydrogen absorption line** to occur in the **visible** part of a star's spectrum, electrons in the hydrogen atoms already need to be in the **n = 2** state.
2) This happens at **high temperatures**, where **collisions** between the atoms give the electrons extra energy.
3) If the temperature is **too high**, though, the majority of the electrons will reach the **n = 3** level (or above) instead, which means there won't be so many Balmer transitions.
4) So the **intensity** of the Balmer lines depends on the **temperature** of the star.
5) For a particular intensity of the Balmer lines, **two temperatures** are possible. Astronomers get around this by looking at the **absorption lines** of **other atoms** and **molecules** as well.

The **Relative Strength** of Absorption Lines gives the **Spectral Class**

Well... quite.

1) For historical reasons the stars are classified into:

spectral classes: O (hottest), **B, A, F, G, K** and **M**

Use a **mnemonic** to remember the order. The standard one is the rather non-PC '**Oh Be A Fine Girl, Kiss Me**'.

2) The graph shows how the **intensity** of the visible spectral lines changes with **temperature**:

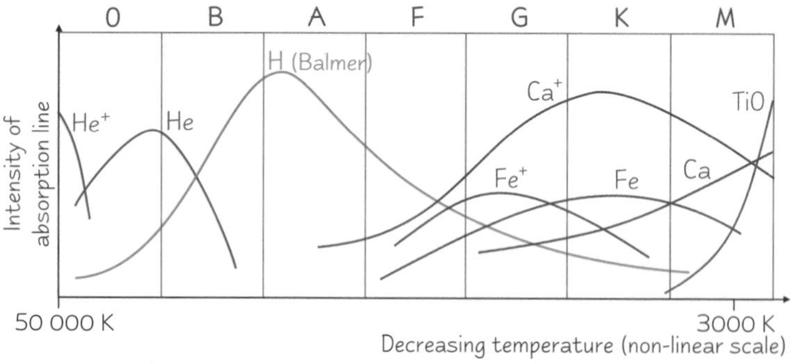

A quick note on the temperature axis: These diagrams, and the H-R diagram (next page), tend to be drawn with spectral class along the horizontal axis. The relationship between spectral class and temperature isn't linear or logarithmic.

THE VISIBLE SPECTRAL CHARACTERISTICS OF SPECTRAL CLASSES

- **O** — **Blue** stars: temperature **25 000 – 50 000 K**. The strongest spectral lines are **helium ion** and **helium atom** absorptions, since these need a really high temperature. They have weak **hydrogen Balmer** lines too.
- **B** — **Blue** stars: **11 000 – 25 000 K**. These spectra show strong **helium atom** and **hydrogen** absorptions.
- **A** — **Blue-white** stars: **7500 – 11 000 K**. Visible spectra are governed by very strong Balmer **hydrogen** lines, but there are also some **metal ion** absorptions.
- **F** — **White** stars: **6000 – 7500 K**. These spectra have strong **metal ion** absorptions.
- **G** — **Yellow-white** stars: **5000 – 6000 K**. These have both **metal ion** and **metal atom** absorptions.
- **K** — **Orange** stars: **3500 – 5000 K**. At this temperature, spectral lines are mostly from neutral **metal atoms**.
- **M** — **Red** stars: **< 3500 K**. **Molecular band** absorptions from compounds like **titanium oxide** are present in the spectra of these stars, since they're cool enough for molecules to form.

Spectral Classes and the H-R Diagram

This page is for** AQA A Unit 5 Option A **and** Edexcel Unit 5 **only.

Absolute Magnitude vs Temperature/Spectral Class — the H-R diagram

1) Independently, Hertzsprung and Russell noticed that a plot of **absolute magnitude** (see p. 90) against **temperature** (or **spectral class**) didn't just throw up a random collection of stars but showed **distinct areas**.

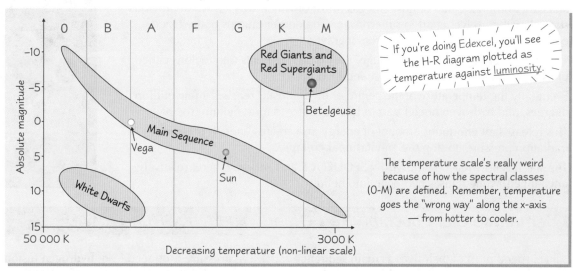

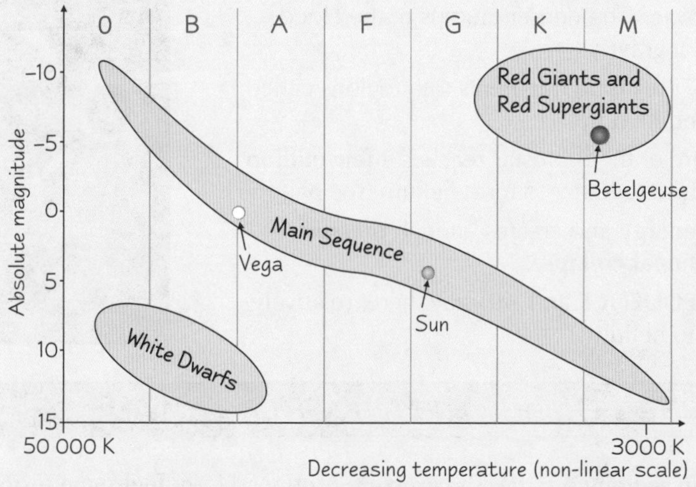

If you're doing Edexcel, you'll see the H-R diagram plotted as temperature against luminosity.

The temperature scale's really weird because of how the spectral classes (O-M) are defined. Remember, temperature goes the "wrong way" along the x-axis — from hotter to cooler.

2) The **long, diagonal band** is called the **main sequence**. Main sequence stars are in their long-lived **stable phase** where they are fusing **hydrogen** into **helium**. The Sun is a main sequence star.
3) Stars that have a **high luminosity** and a relatively **low surface temperature** must have a **huge** surface area because of Stefan's law (page 92). These stars are called **red giants** and are found in the **top-right** corner of the H-R diagram. Red giants are stars that have **moved off** the main sequence and fusion reactions other than hydrogen to helium are also happening in them.
4) Stars that have a **low luminosity** but a **high temperature** must be very **small**, again because of Stefan's law. These stars are called **white dwarfs** and are about the size of the Earth. They lie in the **bottom-left** corner of the H-R diagram. White dwarfs are stars at the **end** of their lives, where all of their fusion reactions have stopped and they are just **slowly cooling down**.

Practice Questions

Q1 Why does hydrogen have to be at a particular temperature before Balmer absorption lines are seen?

Q2 List the spectral classes in order of decreasing temperature and outline their spectral characteristics.

Q3 What is an H-R diagram and what are the three main groups of stars that emerge when the diagram is plotted?

Exam Questions

Q1 The spectral classes of stars can be identified by examining the lines in their absorption spectra.

(a) Explain how temperature affects the strength of the Balmer lines in stellar absorption spectra. [3 marks]

(b) In which two spectral classes of star are strong Balmer lines observed? [2 marks]

(c) Describe the visible spectral characteristics and temperature of a star in class F. [3 marks]

Q2 The spectra of K and M stars have absorption bands corresponding to energy levels of molecules. Explain why this only occurs in the lowest temperature stars. [2 marks]

Q3 Draw the basic features of an H-R diagram, indicating where you would find main sequence stars, red giants and white dwarfs. [5 marks]

'Ospital Bound — A Furious Girl Kicked Me...

Spectral classes are another example of astronomers sticking with tradition. The classes used to be ordered alphabetically by the strength of the Balmer lines. When astronomers realised this didn't quite work, they just fiddled around with the old classes rather than coming up with a sensible new system. Just to make life difficult for people like you and me.

Stellar Evolution

These pages are for AQA A Unit 5 Option A and OCR A Unit 5 only.
(Have a read if you're doing Edexcel Unit 5 as well, but you don't need to know all the details.)

Stars go through several different stages in their lives and move around the H-R diagram as they go (see p. 95).

Stars Begin as Clouds of Dust and Gas

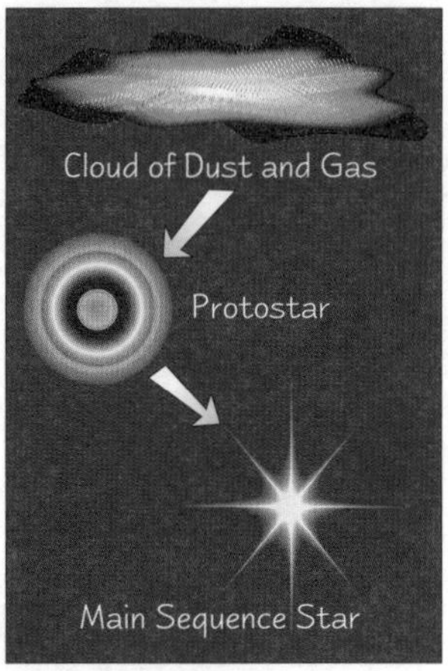

1) Stars are born in a **cloud** of **dust** and **gas**, most of which was left when previous stars blew themselves apart in **supernovae**. The denser clumps of the cloud **contract** (very slowly) under the force of **gravity**.
2) When these clumps get dense enough, the cloud fragments into regions called **protostars**, that continue to contract and **heat up**.
3) Eventually the **temperature** at the centre of the protostar reaches a **few million degrees**, and **hydrogen nuclei** start to **fuse** together to form helium (see page 57).
4) This releases an **enormous** amount of **energy** and creates enough **pressure** (radiation pressure) to stop the **gravitational collapse**.
5) The star has now reached the **MAIN SEQUENCE** and will stay there, relatively **unchanged**, while it fuses hydrogen into helium.

Main Sequence Stars become Red Giants when they Run Out of Fuel

1) Stars spend most of their lives as **main sequence** stars. The **pressure** produced from **hydrogen fusion** in their **core balances** the **gravitational force** trying to compress them. This stage is called **core hydrogen burning**.
2) When the **hydrogen** in the **core** runs out nuclear fusion **stops**, and with it the **outward pressure stops**. The core **contracts** and **heats up** under the **weight** of the star.
3) The material **surrounding** the core still has **plenty of hydrogen**. The **heat** from the contracting **core** raises the **temperature** of this material enough for the hydrogen to **fuse**. This is called **shell hydrogen burning**. (Very low-mass stars stop at this point. They use up their fuel and slowly fade away...)
4) The core continues to contract until, eventually, it gets **hot** enough and **dense** enough for **helium** to **fuse** into **carbon** and **oxygen**. This is called **core helium burning**. This releases a **huge** amount of energy, which **pushes** the **outer layers** of the star outwards. These outer layers **cool**, and the star becomes a **RED GIANT**.
5) When the **helium** runs out, the carbon-oxygen core **contracts again** and heats a **shell** around it so that helium can fuse in this region — **shell helium burning**.

Low Mass Stars (like the Sun) Eject their Shells, leaving behind a White Dwarf

1) In low-mass stars, the **carbon-oxygen core isn't hot enough** for any further **fusion** and so it continues to **contract** under its own **weight**. Once the core has shrunk to about **Earth-size**, **electrons** exert enough pressure (**electron degeneracy pressure**) to stop it collapsing any more (fret not — you don't have to know how).
2) The **helium shell** becomes more and more **unstable** as the core contracts. The star **pulsates** and **ejects** its outer layers into space as a **planetary nebula**, leaving behind the dense core.
3) The star is now a very **hot**, **dense solid** called a **WHITE DWARF**, which will simply **cool down** and **fade away**.

High Mass Stars have a Shorter Life and a more Exciting Death

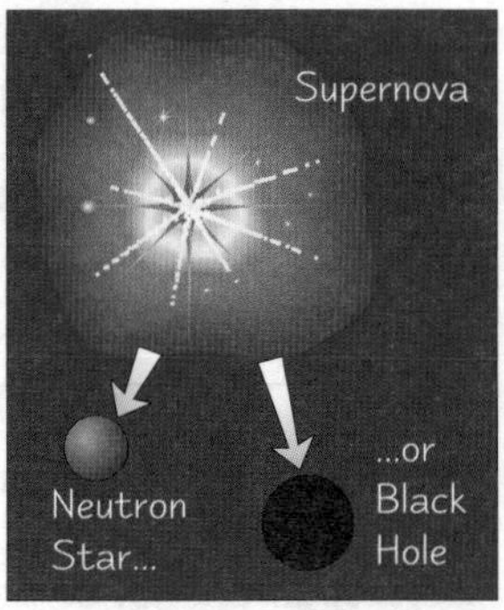

1) Even though stars with a **large mass** have a **lot of fuel**, they use it up **more quickly** and don't spend so long as main sequence stars.
2) When they are **red giants** the **'core burning to shell burning'** process can continue beyond the fusion of helium, building up layers in an **onion-like structure** to become a **SUPER RED GIANT**. For **really massive** stars this can go all the way up to **iron**.
3) Nuclear fusion **beyond iron** isn't **energetically favourable**, though, so once an iron core is formed then very quickly it's goodbye star.
4) The star explodes cataclysmically in a **SUPERNOVA**, leaving behind a **NEUTRON STAR** or (if the star was massive enough) a **BLACK HOLE**.

Stellar Evolution

Massive Stars *go out with a* ***Bit of a Bang***

1) When the core of a star runs out of fuel, it starts to **contract** — forming a white dwarf core.
2) If the star is **massive enough**, though, **electron degeneracy** can't stop the core contracting. This happens when the mass of the core is more than **1.4 times** the mass of the **Sun**.
3) The electrons get **squashed** onto the atomic **nuclei**, combining with protons to form **neutrons** and **neutrinos**.
4) The core suddenly collapses to become a **NEUTRON STAR**, which the outer layers then **fall** onto.
5) When the outer layers **hit** the surface of the **neutron star** they **rebound**, setting up huge **shockwaves**, ripping the star apart and causing a **supernova**. The light from a supernova can briefly outshine an **entire galaxy**.

Neutron stars are incredibly **dense** (about 4×10^{17} kgm^{-3}).
They're **very small**, typically about 20 km across, and they can **rotate very fast** (up to 600 times a second).
They emit **radio waves** in two beams as they rotate. These beams sometimes sweep past the Earth and can be observed as **radio pulses** rather like the flashes of a lighthouse. These rotating neutron stars are called **PULSARS**.

If you're doing OCR A you can go straight to the questions now — AQA A people need to know a little more...

Neutron Stars *are* ***Weird*** *but* ***Black Holes*** *are* ***a Lot Weirder***

1) If the **core** of the star is more than **3 times** the **Sun's mass**, the **neutrons** can't withstand the gravitational forces.
2) There are **no known mechanisms** left to stop the core collapsing to an **infinitely dense** point called a **singularity**. At that point, the **laws of physics** break down completely.
3) Up to a certain distance away (called the **Schwarzschild radius**) the gravitational pull is **so strong** that nothing, not even **light**, can escape its grasp. The **boundary** of this region is called the **event horizon**.

The **Schwarzschild radius** is the **distance** at which the **escape velocity** is the **speed of light**
An object moving at the **escape velocity** has **just enough kinetic energy** to overcome the black hole's gravitational field.

From Newton's law of gravitation we get $\frac{1}{2}mv^2 = \frac{GMm}{r}$

where m = mass of object, M = mass of black hole, v = velocity of object, r = distance from centre of black hole, $G = 6.67 \times 10^{-11}$ Nm^{2}kg^{-2}

Dividing through by m and making r the subject gives: $r = \frac{2GM}{v^2}$

By replacing v with the speed of light, c, you get the Schwarzschild radius, R_s: $R_s = \frac{2GM}{c^2}$.

This derivation is a bit of a fudge (although it gives the right answer, as it happens) — Newton's law of gravity doesn't quite work in intense gravitational fields, so Einstein's general relativity should be used instead (the maths is way too hard to go into here though).

Practice Questions

Q1 Outline how the Sun was formed, how it will evolve and how it will die.

Q2 Describe a white dwarf and a neutron star. What are the main differences between them?

Exam Questions

Q1 Outline the main differences between the evolution of high mass and low mass stars, starting from when they first become main sequence stars. [6 marks]

Q2 (a) What is meant by the Schwarzschild radius of a black hole? [2 marks]

(b) Calculate the Schwarzschild radius for a black hole that has a mass of 6×10^{30} kg. [2 marks]

Live fast — die young...

The more massive a star, the more spectacular its life cycle. The most massive stars burn up the hydrogen in their core so quickly that they only live for a fraction of the Sun's lifetime — but when they go, they do it in style.

The Doppler Effect and Redshift

***This page is for** AQA A Unit 5 Option A, Edexcel Unit 5, OCR A Unit 5 **and** OCR B Unit 4.*

Everyone's heard of the Big Bang theory — well here's some evidence for it.

The **Doppler Effect** — the **Motion** of a Wave's **Source** Affects its **Wavelength**

1) You'll have experienced the Doppler effect **loads of times** with **sound waves**.
2) Imagine an ambulance driving past you. As it moves **towards you** its siren sounds **higher-pitched**, but as it **moves away**, its **pitch** is **lower**. This change in **frequency** and **wavelength** is called the **Doppler shift**.
3) The frequency and the wavelength **change** because the waves **bunch together** in **front** of the source and **stretch out behind** it. The **amount** of stretching or bunching together depends on the **velocity** of the **source**.
4) When a **light source** moves **away** from us, the wavelengths of its light become **longer** and the frequencies become lower. This shifts the light towards the **red** end of the spectrum and is called **redshift**.
5) When a light source moves **towards** us, the **opposite** happens and the light undergoes **blueshift**.
6) The amount of redshift or blueshift, z, is determined by the following formula:

$$z = \frac{\Delta\lambda}{\lambda} = \frac{\Delta f}{f} = \frac{v}{c} \quad \text{if } v << c$$

λ is the emitted wavelength, f is the emitted frequency, $\Delta\lambda$ and Δf are the differences between the observed and emitted wavelengths/frequencies, v is the velocity of the source in the observer's direction and c is the speed of light. ($v << c$ means "v is much less than c".)

7) The way cosmologists tend to look at this stuff, the galaxies aren't actually moving **through space** away from us. Instead, **space itself** is expanding and the light waves are being **stretched** along with it. This is called **cosmological redshift** to distinguish it from **redshift** produced by sources that **are** moving through space.
8) The same formula works for both types of redshift as long as v is much less than c. If v is close to the speed of light, you need to use a nasty, relativistic formula instead (you don't need to know that one).

The **Red Shift** of Galaxies is **Strong Evidence** for the HBB

1) The **spectra** from **galaxies** (apart from a few very close ones) all show **redshift** — the **characteristic spectral lines** of the elements are all at a **longer wavelength** than you would expect. This shows they're all **moving apart**.
2) Hubble realised that the **speed** that **galaxies moved away** from us depended on **how far** they were away. This led to the idea that the Universe started out **very hot** and **very dense** and is currently **expanding**.

THE HOT BIG BANG THEORY (HBB): the Universe started off **very hot** and **very dense** (perhaps as an **infinitely hot**, **infinitely dense** singularity) and has been **expanding** ever since.

Redshift is Used to Study Spectroscopic **Binary Stars**

AQA A Option A only

1) About half of the stars we observe are actually **two stars** that orbit each other. Many of them are too far away from us to be **resolved** with **telescopes** but the **lines** in their **spectra** show a binary star system. These are called **spectroscopic binary stars**.
2) By observing how the **absorption lines** in the spectrum change with **time** the **orbital period** can be calculated:

For simplicity, think about only one absorption line from the spectrum:

a) Both stars are moving at right angles to our line of sight, so there's no redshift.

b) Both stars are moving along our line of sight. Star A shows maximum blueshift. Star B shows maximum redshift.

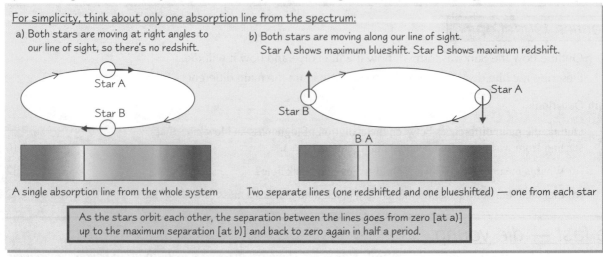

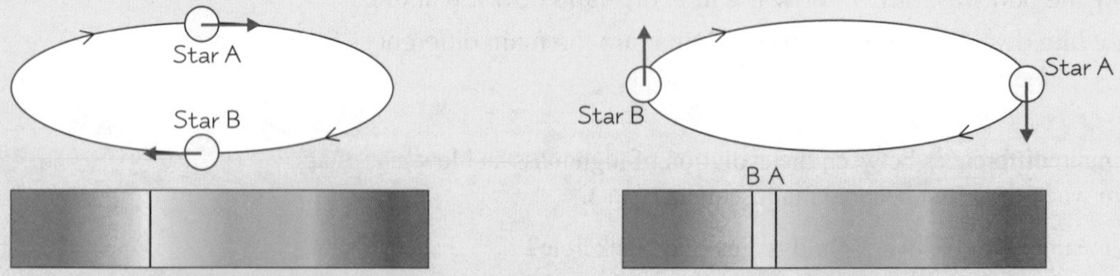

A single absorption line from the whole system

Two separate lines (one redshifted and one blueshifted) — one from each star

As the stars orbit each other, the separation between the lines goes from zero [at a)] up to the maximum separation [at b)] and back to zero again in half a period.

3) Astronomers have used a similar method to find **extrasolar planets**.

The Doppler Effect and Redshift

This page is for** AQA A Unit 5 Option A **only.

The Doppler effect explains quasars too. Read on.

Quasars — Quasi-Stellar Objects

1) **Quasars** were discovered in the late 1950s and were first thought to be **stars in our galaxy**.
2) The puzzling thing was that their spectra were **nothing like** normal stars. They sometimes shot out **jets** of material, and many of them were very active **radio sources**.
3) The 'stars' produced a **continuous spectrum** that was nothing like a black body radiation curve and instead of absorption lines, there were **emission lines** of elements that astronomers **had not seen before**.
4) However, these lines looked strangely familiar and in 1963 Maarten Schmidt realised that they were simply the **Balmer series** of hydrogen (see p.94) but **redshifted** enormously.

Quasars are a Very Long Way Away so they must be Very Bright

1) This **huge redshift** suggests they're a **huge distance away** (see next page) — in fact, the **most distant** objects seen.
2) The measured redshifts give us distances of **billions of light years**.
Using the **inverse square law** for intensity (see p. 92) gives an idea of just how **bright** quasars are:

Example A quasar has the same intensity as a star 20 000 ly away with the same luminosity as the Sun (4×10^{26} W). Its redshift gives a distance of 1×10^{10} ly. Calculate its luminosity.

$I_{quasar} = I_{star}$ so they cancel out of the equation.

$$L \propto Id^2 \Rightarrow \frac{L_{quasar}}{L_{star}} = \frac{d_{quasar}^2}{d_{star}^2} \Rightarrow L_{quasar} = L_{star} \cdot \frac{d_{quasar}^2}{d_{star}^2} = 4\times10^{26} \cdot \frac{1\times10^{20}}{4\times10^{8}} = 1\times10^{38}\ \text{W}$$

That's bright — about **10 times** the **luminosity** of the **entire Milky Way galaxy**!

3) And there's very good evidence to suggest that quasars are only about the size of the **Solar System**.
4) Let me run that past you again. **That's the power of a trillion Suns from something the size of the Solar System**.
5) These numbers caused a lot of controversy in the astrophysics community — they seemed crazy. Many astrophysicists thought there must be a more reasonable explanation. But then evidence for the distance of quasars came when **sensitive CCD** equipment detected the fuzzy cloud of **a galaxy around a quasar**.

The current consensus is that a quasar is a very powerful **galactic nucleus** — a huge **black hole** about 100 million times the mass of the Sun at the centre of a distant galaxy. (**All** galaxies are thought to have these 'supermassive' black holes at their centres.)
This black hole is surrounded by a doughnut shaped mass of **whirling gas** falling into it, which produces the light. In the same way as a pulsar (see p.97), magnetic fields produce jets of radiation streaming out from the poles. The black hole must consume the mass of about **10 Suns per year** to produce the energy observed.

Practice Questions

Q1 What is the Doppler effect? Write down the formula for the redshift and blueshift of light.

Q2 Explain how the spectra of binary stars can be used to calculate their orbital period.

Exam Questions

Q1 The spectra of three objects have been taken. What can you deduce from each of the following?
(a) The absorption lines from object A have been shifted towards the blue end of the spectrum. [1 mark]
(b) The absorption lines from object B oscillate either side of their normal position in the spectrum with a period of two weeks. [2 marks]
(c) The wavelength of the hydrogen alpha line in object C's spectrum is 667.83 nm. In the laboratory, the wavelength of the same line is measured as 656.28 nm. [3 marks]

Q2 (a) What evidence is there to suggest that quasars are a very long distance away? [1 mark]
(b) Use the concept of the inverse square law to suggest why quasars must be very bright. [2 marks]
(c) Outline the main features of a quasar according to the current theory. [2 marks]

Long ago, in a galaxy far, far away — there was a radio-loud, supermassive black hole with a highly luminous arc...

Quasars are weird. There's still some disagreement in the astrophysics community about what they are. There's even some evidence (not generally accepted) that quasars are much nearer than the redshift suggests and are just moving very quickly.

The Big Bang Model of the Universe

These pages are for AQA A Unit 5 Option A, Edexcel Unit 5, OCR A Unit 5 and OCR B Unit 4.

Right, we're moving on to the BIG picture now — we all like a bit of cosmology...

An ***Infinite Universe*** *leads to* ***Olbers' Paradox***

*OCR A **only***

When you read that all the **galaxies** in the Universe are **moving away** from the **Earth** (see p.98 and below), it's easy to imagine that the Earth is at the **centre of the Universe**, or that there's something really **special** about it. **Earth** is special to us because we **live here** — but on a **universal scale**, it's just like any other lump of rock.

1) The **demotion** of **Earth** from anything special is taken to its logical conclusion with the **cosmological principle**...

> **COSMOLOGICAL PRINCIPLE**: on a **large scale** the Universe is **homogeneous** (every part is the same as every other part) and **isotropic** (everything looks the same in every direction) — so it doesn't have a **centre**.

2) Until the **1930s**, cosmologists believed that the Universe was **infinite** in both **space** and **time** (that is, it had always existed) and **static**. This seemed the **only way** it could be **stable** using **Newton's law** of gravitation. Even **Einstein modified** his theory of **general relativity** to make it consistent with the **Steady-State Universe**.

3) In the 1820s, though, an astronomer called **Olbers** noticed a **big problem** with this model of the Universe.

> If stars (or galaxies) are **spread randomly** throughout an **infinite** Universe then **every possible line of sight** must contain a **star**. Calculations show that this should make the **whole** night sky **uniformly bright**.

This problem is called **Olbers' paradox** and clearly there's a **contradiction** with an infinite and static Universe.

Hubble *Realised that the* ***Universe*** *is* ***Expanding***

1) The **spectra** from **galaxies** (apart from a few very close ones) all show **redshift**. The amount of **redshift** gives the **recessional velocity** — how fast the galaxy is moving away (see page 98).

2) A plot of **recessional velocity** against **distance** (found using cepheid variables — see p. 91) showed that they were **proportional**, which suggests that the Universe is **expanding**. This gives rise to **Hubble's law**:

$$v = H_0 d$$

where v = recessional velocity in **kms^{-1}**, d = distance in **Mpc** and H_0 = **Hubble's constant** in **kms^{-1}Mpc^{-1}**.

3) Since distance is very difficult to measure, astronomers disagree on the value of H_0. It's generally accepted that H_0 lies somewhere between 50 kms^{-1}Mpc^{-1} and 100 kms^{-1}Mpc^{-1}.

4) The **SI unit** for H_0 is s^{-1}. To get H_0 in SI units, you need v in ms^{-1} and d in m (1 Mpc = 3.09×10^{22} m).

The ***Expanding Universe*** *gives rise to the* ***Hot Big Bang Model***

1) The Universe is **expanding** and **cooling down** (because it's a closed system). So further back in time it must have been **smaller** and **hotter**. If you trace time back **far enough**, you get a **Hot Big Bang** (see page 98).

2) Since the Universe is **expanding uniformly** away from **us** it seems as though we're at the **centre** of the Universe, but this is an **illusion**. You would observe the **same thing** at **any point** in the Universe.

The ***Age*** *and* ***Observable Size*** *of the* ***Universe*** *Depend on* H_0

1) If the Universe has been **expanding** at the **same rate** for its whole life, the **age** of the Universe is $t = 1/H_0$ (time = distance/speed). This is only an estimate since the Universe probably hasn't always been expanding at the same rate.

2) Unfortunately, since no one knows the **exact value** of H_0 we can only guess the Universe's age. If H_0 **= 75 kms^{-1}Mpc^{-1}**, then the age of the Universe $\approx 1/(2.4 \times 10^{-18}\ \text{s}^{-1}) = 4.1 \times 10^{17}$ s = **13 billion years**.

3) The **absolute size** of the Universe is **unknown** but there is a limit on the size of the **observable Universe**. This is simply a **sphere** (with the Earth at its centre) with a **radius** equal to the **maximum distance** that **light** can travel during its **age**. So if H_0 **= 75 kms^{-1}Mpc^{-1}** then this sphere will have a radius of **13 billion light years**.

4) This gives a very simple solution to **Olbers' paradox**. If the observable Universe is **finite**, then there is **absolutely no reason** why every line of sight should include a star. Actually, most of them don't.

The Big Bang Model of the Universe

If you're doing Edexcel you can skip to the questions now — the rest is for AQA A, OCR A and OCR B.

Cosmic Microwave Background Radiation — More Evidence for the HBB

1) The Hot Big Bang model predicts that loads of **electromagnetic radiation** was produced in the **very early Universe**. This radiation should **still** be observed today (it hasn't had anywhere else to go).
2) Because the Universe has **expanded**, the wavelengths of this cosmic background radiation have been **stretched** and are now in the **microwave** region.
3) This was picked up **accidentally** by Penzias and Wilson in the 1960s.

Properties of the Cosmic Microwave Background Radiation (CMBR)

1) In the late 1980s a satellite called the **Cosmic Background Explorer** (**COBE**) was sent up to have a **detailed look** at the radiation.
2) It found a **perfect blackbody spectrum** corresponding to a **temperature** of **2.73 K** (see page 92).
3) The radiation is largely **isotropic** and **homogeneous**, which confirms the cosmological principle (see page 100).
4) There are **very tiny fluctuations** in temperature, which were at the limit of COBE's detection. These are due to tiny energy-density variations in the early Universe, and are needed for the initial '**seeding**' of galaxy formation.
5) The background radiation also shows a **Doppler shift**, indicating the Earth's motion through space. It turns out that the **Milky Way** is rushing towards an unknown mass (the **Great Attractor**) at over a **million miles an hour**.

Another Bit of Evidence is the Amount of Helium in the Universe

1) The HBB model also explained the **large abundance of helium** in the Universe (which had puzzled astrophysicists for a while).
2) The early Universe had been very hot, so at some point it must have been hot enough for **hydrogen fusion** to happen. This means that, together with the theory of the synthesis of the **heavier elements** in stars, the **relative abundances** of all of the elements can be accounted for.

Practice Questions

Q1 State Olbers' paradox. How does the Hot Big Bang model resolve it?

Q2 What is Hubble's law? How can it be used to find the age of the Universe?

Q3 What is the cosmic background radiation?

Exam Questions

Q1 (a) State Hubble's law, explaining the meanings of all the symbols. [2 marks]

(b) What does Hubble's law suggest about the nature of the Universe? [2 marks]

(c) Assume $H_0 = +50\ \text{kms}^{-1}\text{Mpc}^{-1}$ ($1\ \text{Mpc} = 3.09 \times 10^{22}$ m).

i) Calculate H_0 in SI units. [2 marks]

ii) Calculate an estimate of the age of the Universe, and hence the size of the observable Universe. [3 marks]

Q2 (a) A certain object has a redshift of 0.37. Estimate the speed at which it is moving away from us. [2 marks]

(b) Use Hubble's law to estimate the distance (in light years) that the object is from us.
(Take $H_0 = 2.4 \times 10^{-18}\ \text{s}^{-1}$, $1\ \text{ly} = 9.5 \times 10^{15}$ m.) [2 marks]

(c) With reference to the speed of the object, explain why your answers to a) and b) are estimates. [1 mark]

Q3 Describe the main features of the cosmic background radiation and explain why its discovery was considered strong evidence for the Hot Big Bang model of the Universe.
Marks will be awarded for the quality of your written communication. [7 marks]

My Physics teacher was a Great Attractor — everyone fell for him...

The simple Big Bang model doesn't actually work — not quite, anyway. There are loads of little things that don't quite add up. Modern cosmologists are trying to improve the model using a period of very rapid expansion called inflation.

Evolution of the Universe

These pages are for Edexcel Unit 5 (just the section at the bottom of this page on finding the age of the Universe) and OCR A Unit 5 only.

This page assumes the Standard Big Bang Model — so we can ignore newfangled theories like inflation (for now...)

Gravity Warps Space and Time

1) According to **general relativity** gravity works by changing the **shape** of space and time.
2) To reduce the brain-ache a bit, you can imagine the Universe as a **2-dimensional surface** that's warped in 3 dimensions. This is a handy way of getting an idea of what's going on, but **be careful**. **Space-time** actually has **4 dimensions** (x, y, z and time).
3) On a big scale, there are **three ways** that gravity can warp the Universe: the Universe can be **flat**, **open** or **closed**.
4) This **curvature** of space-time determines the eventual **fate** of the Universe.

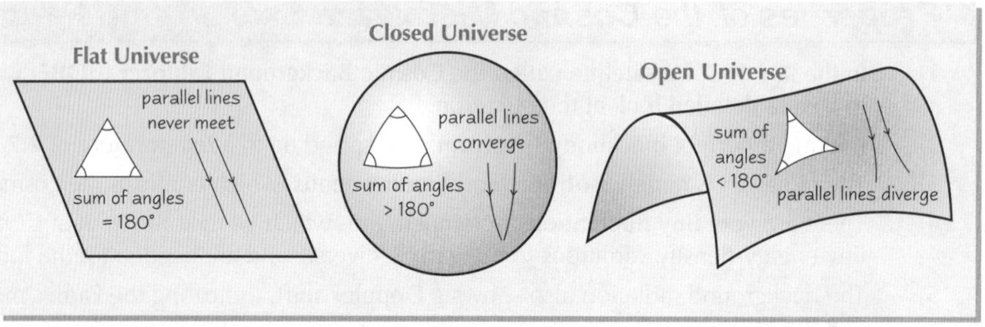

The Curvature depends on the Density of the Universe

1) The amount of **curvature** depends on the **average density** of the Universe, ρ_0.
2) The density required for the Universe to be **flat** is called the **critical density**, ρ_c.

> If $\rho_0 = \rho_c$ the Universe is **flat**, if $\rho_0 < \rho_c$ the Universe is **open** and if $\rho_0 > \rho_c$ it's **closed**.

With a bit of mathematical jiggery-pokery you can get an equation for the critical density of the Universe in terms of the Hubble constant:

$$\rho_0 = \frac{3H_0^2}{8\pi G}$$

G is the gravitational constant — 6.67×10^{-11} Nm^{2}kg^{-2}.

The mists are clearing...

3) The three possible types of **curvature** give three possible **fates** of the Universe:

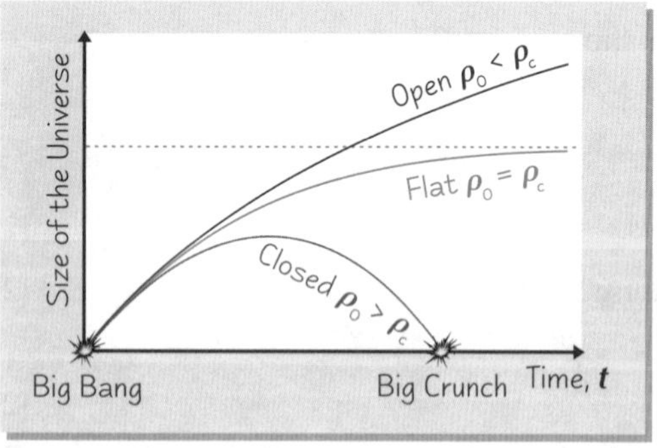

In an **open** Universe, gravity (controlled by the density) is **too weak** to stop the expansion. The Universe will just keep **expanding for ever**.

In a **closed** Universe, gravity is **strong enough** to stop the expansion and start the Universe **contracting** again (ending up with a **Big Crunch**).

In a **flat** Universe, gravity is **just strong enough** to stop the expansion at $t = \infty$ (so the Universe expands for ever, but more and more slowly with time).

We Can't Calculate the Age of the Universe until we know its Density

1) A reasonable **estimate** of the **age** of the Universe is found from $t \approx 1/H_0$ (see page 100). But this formula assumes that the Universe had been expanding at the **same rate** for its whole lifetime.
2) In fact if you look at the **graph** of size against time, the **expansion rate** of the Universe is **slowing down**, even for the **open Universe**. So **in the past** the Universe was expanding **faster** than it is now.
3) That means we've **overestimated** the time it's taken for the Universe to get to the size it is now.
4) The **more dense** the Universe is, the **younger** it must be.
5) If you include all the "**dark matter**" and "**dark energy**" that's been detected **indirectly**, current **estimates** of the actual density of the Universe aren't very far off the **critical density**.

Evolution of the Universe

The Story So Far...

Before 10^{-4} seconds after the Big Bang, this is mainly guesswork. There are plenty of theories around, but not much experimental evidence to back them up. The general consensus at the moment goes something like this:

1) **Big Bang to 10^{-43} seconds.** Well, it's anybody's guess, really. At this sort of size and energy, even general relativity stops working properly. This is the "infinitely hot, infinitely small, infinitely dense" bit.
2) **10^{-43} seconds to 10^{-4} seconds.** At the start of this period, there's no distinction between different types of force — there's just one grand unified force. Then the Universe expands and cools, and the unified force splits into gravity, strong nuclear, weak nuclear and electromagnetic forces. Many cosmologists believe the Universe went through a rapid period of expansion called inflation at about 10^{-34} s.
   The Universe is a sea of quarks, antiquarks, leptons and photons. The quarks aren't bound up in particles like protons and neutrons, because there's too much energy around.
   At some point, matter-antimatter symmetry gets broken, so slightly more matter is made than antimatter.
   Nobody knows exactly how or when this happened, but most cosmologists like to put it as early as possible in the history of the Universe (before inflation, even).

Now we're onto more solid ground

3) **10^{-4} seconds.** This corresponds to a temperature of about 10^{12} K. The Universe is cool enough for quarks to join up to form particles like protons and neutrons. They can never exist separately again. Matter and antimatter annihilate each other, leaving a small excess of matter and huge numbers of photons (resulting in the cosmic background radiation that we observe today).
4) **About 100 seconds.** Temperature has cooled to 10^9 K. The Universe is similar to the interior of a star. Protons are cool enough to fuse to form helium nuclei.
5) **About 300 000 years.** Temperature has cooled to about 3000 K. The Universe is cool enough for electrons (that were produced in the first millisecond) to combine with helium and hydrogen nuclei to form atoms. The Universe becomes transparent since there are no free charges for the photons to interact with. This process is called recombination.
6) **About 14 billion years (now).** Temperature has cooled to about 3 K. Slight density fluctuations in the Universe mean that, over time, clumps of matter have been condensed by gravity into galactic clusters, galaxies and individual stars.

Practice Questions

Q1 What are the three possible fates of the Universe?

Q2 Why does the calculated age of the Universe depend on its density?

Q3 What is recombination?

Exam Questions

Q1 (a) Some cosmologists believe the Universe to be flat. What evidence is there to suggest that this is the case? [2 marks]

(b) Explain what is meant by a flat universe in terms of its geometry, and its evolution. [3 marks]

Q2 The upper limit on Hubble's constant is 100 $\text{kms}^{-1}\text{Mpc}^{-1}$ (1 Mpc = 3.09×10^{22} m).

(a) Work out the average density of the Universe if the Universe is flat and H_0 is 100 $\text{kms}^{-1}\text{Mpc}^{-1}$. [4 marks]

(b) Given that the mass of a hydrogen atom is 1.7×10^{-27} kg, calculate the average number of hydrogen atoms in every m^3 of space if the entire mass of the Universe is hydrogen. [2 marks]

Q3 Starting from the production of matter and antimatter, describe the evolution of the Universe (including its structure) up to the present day.
In your answer, you should use a clear, logical progression of ideas. [10 marks]

It's the end of the world as we know it...

Recently, astronomers have found evidence that the expansion rate is actually accelerating — because of something called dark energy. That means the simple shapes of the graphs on the last page might be a long way from the true picture...

Physics of the Eye

These pages are for AQA A Unit 5 Option B only.

*The eyes contain **converging lenses**, which focus light rays to form images. Page 84 tells you all about lenses — make sure you're confident with that before you start. Here are the two big equations you need to know:*

power of a lens

$$P = \frac{1}{f}$$

lens equation

$$\frac{1}{f} = \frac{1}{u} + \frac{1}{v}$$

You Need to Know the Basic **Structure** of the **Eye**

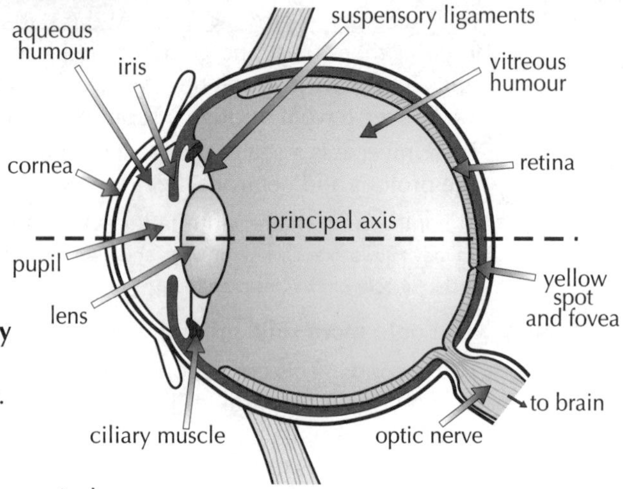

1) The **cornea** is a **transparent** 'window' with a **convex** shape, and a **high refractive index**. The cornea does most of the eye's focusing.
2) The **aqueous humour** is a **watery** substance that lets light pass through the pupil to the lens.
3) The **iris** is the coloured part of the eye. It consists of **radial** and **circular muscles** that control the size of the **pupil** — the hole in the middle of the iris. This regulates the intensity of light entering the eye.
4) The **lens** acts as a **fine focus** and is controlled by the **ciliary muscles**. When the ciliary muscles **contract**, tension is released and the lens takes on a **fat**, more **spherical** shape. When they **relax**, the **suspensory ligaments** pull the lens into a **thin**, **flatter** shape.
5) The **vitreous humour** is a **jelly-like** substance that keeps the eye's shape.
6) Images are formed on the **retina**, which contains **light-sensitive cells** called **rods** and **cones** (see below).
7) The **yellow spot** is a particularly sensitive region of the retina. In the centre of the yellow spot is the **fovea**. This is the part of the retina with the highest concentration of **cones**.
8) The **optic nerve** carries signals from the rods and cones to the **brain**.

The image is upside down but it's interpreted by the brain to seem the right way up.

The **Eye** is an **Optical Refracting System**

1) The **far point** is the **furthest distance** that the eye can focus comfortably. For normally sighted people that's **infinity**. When your eyes are focusing at the far point, they're **'unaccommodated'**. The **near point** is the **closest distance** that the eye can focus on. For young people it's about 9 cm.
2) The **cornea** and **aqueous humour** act as a **fixed converging lens** with a **power** of about **41 D**.
3) The power of the eye's **lens** itself is about **18 D** when **unaccommodated**. By changing shape, it can increase to about **29 D** in young people to view objects at the **near point**.
4) You can **add together** the **powers** of the cornea, aqueous humour and lens. That means you can think of the eye as a **single converging lens** of **power 59 D** at the far point. This gives a **focal length** of **1.7 cm**.
5) When looking at nearer objects, the eye's power **increases**, as the lens changes shape and the **focal length decreases** — but the distance between the lens and the image, ***v***, stays the same, at 1.7 cm.

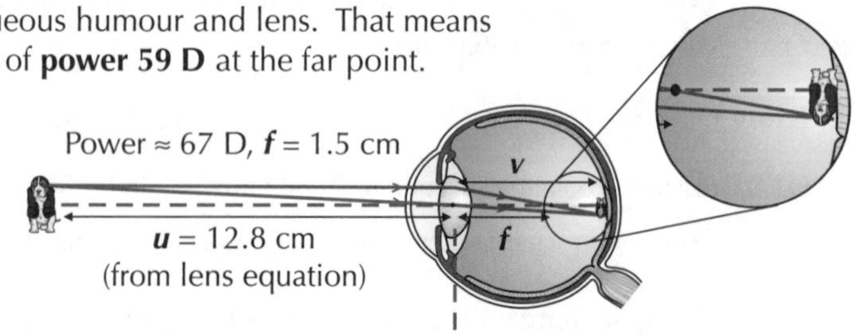

The **Retina** has **Rods** and **Cones**

1) **Rods** and **cones** are cells at the back of the **retina** that respond to **light**. Light travels **through the retina** to the rods and cones at the back.
2) Rods and cones all contain chemical **pigments** that **bleach** when **light** falls on them. This bleaching stimulates the cell to send signals to the **brain** via the **optic nerve**.
3) The cells are **reset** (i.e. unbleached) by enzymes using **vitamin A** from the blood.
4) There's only **one** type of **rod** but there are **three** types of **cone**, which are sensitive to **red**, **green** and **blue** light.

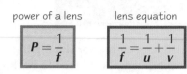

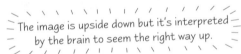

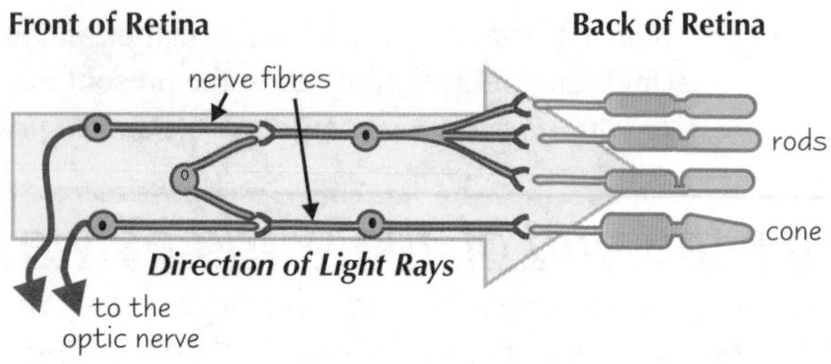

Physics of the Eye

The Cones let you See in Full Colour

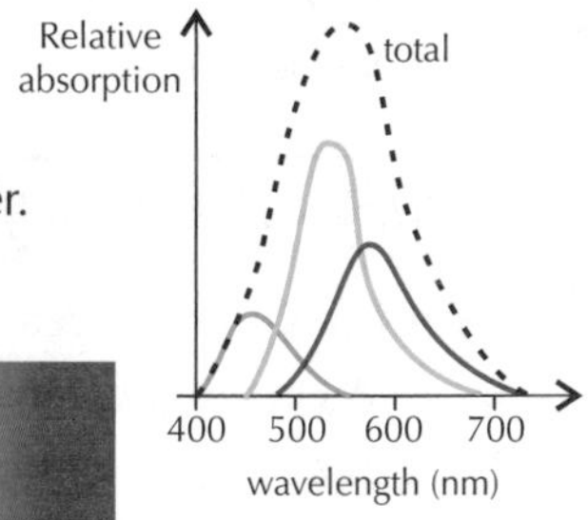

1) The red, green and blue **cones** each absorb a **range of wavelengths**.
2) The eye is **less responsive** to blue light than to red or green, so blues often look dimmer.
3) The brain receives signals from the three types of cone and interprets their **weighted relative strengths** as **colour**...

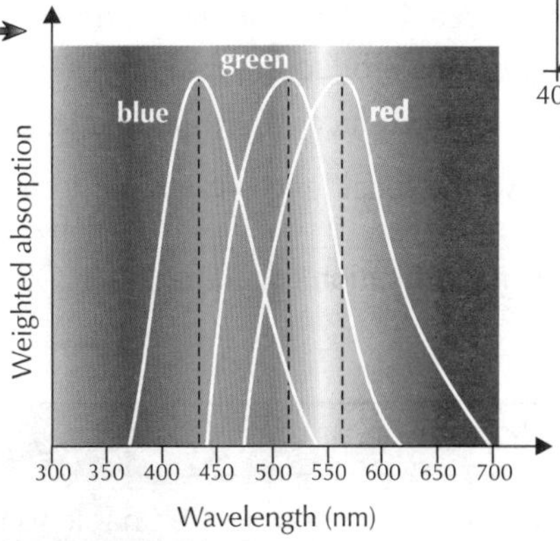

> **Example**
> Yellow light produces almost equal responses from the red and green cones.
> Yellow light can therefore be 'faked' by combining red and green light of almost equal intensity — the electrical signal from the retina will be the same and the brain interprets it as 'yellow'.

4) **Any** colour can be produced by **combining** different intensities of **red**, **green** and **blue** light. Colour televisions work like this.

You Need Good Spatial Resolution to See Details

1) Two objects can only be distinguished from each other if there's **at least one rod** or **cone between** the light from each of them. Otherwise the brain can't **resolve** the two objects and it 'sees' them as one.

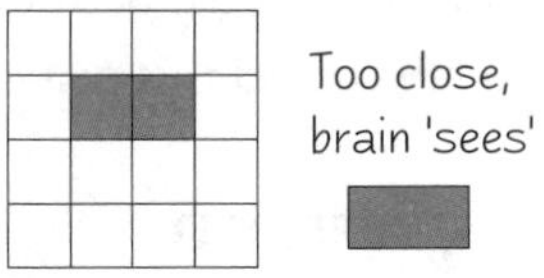

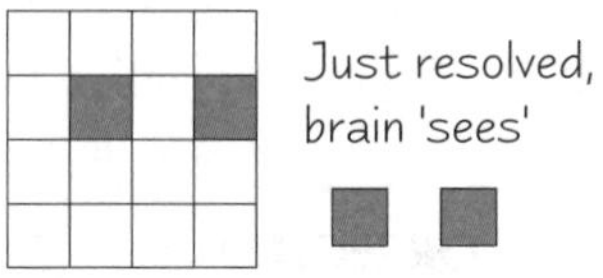

2) **Spatial resolution** is **best** at the **yellow spot** — the **cones** are very **densely packed** here and each cone always has its **own nerve fibre**. There are **no rods in the yellow spot**, though. This means that in **dim light**, when **cones don't work**, resolution is best slightly off the direct line of sight, where the **rods** are more **densely packed**.
3) Away from the yellow spot, resolution is much worse. The light-sensitive cells are **not** as **densely packed** and the rods **share nerve fibres** — there are up to 600 rods per fibre at the edges of the retina.

Persistence of Vision means you Don't See Rapid Flickering

1) **Nerve impulses** from the eye take about a fifth of a second to **decay**. So a very dim light flashing faster than **five times per second** (5 Hz) seems to be **on continuously**. This is called **flicker fusion**.
2) At **higher light intensity**, more nerve cells are 'firing' so a **higher frequency** is needed for flicker fusion to occur.
3) Cinema and TV rely on **persistence of vision** to give the illusion of **smooth** rather than **jerky movements**.

Practice Questions

Q1 Draw a ray diagram to show a young person's eye focusing at the near point.
Assume that the eye's total power is 70 D. Mark on your diagram the distances u, v and f.

Q2 Describe the differences and similarities between rods and cones.

Q3 Sketch a graph showing how the cone cells in the retina respond to different wavelengths of light.

Q4 What is meant by 'persistence of vision'? Give a situation where it is useful.

Exam Questions

Q1 The power of an unaccommodated eye is 60 D.
(a) When the eye focuses at infinity, what will be the image distance, v? [2 marks]
(b) For the eye to focus on an object that is 30 cm away, what extra power must the lens produce? [3 marks]

Q2 The eye is designed to receive incoming light and focus it on the retina.
(a) Outline the path of light through the eye, explaining the purpose of the structures it passes through. [4 marks]
(b) Describe the relationship between the structure of the retina and spatial resolution. [2 marks]

The eyes are the window on the soul...

Or so they said in the 16th century. Sadly, that won't get you far with a question about the spectral response of the retina.

Defects of Vision

These pages are for AQA A Unit 5 Option B only.

Plenty of people don't have perfect vision, and need ***auxiliary lenses*** *to correct their sight.*

Real is Positive, Virtual is Negative

(see p. 84 for more on real and virtual images)

Lenses can produce **real** or **virtual** images, and you need to follow the "**real** is **positive**, **virtual** is **negative**" rule.

1) A **converging lens** produces a **real image**, so its **focal length**, ***f***, is **positive**.
2) A **diverging lens** produces a **virtual image**, so it has a **negative focal length**.
3) As you know, the focal length is related to object and image distances by the **lens equation**... $\frac{1}{f} = \frac{1}{u} + \frac{1}{v}$
4) The **linear magnification** of a lens is $m = \frac{\text{size of image}}{\text{size of object}}$ and $m = \frac{v}{u}$

Myopia is Corrected with Diverging Lenses

1) **Short-sighted** (myopic) people are unable to focus on distant objects — this happens if their **far point** is **closer** than infinity (see p. 104).
2) Myopia occurs when the **cornea** and **lens** are too **powerful** or the **eyeball** is too **long**.
3) The focusing system is **too powerful** and images of distant objects are brought into focus in **front** of the retina.
4) A lens of **negative power** is needed to correct this defect — so a **diverging** lens is placed in front of the eye.

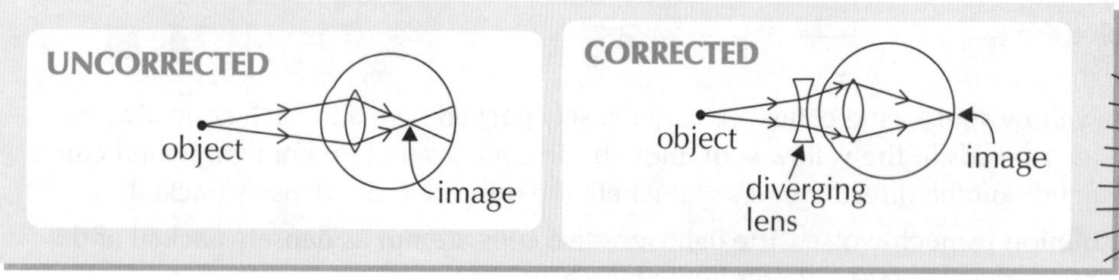

As well as correcting the far point, the diverging lens also makes the near point a little further away than it was. This isn't usually a problem — short-sighted people usually have a near point that is closer than normal anyway.

Hypermetropia is corrected with Converging Lenses

1) **Long-sighted** (hypermetropic) people are unable to focus clearly on near objects. This happens if their **near point** is **further** away than normal (25 cm or more).
2) Long sight occurs because the **cornea** and **lens** are too **weak** or the **eyeball** is too **short**.
3) The focusing system is **too weak** and images of near objects are brought into focus **behind** the retina.
4) A lens of **positive power** is needed to correct the defect — so a **converging** lens is placed in front of the eye.

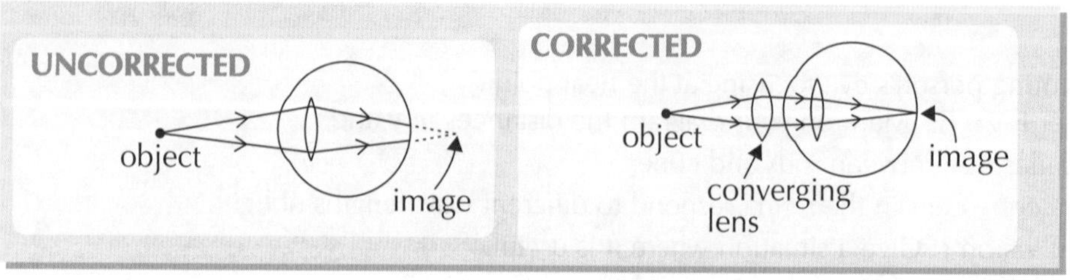

Long-sightedness is common among young children whose lenses have grown quicker than their eyeballs.

Astigmatism is Corrected with Cylindrical Lenses

1) **Astigmatism** is caused by an irregularly shaped **cornea** or **lens** which has **different focal lengths** for different **planes**. For instance, when **vertical lines** are in focus, **horizontal** lines might not be.
2) The condition is corrected with **cylindrical lenses**.

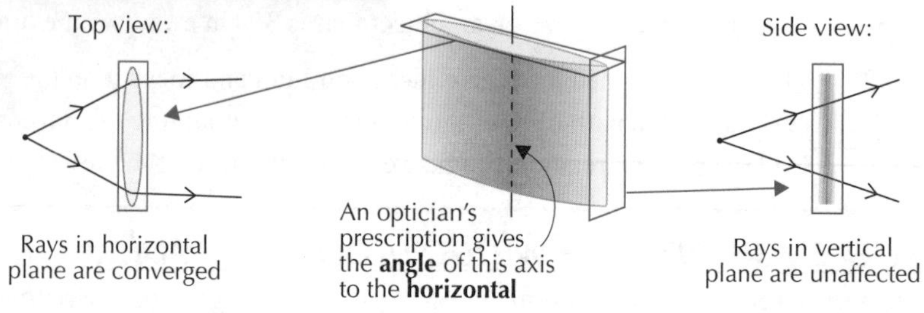

Top view:
Side view:
Rays in horizontal plane are converged
An optician's prescription gives the angle of this axis to the horizontal
Rays in vertical plane are unaffected

Defects of Vision

Choosing a **Lens** to Correct for **Short Sight** Depends on the **Far Point**

1) To correct for **short sight**, a **diverging** lens is chosen which has its **principal focus** at the eye's **faulty far point**.
2) The **principal focus** is the point that rays from a distant object **appear** to have come from (see p.84).
3) The lens must have a **negative focal length** which is the same as the **distance to the eye's far point**. This means that objects at **infinity**, which were out of focus, now seem to be in focus at the far point.

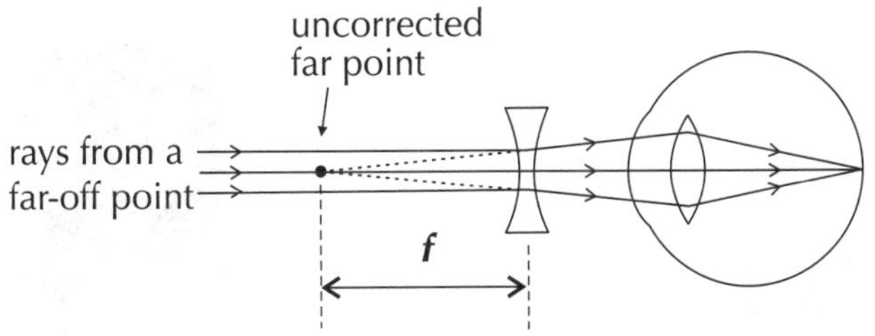

Example

Ben is short-sighted. His far point is 5 m.
Calculate the power of lens he needs to correct his vision.

Focal length, f = far point = −5 m

Power needed = $\frac{1}{f}$ = **−0.2 D**

The power's always **negative** to correct for **short** sight.

Calculations Involving **Long Sight** Use the **Lens Equation**

1) People with these conditions have a near point which is too far away. An 'acceptable' near point is 25 cm.
2) A **converging lens** is used to produce a **virtual image** of objects 0.25 m away **at the eye's near point.** This means that close objects, which were out of focus, now seem to be in focus at the near point.
3) You can work out the **focal length**, and hence the **power** of lens needed, using the **lens equation** $\frac{1}{f} = \frac{1}{u} + \frac{1}{v}$

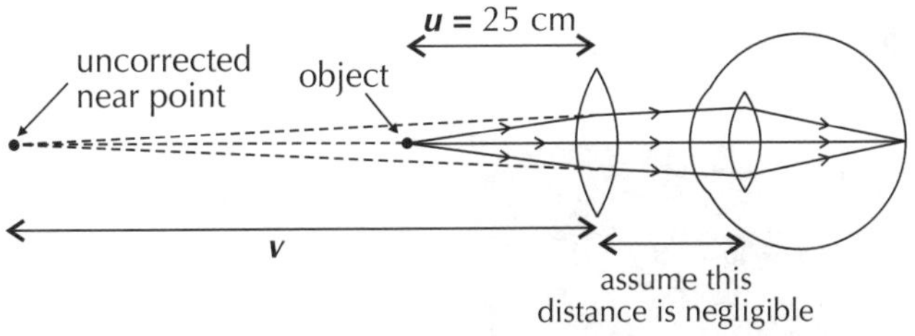

Example

Mavis can't read her book — her near point is 5 m.
What power of lens does she need?

u = 0.25 m, v = −5 m (real is positive, virtual is negative)

$\frac{1}{f} = \frac{1}{0.25} - \frac{1}{5}$

$\frac{1}{f} = 3.8$ so power = **+3.8 D**

The power's always **positive** to correct for **long** sight.

Practice Questions

Q1 Define the terms myopia, hypermetropia and astigmatism.
Q2 What type of auxiliary lenses are used to correct these conditions?
Q3 Define the terms near point and far point.

Exam Questions

Q1 A man with short sight has a far point of 4 m.
Calculate the power of auxiliary lens needed to correct his far point. [3 marks]

Q2 A girl has a near point of 2 m.
Calculate the power of lens required to correct her near point to 25 cm. [3 marks]

Q3 Claire suffers from astigmatism.
(a) What type of lenses are used to correct astigmatism? [1 mark]
(b) Draw a diagram of a lens that would converge rays in the vertical plane but not in the horizontal plane. [2 marks]

You can't fly fighter planes if you wear glasses...

There's a hidden bonus to having dodgy eyes — in the exam, you can take your specs off (discreetly) and have a look at the lenses to remind yourself what type is needed to correct short sight, long sight, or whatever it is you have. Cunning.

Physics of the Ear

These pages are for AQA A Unit 5 Option B only.

Ears are pretty amazing — they convert sound into electrical energy, using some tiny bones and lots of even tinier hairs.

The Intensity of Sound is Power per Unit Area

The **intensity** of a sound wave is defined as the amount of sound **energy** that passes **per second per unit area** (perpendicular to the direction of the wave). That's **power per unit area**.

1) If the sound energy arriving at the ear per second is ***P***, then the intensity of the sound is:

$$I = \frac{P}{A}$$

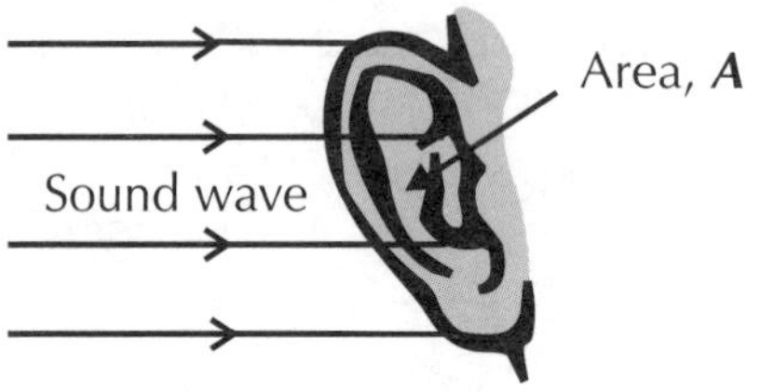

Felicity thought her waves were sound.

2) The SI unit of intensity is Wm^{-2}, but you'll often see decibels used instead (see p. 110).
3) For any wave, **intensity** $\propto$ **amplitude²** — so doubling the amplitude will result in four times the intensity.
4) Intensity is related to the **loudness** of sound (see p. 110).

The Ear has Three Main Sections

The ear consists of three sections: the **outer** ear (**pinna** and **auditory canal**), the **middle ear** (**ossicles** and **Eustachian tube**) and the **inner ear** (**semicircular canals**, **cochlea** and **auditory nerve**).

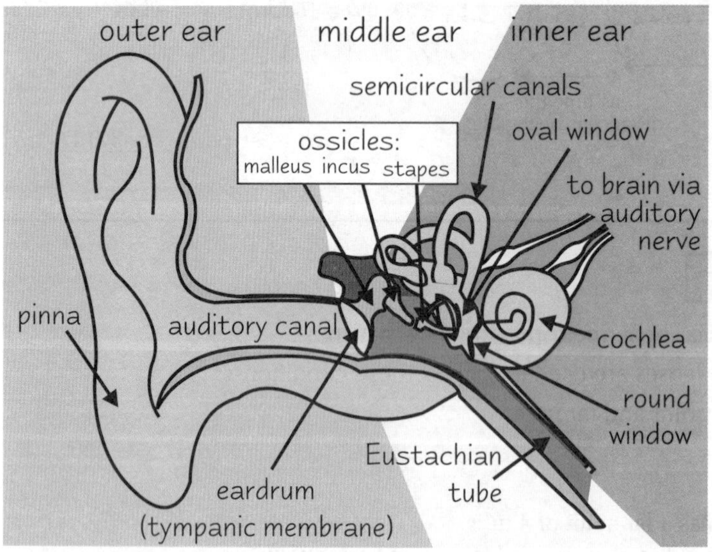

1) The **tympanic membrane** (eardrum) separates the **outer** and **middle** ears.
2) Although separated, the **outer** and **middle** ears both contain **air** at **atmospheric pressure**, apart from slight pressure variations due to sound waves. This pressure is maintained by **yawning** and **swallowing** — the middle ear is opened up to the outside via the **Eustachian tube** (which is connected to the throat).
3) The **oval** and **round windows** separate the **middle** and **inner** ears.
4) The **inner ear** is filled with fluid called **perilymph** (or **endolymph** in the **cochlear duct**). This fluid allows **vibrations** to pass to the basilar membrane in the **cochlea**.
5) The **semicircular canals** are involved with **maintaining balance**.

Physics of the Ear

The **Ear** acts as a **Transducer,** converting **Sound Energy**...

1) The **pinna** (external ear) acts like a funnel, channelling sound waves into the auditory canal — this **concentrates** the energy onto a **smaller area**, which increases the **intensity**.
2) The sound waves consist of **variations** in **air pressure**, which make the **tympanic membrane** (eardrum) **vibrate**.
3) The tympanic membrane is connected to the **malleus** — one of the **three tiny bones** (**ossicles**) in the middle ear. The malleus then passes the **vibrations** of the eardrum on to the **incus** and the **stapes** (which is connected to the **oval window**).
4) As well as **transmitting vibrations**, the **ossicles** have **two** other functions — **amplifying** the sound signal and **reducing** the **energy reflected back** from the inner ear.
5) The **oval window** has a much **smaller area** than the **tympanic membrane**. Together with the **increased force** produced by the ossicles, this results in **greater pressure variations** at the oval window.
6) The **oval window** transmits vibrations to the **fluid** in the **inner ear**.

...into **Electrical Energy**

1) Pressure waves in the fluid of the **cochlea** make the **basilar membrane** vibrate. Different regions of this membrane have different **natural frequencies**, from 20 000 Hz near the middle ear to 20 Hz at the other end.
2) When a sound wave of a particular **frequency** enters the inner ear, one part of the basilar membrane **resonates** and so vibrates with a **large amplitude**.
3) **Hair cells** attached to the basilar membrane trigger **nerve impulses** at this point of greatest vibration.
4) These **electrical impulses** are sent, via the **auditory nerve**, to the **brain**, where they are interpreted as **sounds**.

THE INNER EAR (UNROLLED):

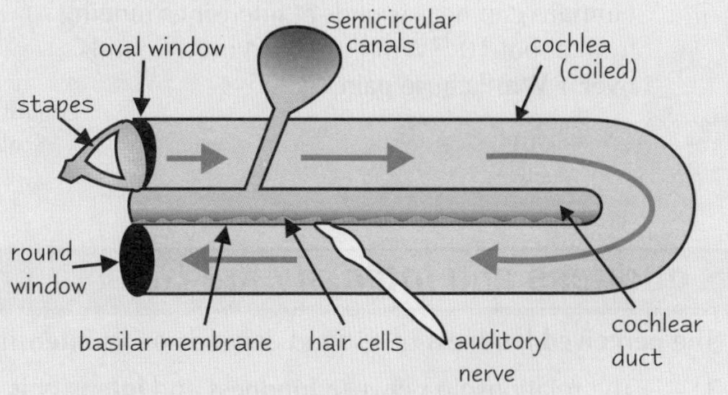

Practice Questions

Q1 What is meant by the 'intensity' of sound? What is the formula for intensity?

Q2 Sketch a diagram of the ear, labelling the structures within it.

Q3 Describe the function of the ossicles.

Q4 Explain why the relative size of the oval window and tympanic membrane is important.

Exam Question

Q1 The ear is designed to transduce sound energy into electrical energy.

(a) What is the function of the pinna? [1 mark]

(b) Describe how sound energy is transmitted through the middle ear. [3 marks]

(c) The surface area of the tympanic membrane is around 14 times the area of the oval window. Show that this increases the amplitude of vibrations in the ear by a factor of approximately 3.74. [3 marks]

(d) Describe how pressure waves in the cochlea are converted to electrical impulses. [2 marks]

(e) Explain how the ear is able to encode the frequency of a sound in the information sent to the brain. [2 marks]

Ears are like essays — they have a beginning, middle and end...

Or outer, middle and inner, if we're being technical. Learn what vibrates where, and you'll be fine.

Intensity and Loudness

These pages are for AQA A Unit 5 Option B only.

*The ear's sensitivity depends on the **frequency** and **intensity** of sounds, and deteriorates as you get older.*

Humans can Hear a Limited Range of Frequencies

1) Young people can hear frequencies ranging from about **20 Hz** (low pitch) up to **20 000 Hz** (high pitch). As you get older, the upper limit decreases.
2) Our ability to **discriminate between frequencies** depends on how **high** that frequency is. For example, between 60 and 1000 Hz, you can hear frequencies 3 Hz apart as **different pitches**. At **higher** frequencies, a **greater difference** is needed for frequencies to be distinguished. Above 10 000 Hz, pitch can hardly be discriminated at all.
3) The **loudness** of sound you hear depends on the **intensity** and **frequency** of the sound waves.
4) The **weakest intensity** you can hear — the **threshold of hearing, I_0** — depends on the **frequency** of the sound wave.
5) The ear is **most sensitive** at around **3000 Hz**. For any given intensity, sounds of this frequency will be **loudest**.
6) Humans can hear sounds at intensities ranging from about 10^{-12} Wm^{-2} to 100 Wm^{-2}. Sounds **over 1 Wm^{-2}** cause **pain**.

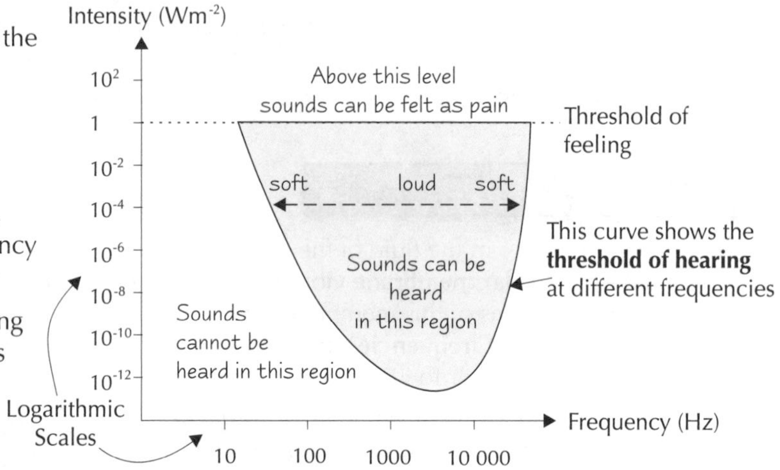

Loudness and Intensity are Related Logarithmically

The **perceived loudness** of a sound depends on its **intensity** (and its frequency — see above).

1) The relationship between **loudness** and **intensity** is **logarithmic**.
2) This means that **loudness, L,** goes up in **equal intervals** if **intensity, I,** increases by a **constant factor** (provided the frequency of the sound doesn't change).
3) E.g. if you **double** the intensity, **double it again** and so on, the **loudness** keeps going up in **equal steps**.

$$\Delta L \propto \log\left(\frac{I_2}{I_1}\right)$$

I_1 is the original intensity
I_2 is the new intensity
ΔL is increase in loudness

The Decibel Scale is used for Measuring Intensity Level

1) You can often measure loudness using a **decibel meter**. The **decibel scale** is a **logarithmic scale** which actually measures **intensity level**.
2) The **intensity level, IL,** of a sound of intensity I is defined as

$$IL = 10\log\left(\frac{I}{I_0}\right)$$

I = intensity
I_0 = threshold of hearing

3) I_0 is the **threshold of hearing** (the **lowest intensity** of sound that can be heard) at a frequency of **1000 Hz**.
4) The value of I_0 is **1×10^{-12} Wm^{-2}**.
5) The units of IL are **decibels** (dB). Intensity level can be given in **bels** — one decibel is a tenth of a bel — but decibels are usually a more convenient size.

The dBA Scale is an Adjusted Decibel Scale

1) The **perceived loudness** of a sound depends on its **frequency** as well as its intensity. Two different frequencies with the **same loudness** will have **different intensity levels** on the dB scale.
2) The **dBA** scale is an **adjusted decibel scale** which is designed to take into account the **ear's response** to **different frequencies**.
3) On the **dBA scale**, sounds of the **same intensity level** have the **same loudness** for the average human ear.

Intensity and Loudness

You can Generate **Curves of Equal Loudness**

1) Start by generating a **control frequency** of **1000 Hz** at a particular **intensity level**.
2) Generate another sound at a different frequency. Vary the volume of this sound until it appears to have the **same loudness** as the 1000 Hz frequency. Measure the **intensity level** at this volume.
3) Repeat this for several different frequencies, and plot the resulting curve on a graph.
4) Change the **intensity level** of the **control frequency** and repeat steps two and three.
5) If you measure **intensity level** in **decibels**, then the **loudness** of the sound is given in **phons**.

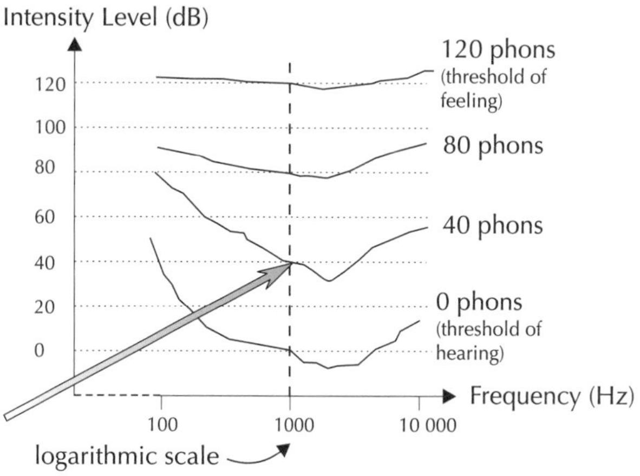

At 1000 Hz, the loudness in phons is the same value as the intensity level in decibels.

Hearing Deteriorates with **Age** and **Exposure** to **Excessive Noise**

1) As you get **older**, your hearing deteriorates **generally**, but **higher frequencies** are affected **most**.
2) Your ears can be damaged by **excessive noise**. This results in general hearing loss, but frequencies around **4000 Hz** are usually worst affected.
3) People who've worked with very **noisy machinery** have most hearing loss at the **particular frequencies** of the noise causing the damage.
4) **Equal loudness curves** can show hearing loss.
5) For a person with hearing loss, **higher intensity levels** are needed for the **same loudness**, when compared to a normal ear. A **peak** in the curve shows damage at a **particular** range of **frequencies**.

Equal loudness curves at 0 phons

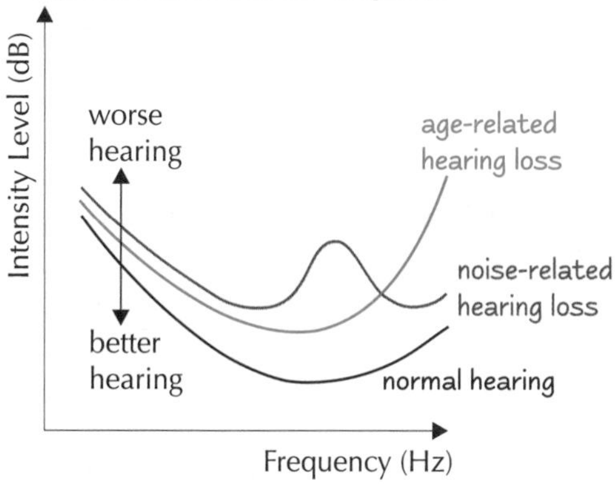

Practice Questions

Q1 Define the threshold of hearing and sketch a graph that shows how it depends on frequency.

Q2 How are curves of equal loudness generated?

Q3 What is the dB scale? How is the dBA scale different?

Exam Questions

Q1 A small siren, which can be regarded as a point source, emits sound waves at a frequency of 3000 Hz. The intensity of the sound is 0.94 Wm^{-2} at a distance of 10 m.

(a) State the accepted value of the threshold of hearing at 1000 Hz, I_0, in Wm^{-2}. [1 mark]

(b) Calculate the intensity level of the sound of the siren. [2 marks]

(c) Why does the siren use a frequency of 3000 Hz? [1 mark]

Q2 The diagram shows an equal loudness curve for a person suffering hearing loss and a person with normal hearing. The patient believes his hearing may have been damaged by working with noisy machinery. Does his equal loudness curve support this? Explain your answer. [3 marks]

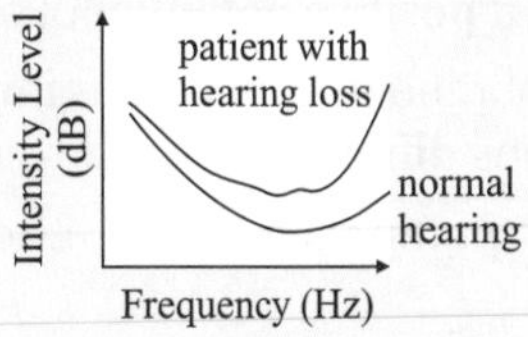

Saved by the decibel....

It's medical fact that prolonged loud noise damages your hearing, so you should really demand ear protection before you agree to do the housework — some vacuum cleaners are louder than 85 dBA — the 'safe' limit for regular exposure.

Physics of the Heart

These pages are for AQA A Unit 5 Option B only.

There's a bit of biochemistry on this page — my, my, aren't you lucky people...

The **Heart** is a **Double Pump**

1) The heart is a **large muscle**. It acts as a **double pump**, with the **left**-hand side pumping blood from the **lungs** to the **rest of the body** and the **right**-hand side pumping blood from the **body** back to the **lungs**.
2) Traditionally, a diagram of the heart is drawn as though you're looking at it **from the front**, so the **right**-hand side of the heart is drawn on the **left**-hand side of the **diagram** and vice versa (just to confuse you).
3) Each side of the heart has **two chambers** — an **atrium** and a **ventricle** — separated by a **valve**.
4) **Blood** enters the **atria** from the veins, then the atria **contract**, squeezing blood into the **ventricles**. The **ventricles** then **contract**, squeezing the blood **out** of the heart into the **arteries**. The **valves** are there so that the blood doesn't go back into the atria when the ventricles contract.

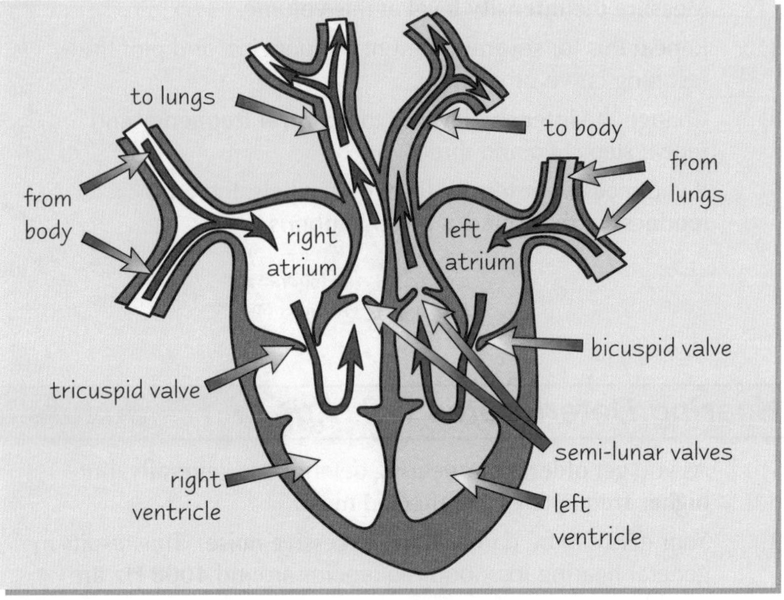

The Movement of **Sodium** and **Potassium Ions** Generates **Electrical Signals**

1) The movement of **sodium** and **potassium ions** across **cell membranes** in the heart is controlled by **diffusion** and a **sodium-potassium pump**.
2) The **pump** uses a series of **chemical reactions** to move **sodium ions** (Na^+) through the membrane and out of the cell, and to move **potassium ions** (K^+) into the cell.
3) By **diffusion**, particles tend to move from **high** to **low concentrations** (along a **concentration gradient**). So, as the pump builds up the ion concentrations, the ions try to **diffuse back** in the **opposite** direction.
4) So far, so good — but here's where it gets a bit more complicated.
5) For most of the time, the membrane **only lets K^+ ions** diffuse through, and **not** the Na^+ ions. That means there's a **net flow** of **positive charge out of** the cell and a **voltage** builds up until equilibrium is reached.
6) By convention, the potential on the **outside** of the membrane (where there's lots of sodium) is taken to be **0 V**, so the membrane potential on the inside is **negative** (–80 mV for heart muscle). You've now got a **polarised** membrane.

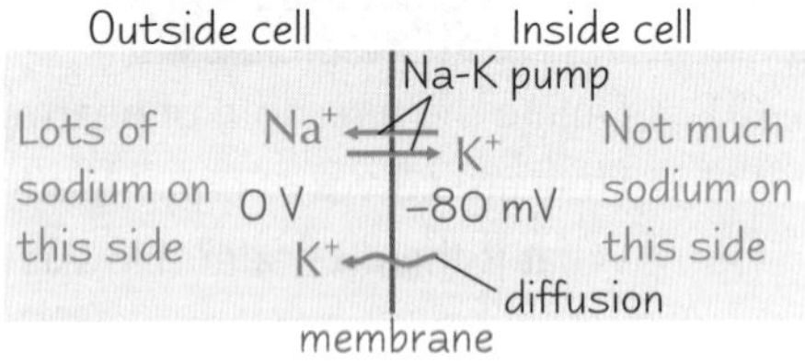

7) If the membrane is **stimulated** by an **electrical signal** it suddenly becomes **permeable** to **Na^+** as well. The sodium ions **rush** across the membrane towards the **negative side** (inside the cell), pushed by both the **Na^+ concentration gradient** and **electrostatic forces**.
8) This first **depolarises** the membrane, then **charges it up** the **other way** (called reverse-polarisation), reaching a **positive potential** of about 40 mV. This makes the heart muscle **CONTRACT**.
9) The membrane then becomes **impermeable** to **Na^+** ions again, but **very permeable** to **K^+** ions. The K^+ ions **diffuse** very quickly, repolarising the membrane, and the heart muscle **RELAXES**.
10) The Na-K pump then slowly restores the potential back to its **equilibrium polarised state**.

The sudden flip in potential is called the **action potential**. When this happens at one part of a membrane, it triggers the part next to it to do the same and so an electrical signal passes down the membrane.

Physics of the Heart

The Heart's **Pacemaker** is the **Sinoatrial Node**

1) A group of specialised cells at the **sinoatrial (SA) node** (in the wall of the right atrium) produce **electrical signals** that pulse about **70 times a minute**.
2) These signals spread through the **atria** and make them **contract** via the **action potential** (see previous page).
3) The signals then pass to the **atrioventricular (AV) node**, which **delays** the pulse for about **0.1 seconds** before passing it on to the **ventricles**.
4) The ventricles **contract** and the process repeats.

The Heart can be **Monitored** by an **Electrocardiograph (ECG)**

1) The **potential difference** between the **polarised** and **depolarised** heart cells produces a **weak electrical signal** at the surface of the body. This is plotted against time to give an **electrocardiogram (ECG)**, which can provide useful information about the **condition** of the heart.
2) A **normal** ECG, covering a **single heartbeat**, has **three** separate parts: a **P** wave, a **QRS** wave and a **T** wave.
3) The **P wave** corresponds to the **depolarisation** and **contraction** of the **atria**.
4) The **QRS wave** (about 0.2 seconds later) corresponds to the **depolarisation** and **contraction** of the **ventricles**. This completely swamps the trace produced by the repolarisation and relaxation of the atria.
5) Finally, the **T wave** (another 0.2 seconds later) corresponds to the **repolarisation** and **relaxation** of the **ventricles**.

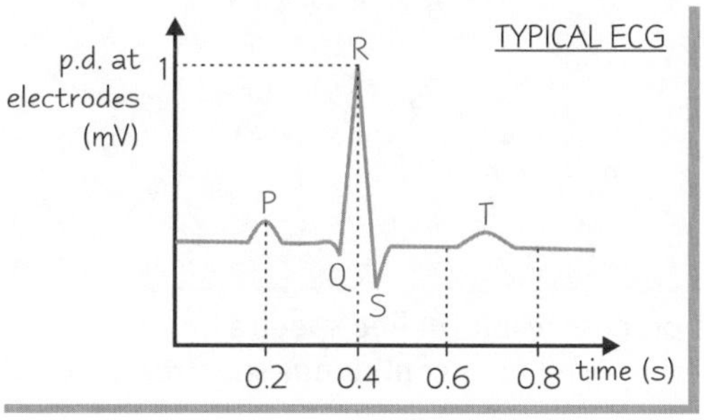

6) There are **12** standard ways of placing electrodes on the body to obtain an **ECG**, each producing a slightly different waveform. In all cases the signal is **heavily attenuated** (absorbed and weakened) by the body and needs to be amplified by a high impedance **amplifier**.
7) **Electrodes** are placed on the **chest** and the **limbs** where the arteries are close to the surface. The **right leg** is **never** used since it is **too far away** from the heart.
8) In order to get a **good electrical contact**, **hairs** and **dead skin** cells are removed and a **conductive gel** is used.

Practice Questions

Q1 Describe the basic structure of the heart, and the passage of blood through the heart, lungs and the body.

Q2 Describe how a membrane in heart muscle is initially polarised and what happens when it is stimulated.

Q3 Sketch a typical ECG trace and indicate the main features.

Exam Questions

Q1 A patient with a suspected heart condition is given an ECG.

(a) Describe how the patient's skin is prepared to ensure a good electrical contact with the electrodes. [2 marks]

(b) The patient's ECG shows a pause between the P and QRS waves.
Describe how the action of the heart corresponds to these waves. [3 marks]

Q2 Explain the processes of depolarisation and repolarisation in the formation of an action potential.
The quality of your written answer will be assessed in this question. [6 marks]

Q3 Outline how electrical signals are involved in the function of the heart. [4 marks]

Be still my beating sinoatrial node...

If you rely on the cast of ER to get your heart beating faster, console yourself that it's all very educational. Listen out for the machine that goes 'bip, bip, bip', and look for the P waves, QRS waves and T waves on the screen. If there aren't enough waves, the brave docs have to start shouting 'clear' and waving defibrillators around.

X-Ray Imaging

These pages are for AQA A Unit 5 Option B and OCR A Unit 5 only.

X-ray imaging is one kind of non-invasive diagnostic technique — these techniques let doctors see what's going on (or going wrong) inside your body, without having to open you up and have a look.

X-rays are Produced by Bombarding Tungsten with High Energy Electrons

1) In an X-ray tube, **electrons** are emitted from a **heated filament** and **accelerated** through a high **potential difference** (the **tube voltage**) towards a **tungsten anode**.
2) When the **electrons** smash into the **tungsten anode**, they **decelerate** and some of their **kinetic energy** is converted into **electromagnetic energy**, as **X-ray photons**. The tungsten anode emits a **continuous spectrum** of **X-ray radiation** — this is called **bremsstrahlung** ('braking radiation').

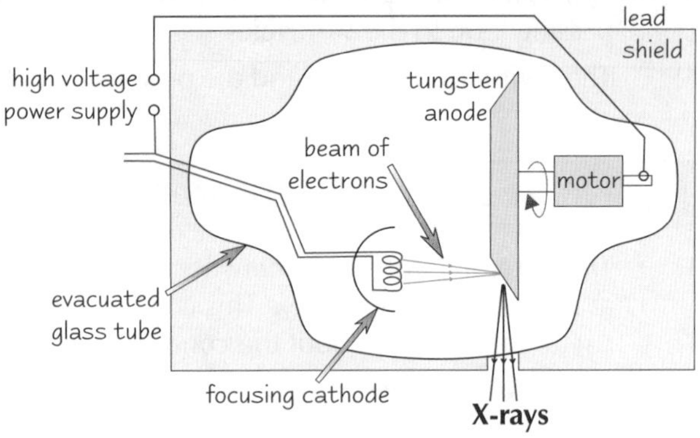

3) 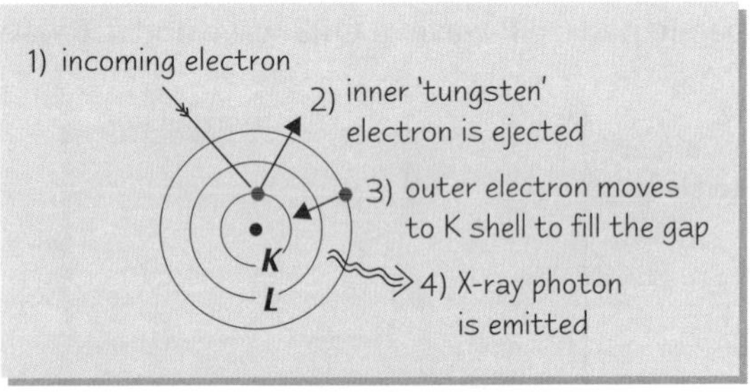

X-rays are also produced when beam electrons **knock out** other electrons from the **inner shells** of the **tungsten atoms**. Electrons in the atoms' **outer shells** move into the **vacancies** in the **lower energy levels**, and **release energy** in the form of **X-ray photons**.

4) This process results in **line spectra** superimposed on a **continuous spectrum**.
5) Only about **1%** of the electrons' **kinetic energy** is converted into **X-rays**. The rest is converted into **heat**, so, to avoid overheating, the tungsten anode is **rotated** at about 3000 rpm. It's also **mounted** on **copper** — this **conducts** the heat away effectively.

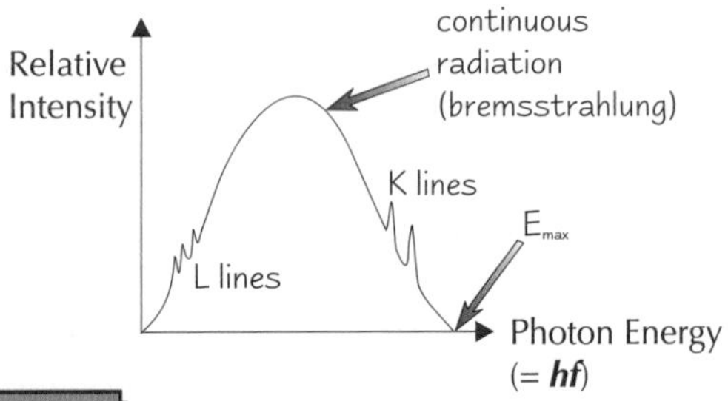

Beam Intensity and Photon Energy can be Varied

The **intensity** of the X-ray beam is the **energy per second per unit area** passing through a surface (at right angles). There are two ways to increase the **intensity** of the X-ray beam:

1) Increase the **tube voltage**. This gives the electrons **more kinetic energy**. Higher energy electrons can **knock out** electrons from shells **deeper** within the tungsten atoms — giving more 'spikes' on the graphs. Individual **X-ray photons** also have **higher maximum energies**.
   Intensity is approximately **proportional** to **voltage squared**.
2) Increase the **current** supplied to the filament. This liberates **more electrons per second**, which then produce **more X-ray photons per second**. Individual **photons** have the **same energy** as before.
   Intensity is approximately **proportional** to **current**.
   The **intensity** of the X-ray beam is related to the **area under** the **graph**.

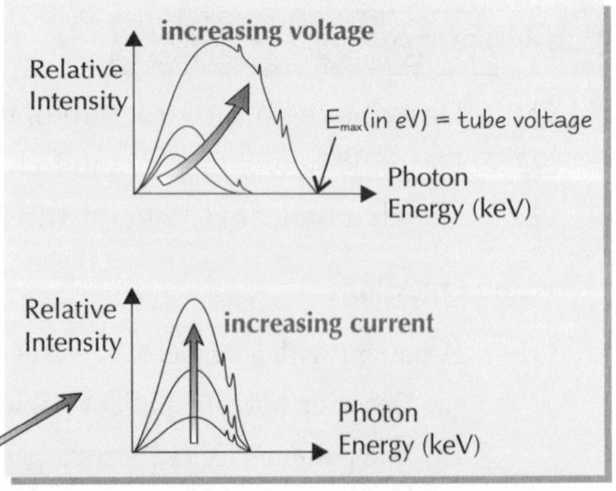

Radiographers try to Produce a Sharp Image and Minimise the Radiation Dose

Medical X-rays are a compromise between producing really sharp, clear images, whilst keeping the amount of radiation the patient is exposed to as low as possible. To do this, radiographers:

1) Put the **detection plate close** to and the **X-ray tube far** from the patient and make sure the patient **keeps still**.
2) Put a **lead grid** between the patient and film to **stop** scattered radiation '**fogging**' the film and **reducing contrast**.
3) Use an **intensifying screen** next to the film surface. This consists of crystals that **fluoresce** — they **absorb X-rays** and re-emit the energy as **visible light**, which helps to develop the photograph quickly. A shorter exposure time is needed, keeping the patient's radiation dose lower.

X-Ray Imaging

X-Rays are Attenuated when they Pass Through Matter

When X-rays pass through matter (e.g. a patient's body), they are **absorbed** and **scattered**. The intensity (I) of the X-ray beam **decreases** (attenuates) **exponentially** with **distance from** the **surface** (x), according to the material's attenuation coefficient (μ), as the equation shows.

$$I = I_0 e^{-\mu x}$$

1) **Half-value thickness**, $x_{\frac{1}{2}}$, is the thickness of material required to **reduce** the **intensity** to **half** its **original value**.
   This depends on the **attenuation coefficient** of the material, and is given by: $x_{\frac{1}{2}} = \frac{\ln 2}{\mu}$
2) The **mass attenuation coefficient**, μ_m, for a material of density ρ is given by: $\mu_m = \frac{\mu}{\rho}$

X-rays are Absorbed More by Bone than Soft Tissue

The details of absorption processes are just for OCR A.

X-rays are **attenuated** by **absorption** and **scattering**. The **three** main **causes** of this are:

1) The **photoelectric effect** — a **photon** with around **30 keV** of energy is absorbed by an **electron**, which is **ejected** from its atom. The gap in the **electron shell** is filled by another **electron**, which emits a **photon**.
2) **Compton scattering** — a **photon** with around **0.5-5 MeV** of energy knocks an **electron** out of an **atom**, which causes the **photon** to **lose energy** and be **scattered**.
3) **Pair production** — a **high** (> 1.1 MeV) **energy** photon **decays** into an **electron** and a **positron**.

How much **energy is absorbed** by a **material** depends on its **atomic number** — so tissues containing atoms with **different atomic numbers** (e.g. **soft tissue** and **bone**) will **contrast** in the X-ray image. If the tissues in the region of interest have similar attenuation coefficients then artificial **contrast media** can be used — e.g. **barium meal**. **Barium** has a **high atomic number**, so it shows up clearly in X-ray images and can be followed as it moves along the patient's digestive tract.

Fluoroscopy and CT Scans use X-rays

1) **Moving images** can be created by **X-ray fluoroscopy**, using a **fluorescent screen** and an **image intensifier**.
2) **Computerised axial tomography** (CT or CAT) scans produce an image of a **two-dimensional slice** through the body. An **X-ray beam rotates** around the body and is picked up by thousands of **detectors**. A computer works out how much attenuation has been caused by each part of the body and produces a very **high quality** image. However, the machines are **expensive**.
3) Both these techniques involve a **high radiation dose** for the patient.

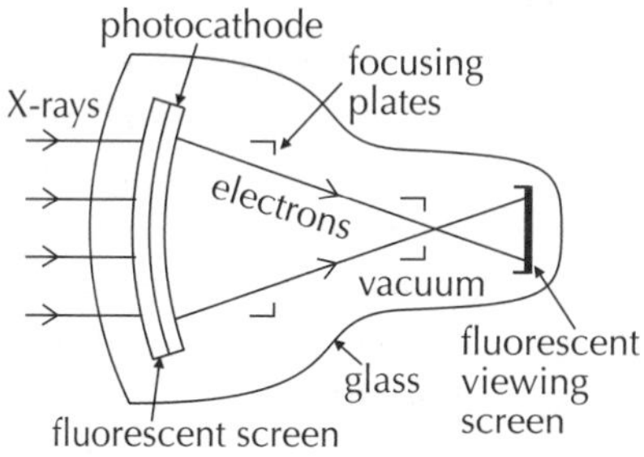

Practice Questions

Q1 Draw a diagram of an X-ray tube and explain how a typical X-ray spectrum is produced.

Q2 What measures can be taken to produce a high quality X-ray image while reducing the patient's radiation dose?

Exam Questions

Q1 An X-ray tube is connected to a potential difference of 30 kV.

(a) Sketch a graph of relative intensity against photon energy (in eV) for the resulting X-ray spectrum, and indicate its main features. [3 marks]

(b) Calculate the velocity of the electrons arriving at the anode. [4 marks]

Q2 The half-value thickness for aluminium is 3 mm for 30 keV X-ray photons.

(a) Explain what is meant by the term 'half-value thickness'. [1 mark]

(b) What thickness of aluminium would reduce the intensity of a homogeneous beam of X-rays at 30 keV to 1% of its initial value? [4 marks]

I've got attenuation coefficient disorder — I get bored really easily...

X-ray images are just shadow pictures — bones absorb X-rays, stop them reaching the film and create a white 'shadow'.

Ultrasound Imaging

These pages are for AQA A Unit 5 Option B and OCR A Unit 5 only.

Ultrasound is a 'sound' with higher frequencies than we can hear.

Ultrasound has a Higher Frequency than Humans can Hear

1) Ultrasound waves are **longitudinal** waves with **higher frequencies** than humans can hear (>20 000 Hz).
2) For **medical** purposes, frequencies are usually from **1** to **15 MHz**.
3) When an ultrasound wave meets a **boundary** between two **different materials**, some of it is **reflected** and some of it passes through (undergoing **refraction** if the **angle of incidence** is **not 90°**).
4) The **reflected waves** are detected by the **ultrasound scanner** and are used to **generate an image**.

The Amount of Reflection depends on the Change in Acoustic Impedance

1) The **acoustic impedance**, Z, of a medium is defined as: $Z = \rho c$
   Z has units of $kgm^{-2}s^{-1}$.
2) Say an ultrasound wave travels through a material with an impedance Z_1. It hits the boundary between this material and another with an impedance Z_2. The incident wave has an intensity of I_i.
3) If the two materials have a **large difference** in **impedance**, then **most** of the energy is **reflected** (the intensity of the reflected wave I_r will be high). If the impedance of the two materials is the **same** then there is **no reflection**.
4) The **fraction** of wave **intensity** that is reflected is called the **intensity reflection coefficient**, α.

$$\alpha = \frac{I_r}{I_i} = \left(\frac{Z_2 - Z_1}{Z_2 + Z_1}\right)^2$$

You don't need to learn this equation. Just practise using it.

There are Advantages and Disadvantages to Ultrasound Imaging

ADVANTAGES:

1) There are **no** known **hazards** — in particular, **no** exposure to **ionising radiation**.
2) It's good for imaging **soft tissues**, since you can obtain **real-time** images — X-ray fluoroscopy can achieve this, but involves a huge dose of radiation.
3) Ultrasound devices are relatively **cheap** and **portable**.

DISADVANTAGES:

1) Ultrasound **doesn't penetrate bone** — so it **can't** be used to **detect fractures** or examine the **brain**.
2) Ultrasound **cannot** pass through **air spaces** in the body (due to the **mismatch** in **impedance**) — so it can't produce images from behind the lungs.
3) The **resolution** is **poor** (about 10 times worse than X-rays), so you **can't see** fine **detail**.

Ultrasound Images are Produced Using the Piezoelectric Effect

1) **Piezoelectric crystals** produce a **potential difference** when they are **deformed** (squashed or stretched) — the rearrangement in structure displaces the **centres of symmetry** of their electric **charges**.

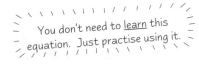

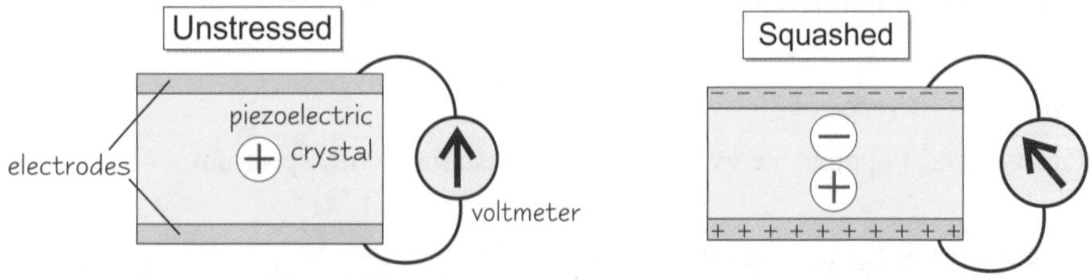

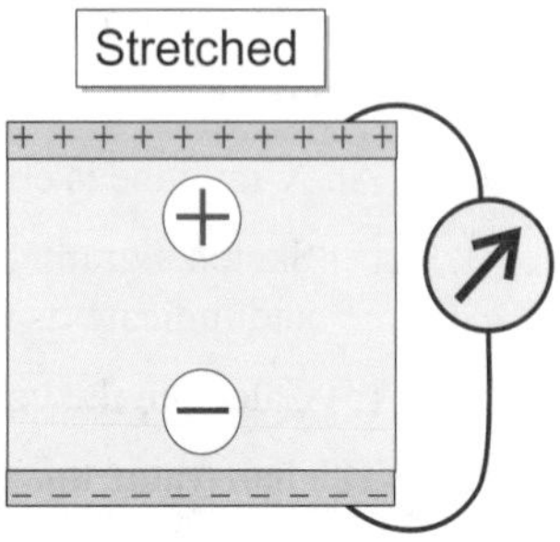

2) When you **apply a p.d.** across a piezoelectric crystal, the crystal **deforms**. If the p.d. is **alternating**, then the crystal **vibrates** at the **same frequency**.
3) A piezoelectric crystal can act as a **receiver** of **ultrasound**, converting **sound waves** into **alternating voltages**, and also as a **transmitter**, converting **alternating voltages** into **sound waves**.
4) Ultrasound devices use **lead zirconate titanate** (**PZT**) crystals. The **thickness** of the crystal is **half the wavelength** of the ultrasound that it produces. Ultrasound of this frequency will make the crystal **resonate** (like air in an open pipe — see p.14) and produce a large signal.
5) The PZT crystal is **heavily damped**, to produce **short pulses** and **increase** the **resolution** of the device.

Ultrasound Imaging

You need a Coupling Medium between the Transducer and the Body

1) **Soft tissue** has a very different **acoustic impedance** from **air**, so almost all the ultrasound **energy** is **reflected** from the surface of the body if there is air between the **transducer** and the **body**.
2) To avoid this, you need a **coupling medium** between the transducer and the body — this **displaces** the **air** and has an impedance much closer to that of body tissue. **Coupling media** are an example of **impedance matching**.
3) The coupling medium is usually an **oil** or **gel** that is smeared onto the skin.

The A-Scan is a Range Measuring System

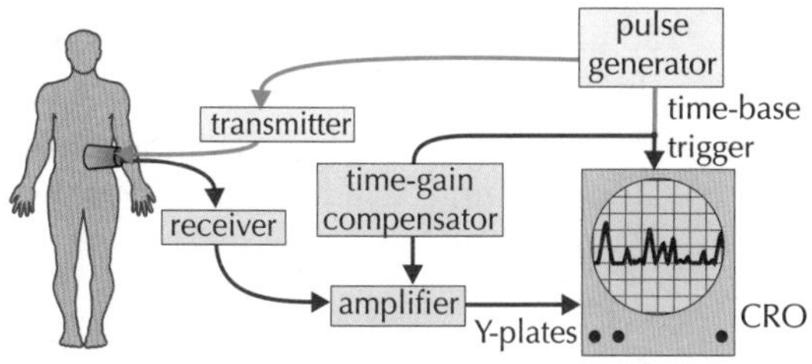

1) The **amplitude scan** (**A-Scan**) sends a short **pulse** of ultrasound into the body simultaneously with an **electron beam** sweeping across a cathode ray oscilloscope (**CRO**) screen.
2) The scanner receives **reflected** ultrasound pulses that appear as **vertical deflections** on the CRO screen.
3) **Weaker** pulses (that have travelled further in the body and **arrive later**) are **amplified** more to avoid the loss of valuable data — this process is called **time-gain compensation** (**TGC**).
4) The **horizontal positions** of the reflected pulses indicate the **time** the 'echo' took to return, and are used to work out **distances** between structures in the body (e.g. the **diameter** of a **baby's head** in the uterus).
5) A **stream** of pulses can produce a **steady image** on the screen (due to **persistence of vision** — see p.105), although modern CROs can store a digital image after just one exposure.

In a B-Scan, the Brightness Varies

1) In a **brightness scan** (**B-Scan**), the electron beam sweeps **down** the screen rather than across.
2) The amplitude of the reflected pulses is displayed as the **brightness** of the spot.
3) You can use a **linear array** of transducers to produce a **two-dimensional** image.

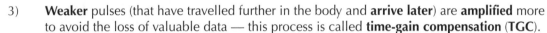

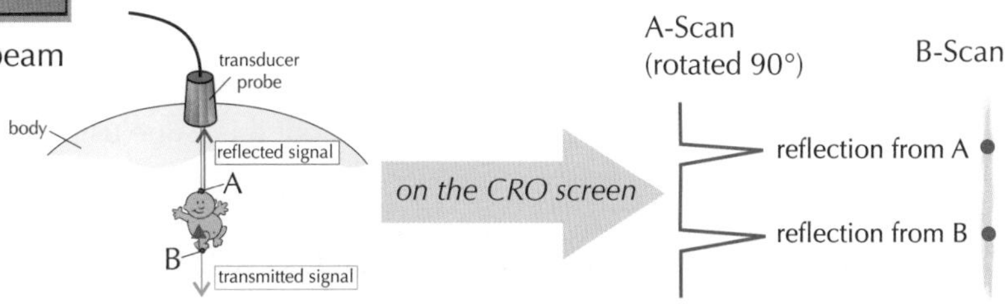

OCR A only — **Ultrasound imaging** can also be used to measure the **speed of blood flow**.
If the **ultrasound waves** reflect off something that is **moving** (e.g. **blood**), their **frequency** will be **shifted** according to the **Doppler effect** (see p.98-99). **How much** the reflected waves are **shifted** depends on **how fast** the blood is moving — so by **measuring the shift**, you can work out the **speed of blood flow**.

Practice Questions

Q1 What are the main advantages and disadvantages of imaging using ultrasound?

Q2 How are ultrasound waves produced and received in an ultrasound transducer?

Q3 Define acoustic impedance.

Exam Questions

Q1 (a) What fraction of intensity is reflected when ultrasound waves pass from air to soft tissue?
Use $\boldsymbol{Z}_{air} = 0.430 \times 10^3$ kgm^{-2}s^{-1}, $\boldsymbol{Z}_{tissue} = 1630 \times 10^3$ kgm^{-2}s^{-1}. [2 marks]

(b) Calculate the ratio between the intensity of the ultrasound that **enters** the body when a coupling gel is used ($\boldsymbol{Z}_{gel} = 1500 \times 10^3$ kgm^{-2}s^{-1}) and when none is used. Give your answer to the nearest power of ten. [4 marks]

Q2 (a) The acoustic impedance of a certain soft tissue is 1.63×10^6 kgm^{-2}s^{-1} and its density is 1.09×10^3 kgm^{-3}.
Show that ultrasound travels with a velocity of 1.50 kms^{-1} in this medium. [2 marks]

(b) The time base on a CRO was set to be 50 μscm^{-1}. Reflected pulses from either side of a fetal head are 2.4 cm apart on the screen. Calculate the diameter of the fetal head if the ultrasound travels at 1.5 kms^{-1}. [4 marks]

Ultrasound — Mancunian for 'très bien'

You can use ultrasound to make images in cases where X-rays would do too much damage — like to check up on the development of a baby in the womb. You have to know what you're looking for though, or it just looks like a blob.

Endoscopy

These pages are for AQA A Unit 5 Option B only.

Phew, that ultrasound stuff wasn't exactly a walk in the park — luckily, endoscopes are easier to understand...

Optical Fibres Use Total Internal Reflection to Transmit Light

1) **Optical fibres** are a bit like electric wires — but instead of carrying current they **transmit light**.
2) A typical optical fibre consists of a **glass core** (about 5 μm to 50 μm in diameter) **surrounded** by a **cladding**, which has a slightly **lower refractive index**.
3) The **difference** in refractive index means that light travelling along the fibre will be **reflected** at the **cladding-core interface**.

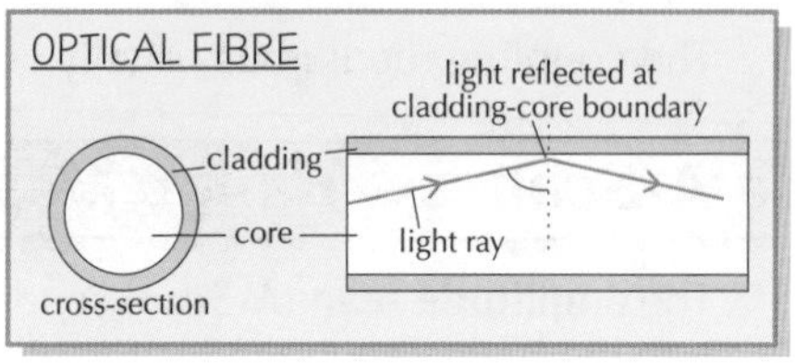

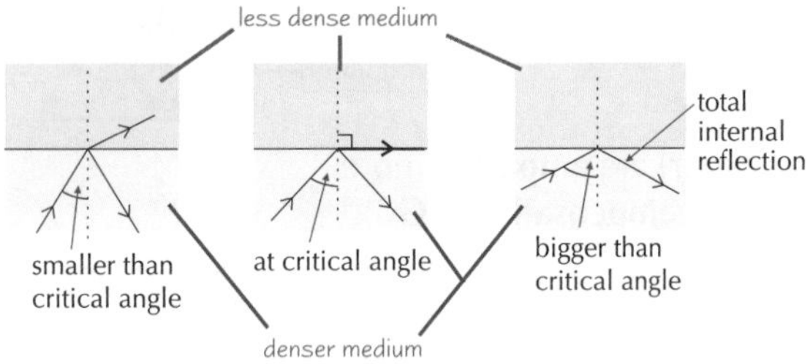

4) If the light ray's **angle of incidence** is **less than or equal** to a **critical angle**, some light will be **lost** out of the fibre.
5) But if the **angle of incidence** is **larger** than the **critical angle**, the light ray will be **completely reflected** inside the fibre.
6) This phenomenon is called **total internal reflection** and means that the ray **zigzags** its way along the fibre — so long as the fibre isn't too curved.

The Critical Angle for an Optical Fibre can be Worked Out

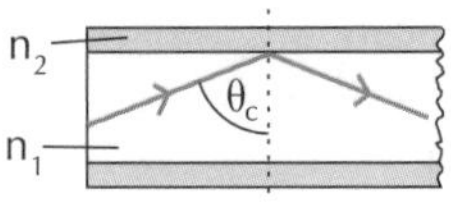

1) The **critical angle**, θ_c, depends on the **refractive index** of the **core**, n_1, and **cladding**, n_2, in an optical fibre.
2) You can work out this value using the formula:

$$\sin\theta_c = \frac{n_2}{n_1}$$

Example

An optical fibre consists of a core with a refractive index of 1.5 and cladding with a refractive index of 1.4.

a) What is the critical angle at the core-cladding boundary?

$$\theta_c = \sin^{-1}\left(\frac{n_2}{n_1}\right) = \sin^{-1}\left(\frac{1.4}{1.5}\right) = 69°$$

b) Would total internal reflection occur if the incident angle of light is 70°?

70° > θ_c, so total internal reflection would occur.

If some of this is sounding familiar, it's because you did it in AS. The equation for critical angle is derived from Snell's law of refraction.

Lots of Optical Fibres can be Bundled Together

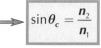

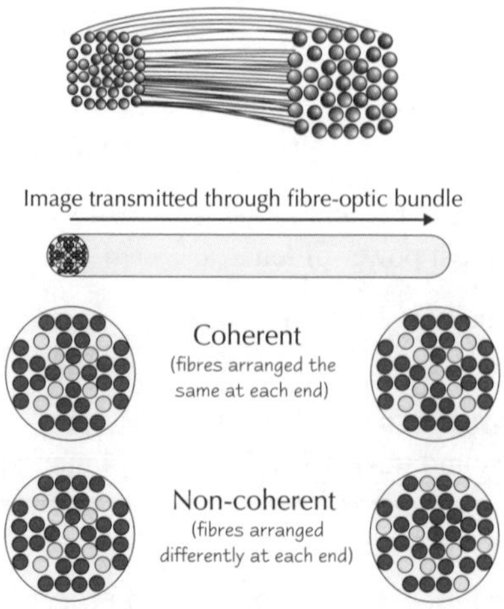

1) An **image** can be transmitted along a **bundle** of optical fibres.
2) This can only happen if the **relative positions** of fibres in a bundle are the **same** at each end (otherwise the image would be jumbled up) — a fibre-optic bundle in this arrangement is said to be **coherent**.
3) The **resolution** (i.e. how much detail can be seen) depends on the **thickness** of the fibres. The thinner the fibres, the **more detail** that can be resolved — but thin fibres are more **expensive** to make.
4) Images can be **magnified** by making the diameters of the fibres get **gradually larger** along the length of the bundle.
5) If the relative **position** of the fibres **does not** remain the same between each end the bundle of fibres is said to be **non-coherent**.
6) **Non-coherent bundles** are much easier and **cheaper** to make. They **can't** transmit an **image** but they can be used to get **light** to hard-to-reach places — kind of like a flexible **torch**.

Endoscopy

Endoscopes Use Optical Fibres to Create an *Image*

1) An **endoscope** consists of a **long tube** containing **two bundles** of fibres — a **non-coherent** bundle to carry **light** to the area of interest and a **coherent** bundle to carry an **image** back to the eyepiece.
2) Endoscopes are widely used by surgeons to examine inside the body
3) An **objective lens** is placed at the **distal** end (**furthest from the eye**) of the **coherent** bundle to form an image, which is then transmitted by the fibres to the **proximal** end (**closest to the eye**) where it can be **viewed** through an **eyepiece**.
4) The **endoscope tube** can also contain a **water channel**, for cleaning the objective lens, a **tool aperture** to perform **keyhole surgery** and a **CO_2 channel** which allows CO_2 to be pumped into the area in front of the endoscope, making more room in the body.

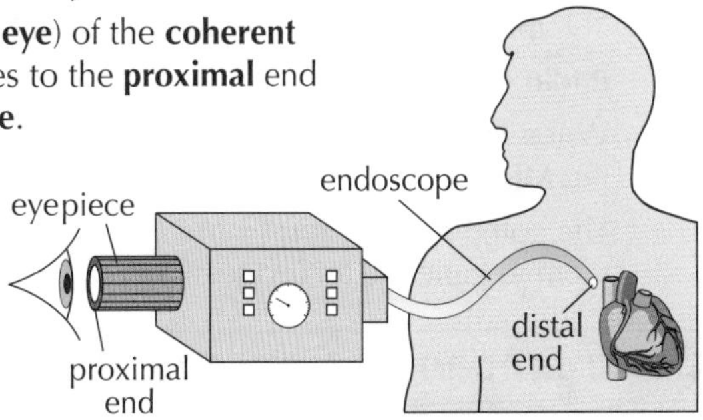

Endoscopes are Used in *Keyhole Surgery*

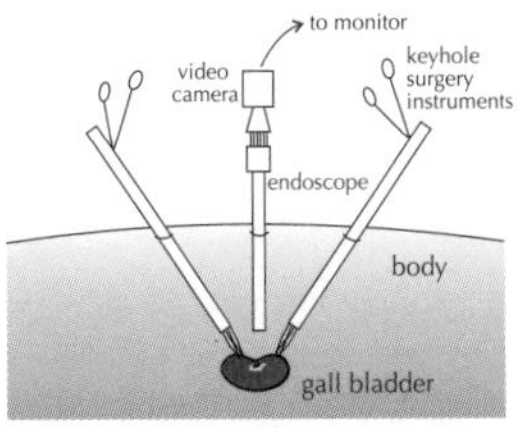

1) **Traditional** surgery needs a **large cut** to be made in the body so that there's **room** for the surgeons to get in and perform an **operation**.
2) This means that there's a **large risk of infection** to the exposed tissues and that permanent **damage** could be done to the patient's **body**.
3) New techniques in **minimally invasive surgery** (MIS or **keyhole surgery**) mean that only a **few small holes** need to be cut into the body.
4) An **endoscope** can be used in keyhole surgery to show the surgeon an **image** of the area of interest. **Surgical instruments** are passed through the endoscope tube, or through additional **small holes** in the body, so that the **operation** can be carried out.
5) **Common procedures** include the removal of the **gall bladder**, investigation of the **middle ear**, and removal of abnormal polyps in the **colon** so that they can be investigated for **cancer**.
6) **Recovery times** tend to be **quicker** for keyhole surgery, so the **patient** can usually **return home** on the **same day** — which makes it much **cheaper** for the hospital and **nicer** for the patient.

Practice Questions

Q1 What condition must be satisfied for total internal reflection to occur?

Q2 Explain the difference between a coherent and a non-coherent bundle of fibres.

Q3 What are the main features of an endoscope?

Q4 How have endoscopes revolutionised some surgical techniques?

Exam Questions

Q1 A beam of light is transmitted through an optical fibre.
The refractive index of the fibre's core is 1.35 and the refractive index of its cladding 1.30.
(a) What is the critical angle for the core-cladding boundary? [1 mark]
(b) Explain why the angle of incidence of the beam of light should be kept at or above the critical angle. [2 marks]

Q2 Coherent fibre-optic bundles can be used to transmit images.
Describe the main features of the structure of a coherent fibre-optic bundle,
and explain why each feature is important for the bundle's function. [4 marks]

If you ask me, physics is a whole bundle of non-coherentness...

If this is all getting too much, and your brain is as fried as a pork chipolata, just remember the wise words of revision wisdom from the great Spike Milligan — Ying tong, ying tong, ying tong, ying tong, ying tong, iddly-I-po, iddly-I-po...

Magnetic Resonance Imaging

These pages are for AQA A Unit 5 Option B and OCR A Unit 5 only.

Magnetic Resonance Imaging, or MRI to you and me, is yet another form of non-invasive diagnostic imaging — enjoy.

Magnetic Resonance** can be used to Create **Images

1) The patient lies in the centre of a huge **superconducting magnet** that produces a **uniform magnetic field**. The magnet needs to be **cooled** by **liquid helium** — this is partly why the scanner is so **expensive**.
2) Radio frequency **coils** are used to transmit **radio waves**, which **excite hydrogen nuclei** in the patient's body.
3) When the radio waves are switched off, the hydrogen nuclei relax and emit electromagnetic energy — this is the **MRI signal** (more details below). The radio frequency coils **receive the signal** and send it to a **computer**.
4) The computer **measures** various quantities of the MRI signal — amplitude, frequency, phase — and **analyses** them to generate an **image** of a **cross-section** through the body.

Contrast** can be Controlled by Varying the **Pulses** of **Radio Waves

1) Radio waves are applied in **pulses**. Each short pulse **excites** the hydrogen nuclei and then allows them to **relax** and emit a signal. The response of **different tissue types** can be enhanced by varying the **time between pulses**.
2) Tissues consisting of **large molecules** such as **fat** are best imaged using **rapidly repeated pulses**. This technique is used to image the internal **structure** of the body.
3) Allowing **more time** between pulses enhances the response of **watery** substances. This is used for **diseased** areas.

MRI** has **Advantages** and **Disadvantages

ADVANTAGES:

1) There are **no** known **side effects**.
2) An image can be made for any slice in any **orientation** of the body.
3) High quality images can be obtained for **soft tissue** such as the **brain**.
4) **Contrast** can be **weighted** in order to investigate different situations.

DISADVANTAGES:

1) The imaging of **bones** is very **poor**.
2) Some people suffer from **claustrophobia** in the scanner.
3) Scans can be **noisy** (due to the switching of the gradient magnets, see page 121) and take a **long time**.
4) MRI can't be used on people with **pacemakers** or some **metal implants** — the strong magnetic fields would be very harmful.
5) Scanners **cost millions** of pounds.

If you're doing AQA you can skip straight to the questions now — OCR A people need to know some more details about exactly where the MRI signal comes from.

Atomic Nuclei** can Behave like **Magnets

1) **Protons** and **neutrons** possess a quantum property called **spin**, which makes them behave like **tiny magnets**.
2) If a nucleus has **even numbers** of **protons** and **neutrons** then the magnetic effects **cancel out**. A nucleus with an **odd number** of **protons** or **neutrons** has a **net spin** and is slightly **magnetic**.
3) The most important nucleus for **magnetic resonance imaging (MRI)** is **hydrogen**, which human bodies contain a lot of. A **hydrogen nucleus** has just **one proton**.

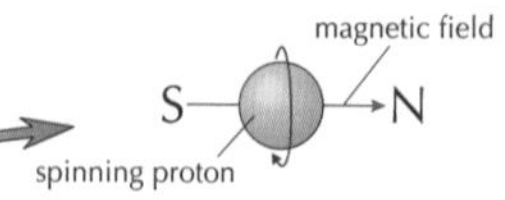

Protons Align** themselves in a **Magnetic Field

1) Normally, protons are orientated **randomly**, so their magnetic fields cancel out. When a strong **external magnetic field** is applied, as in an MRI scanner, the protons **align** themselves with the **magnetic field lines**.
2) Protons in **parallel alignment** point in the **same direction** as the external **magnetic field**. **Antiparallel alignment** means the protons point in the **opposite direction to the field**.

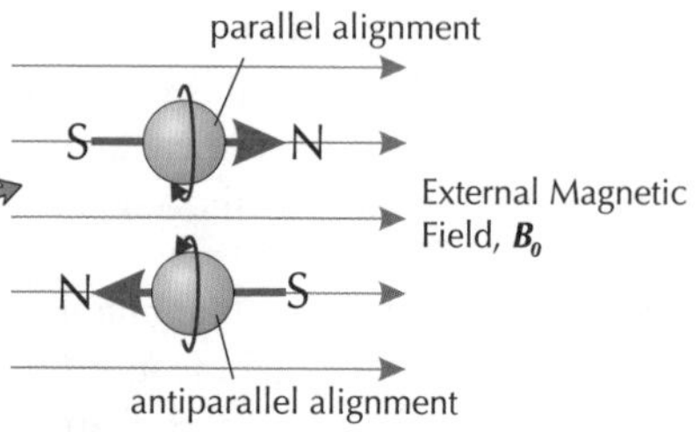

3)

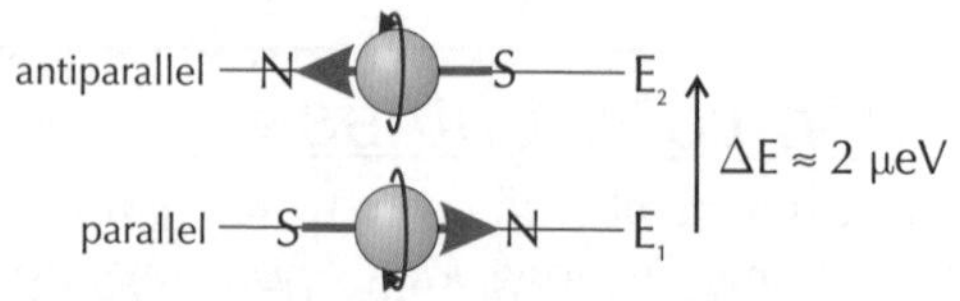

Protons align in these two directions in almost equal numbers (about 7 more per million are parallel). The **different alignments** correspond to **different energy levels**. The nuclei can **flip** between the two by **emitting** or **absorbing** a specific amount of **energy**.

Magnetic Resonance Imaging

Protons in a Magnetic Field Precess at the Larmor Frequency

1) Nuclei in a magnetic field don't just stay still — they **precess** (wobble) **around** the **magnetic field lines** (like a **spinning top** precessing around gravitational field lines).
2) They **don't** all precess **in phase** with each other.
3) All the protons **precess** at the **same frequency** — the **Larmor frequency**, ***f***. The value of ***f*** depends on the **strength** of the **magnetic field**, B_0.

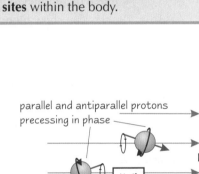

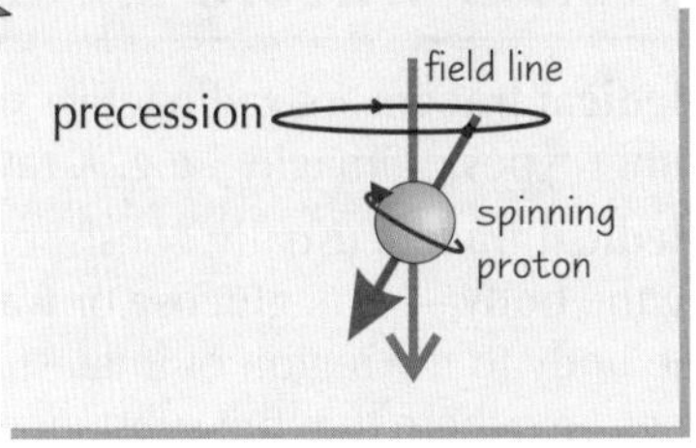

$$f = \frac{\gamma B_0}{2\pi}$$

γ = gyromagnetic ratio (in HzT^{-1}),
B_0 = magnetic flux density of the external field (in T).

4) For protons, $\frac{\gamma}{2\pi} = 42.57\ \text{MHzT}^{-1}$.

In an MRI scanner, the magnetic field, B_0 is about **1-2 teslas**, which puts ***f*** in the **radio** frequency range. There are also three **gradient magnets** — electromagnets which produce a very small field (superimposed on the main one) that gradually **varies** from place to place. The **Larmor frequency** depends on the **total magnetic flux density**, so **different frequencies** of radio wave can be used to target **different sites** within the body.

Radio Waves can Make Protons Resonate

1) Protons have a **natural frequency** of oscillation in a magnetic field which is **equal** to the **Larmor frequency**, **f**. **Radio waves** at this frequency can make protons **resonate**.
2) The protons **absorb energy** from the radio waves and **flip** from **parallel** to **antiparallel alignment**.
3) Radio waves at the Larmor frequency also make the protons precess **in phase** with each other, producing a **rotating magnetic field** at **right angles** to the external field.
4) When the **external radio waves stop**, the protons return to their **original states** and **emit electromagnetic energy** as they do so — this emitted energy is the MRI signal.
5) The time taken for the protons to return to their original state is called the **relaxation time**, and is about **one second**.
6) **Relaxation times** depend on what molecules surround the protons, so they **vary** for **different tissue types**.

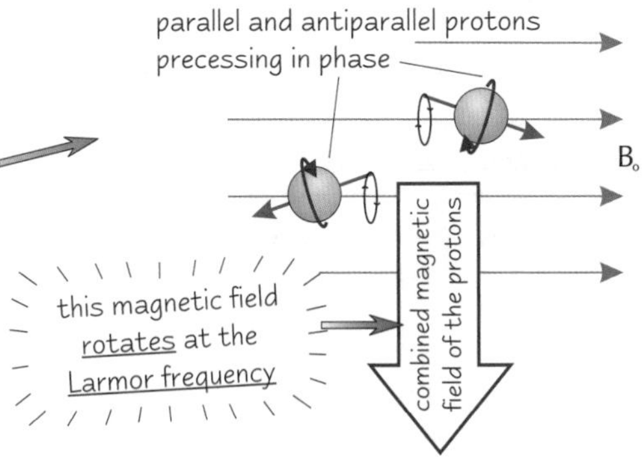

Practice Questions

Q1 Define the Larmor frequency and explain how radio waves at this frequency can cause resonance.

Q2 What is 'relaxation time' and how is this used to generate contrast within the images?

Q3 How do MRI scanners target protons from particular parts of the body?

Q4 Give two advantages of MRI compared to X-ray imaging.

Exam Questions

Q1 (a) Using a diagram, explain what is meant by the term 'precession'. [2 marks]

(b) What is the 'Larmor frequency'? Suggest a typical value for the Larmor frequency in an MRI scanner. [2 marks]

Q2 Outline how an MRI scanner is used to produce an image of a section of a patient's body.
The quality of your written answer will be assessed in this question. [6 marks]

Q3 Discuss the advantages and disadvantages of MRI scanning as a medical imaging technique. [6 marks]

Precession — protons on parade...

OK, so it hasn't been the easiest of pages. But at least now you know why people sit in vats of baked beans to raise money for their local hospital to buy an MRI scanner. Though perhaps you need A2 Psychology to understand the beans part.

Medical Uses of Nuclear Radiation

These pages are for AQA A Unit 5, OCR A Unit 5 and OCR B Unit 5 only.

Radiation can be incredibly useful in medicine, but any use of ionising radiation carries some risk.

Medical Tracers are Used to Diagnose the Function of Organs

Medical tracers are **radioactive substances** that are used to show tissue or **organ function**.
Other types of imaging, **e.g. X-rays**, only show the **structure** of organs — medical tracers show **structure and function**.

Medical tracers usually consist of a **radioactive isotope** — e.g. **technetium-99m** — bound to a **substance** that is **used** by the **body** — e.g. **glucose** or **water**. The tracer is **injected** into or **swallowed** by the patient and then **moves** through the **body** to the region of interest. **Where** the tracer goes depends on the **substance** the isotope is bound to — i.e. it goes anywhere that the substance would **normally go**, and is used how that substance is **normally used**. The **radiation emitted** is **recorded** (e.g. by a **gamma camera** or **PET scanner**, see below) and an **image** of inside the patient produced.

1) Tracers can show areas of **damaged tissue** in the heart by detecting areas of **decreased blood flow**. This can reveal **coronary artery disease** and damaged or dead heart muscle caused by **heart attacks**.
2) They can identify **active cancer tumours** by showing **metabolic activity** in tissue. **Cancer cells** have a **much higher metabolism** than healthy cells because they're growing fast, so take up more tracer.
3) Tracers can show **blood flow and activity** in the **brain**. This helps **research** and **treat** neurological conditions like Parkinson's, Alzheimer's, epilepsy, depression, etc.

Technetium-99m is widely used in medical tracers because it emits **γ-radiation**, has a **half-life of 6 hours** (long enough for data to be recorded, but short enough to limit the radiation to an acceptable level) and **decays** to a **much more stable isotope**.

The rest of these pages are just for OCR A and OCR B. If you're doing AQA then, sorry, but that's it for this section.

Gamma Cameras Detect Gamma Radiation

OCR A only

The **γ-rays** emitted by **radiotracers** injected into a patient's body are detected using a **gamma camera**.
Gamma cameras (like the one shown **below**) consist of **five** main parts:

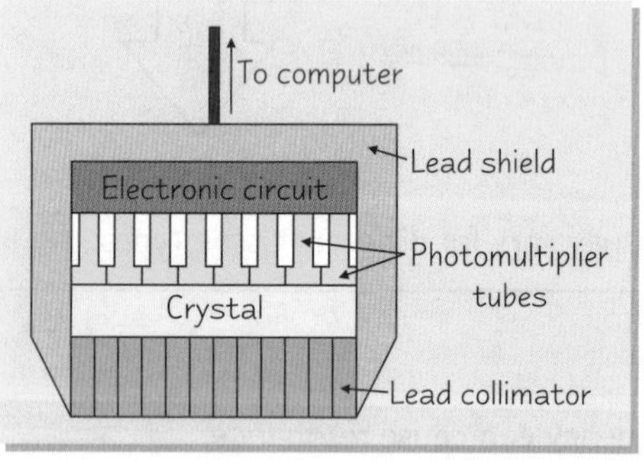

1) **Lead shield** — **stops radiation** from **other sources** entering the camera.
2) **Lead collimator** — a **piece of lead** with thousands of **vertical holes** in it — only γ-rays **parallel** to the holes can **pass through**.
3) **Sodium iodide crystal** — emits a **flash of light** (**scintillates**) whenever a **γ-ray** hits it.
4) **Photomultiplier tubes** — **detect** the flashes of **light** from the crystal and turn them into **pulses of electricity**.
5) **Electronic circuit** — **collects** the **signals** from the photomultiplier tubes and sends them to a **computer** for processing into an **image**.

PET Scanning Involves Positron/Electron Annihilation

OCR A only

1) The patient is injected with a substance used by the body, e.g. glucose, containing a **positron-emitting** radiotracer with a **short half-life**, e.g. ^{13}N, ^{15}O, ^{18}F.
2) The patient is left for a time to allow the radiotracer to **move through the body** to the organs.
3) **Positrons** emitted by the radioisotope collide with **electrons** in the organs, causing them to **annihilate**, emitting **high-energy gamma rays** in the process.
4) **Detectors** around the body record these **gamma rays**, and a computer builds up a **map of the radioactivity** in the body.

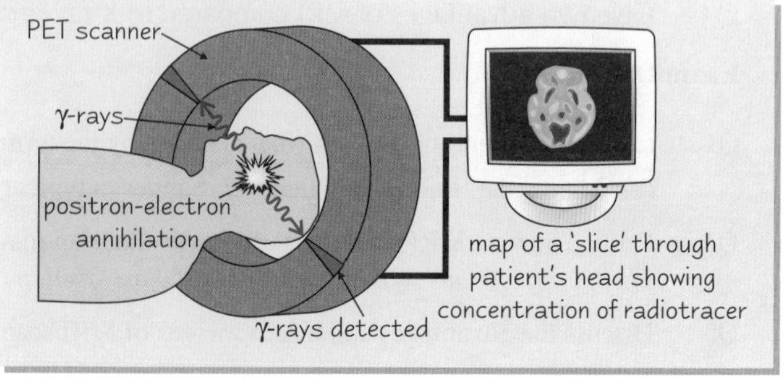

5) The **distribution of radioactivity** matches up with **metabolic activity**. This is because **more** of the radioactive glucose (or whatever) injected into the patient is taken up and **used** by cells that are **doing more work** (cells with an **increased metabolism**, in other words).

Medical Uses of Nuclear Radiation

Ionising Radiation is Used When the *Benefits* Outweigh the *Risks*

X-rays, **γ-rays**, and α and β **particles** are all classed as **ionising radiation**. When they **interact** with matter they **ionise atoms** or **molecules** to form **ions** — usually by **removing an electron** — and this can **damage** cells.

Cell damage is bad news — it can cause:

1) **Cell mutations** and **cancerous tumours** by altering or damaging the cell's DNA.
2) **Cell sterility** by stopping the cell from reproducing.
3) **Cell death** — the cell is destroyed completely.

The **macroscopic effects** of ionising radiation (i.e. the large-scale effects) include **tumours**, **skin burns**, **sterility**, **radiation sickness**, **hair loss** and **death** — nice. The result is that radiation is only used when the **benefits** to the patient **outweigh** the **risks** — i.e. **radiation** doses are **limited** and only used when it's **absolutely necessary**.

Exposure, *Absorbed Dose* and *Effective Dose*

Air is used since its average atomic number is similar to that of body tissue.

1) **Exposure** is defined as the **total charge produced** by ionising radiation **per unit mass of air**. The unit of exposure is the C kg^{-1}.
2) The **absorbed dose** is more useful in medical physics because it is a measure of the **energy absorbed per unit mass**. The unit is the **gray** (**Gy**) where 1 Gy = 1 Jkg^{-1}.
3) The **effective dose**, ***H***, takes into account the fact that the **amount of damage** to body tissue depends on the **type of ionising radiation**. The unit is the **sievert** (**Sv**) where 1 Sv = 1 Jkg^{-1}.

$$H = Q \times D$$

where H is the effective dose (Sv), Q is the quality factor, and D is the absorbed dose (Gy)

4) **Each type** of radiation is assigned a weighted **quality factor**, ***Q*** — the **greater** the **damage** produced by a type of radiation, the **higher** the quality factor.

Radiation	Q
X-ray, β, γ	1
neutrons	5 - 20
α	20

Example Which absorbed dose would cause the greatest damage to a cell, 5 Gy of α or 10 Gy of β radiation?

To compare the potential damage to the cell you need to look at the effective dose of each type of radiation.

$H_\alpha = 20 \times 5 = 100$ Sv $\quad H_\beta = 10 \times 1 = 10$ Sv

So **5 Gy of α** radiation would cause **more** cell damage than **10 Gy of β**.

Practice Questions

Q1 Why are medical tracers useful? Why are they dangerous?

Q2 What are the five main parts of a gamma camera?

Q3 Describe how an image is formed in PET scanning.

Q4 What's the difference between absorbed dose and effective dose?

Exam Questions

Q1 A doctor suspects that his patient has a cancerous tumour.
Describe a non-invasive technique that could be used to confirm the doctor's diagnosis. [3 marks]

Q2 A man of mass 70 kg accidentally swallows a source of α radiation (with a radiation quality factor of 20).
The source emits 3×10^{10} particles per second (constant over this time period) and the energy of each particle is 8×10^{-13} J. The source is removed after 1000 seconds.
(a) Assuming that all the ionising energy is distributed uniformly around the man's body, what is the absorbed dose that he receives? [2 marks]
(b) Calculate the effective dose. [1 mark]

The biological effects of a page on radiation — a sore head...

Hoo-bleeding-rah — at last, you've made it to the end of a proper beast of a section. But before you tootle off, just make sure you know the difference between absorbed dose and effective dose and can work each one out — there's bound to be a question on them in your exam. Oh, and don't forget to come back for the next section — it's a real good 'un.

Charge/Mass Ratio of the Electron

These pages are for AQA A Unit 5 Option D and Edexcel Unit 4.

***e/m** was known for quite a long time before anyone came up with a way to measure e or m separately.*

Cathode Ray is an *Old-Fashioned* name for a Beam of *Electrons*

AQA A only

1) The phrase '**cathode ray**' was first used in 1876, to describe the **glow** that appears on the wall of a discharge tube like the one in the diagram, when a **potential difference** is applied across the terminals.
2) The **rays** seemed to come from the **cathode** (hence their name) and there was a lot of argument about **what** the rays were made of.

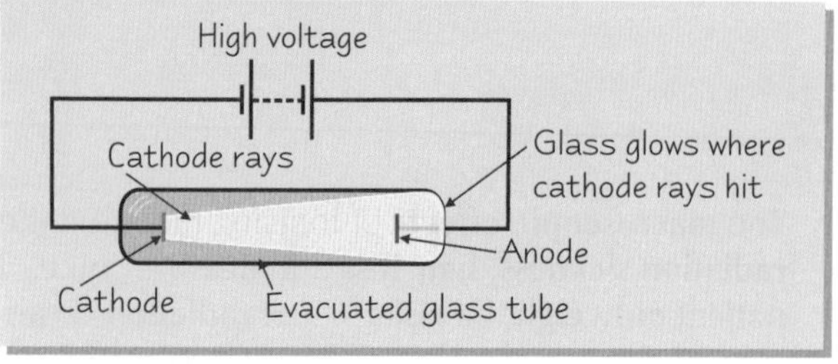

3) **J. J. Thomson** ended the debate in 1897, when he demonstrated (see opposite) that cathode rays:

a) have **energy**, **momentum** and **mass**,
b) have a **negative charge**,
c) have the **same properties**, no matter **what gas** is in the tube and what the **cathode** is made of,
d) have a **charge to mass ratio** much **bigger** than that of **hydrogen** ions. So they either have a **tiny mass**, or a much higher charge — Thomson assumed they had the same size charge as hydrogen ions.

Thomson concluded that **all atoms** contain these 'cathode ray particles', that were later called **electrons**.

Electron Beams are Produced by *Thermionic Emission*

1) When you **heat** a **metal**, its **free electrons** gain a load of **thermal energy**.
2) Give them **enough energy** and they'll **break free** from the surface of the metal — this is called **thermionic emission**. (Try breaking the word down — think of it as '**therm**' [to do with heat] + '**ionic**' [to do with charge] + '**emission**' [giving off] — so it's 'giving off charged particles when you heat something'.)
3) Once they've been emitted, the electrons can be **accelerated** by an **electric field** in an **electron gun**:

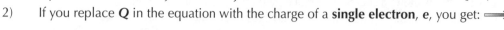

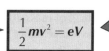

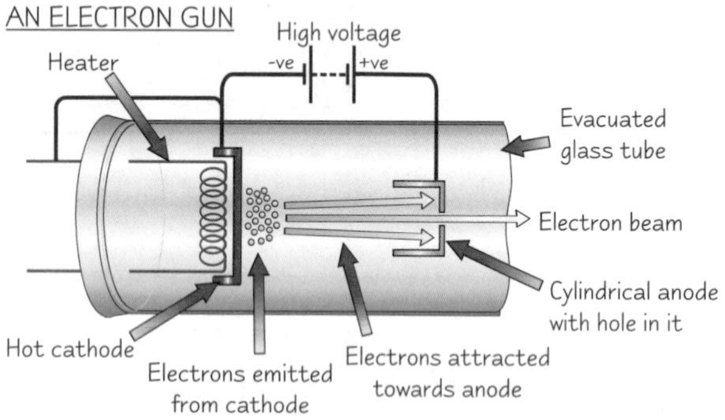

A **heating coil** heats the metal cathode. The electrons that are emitted are **accelerated** towards the **cylindrical anode** by the electric field set up by the high voltage.

Some electrons pass through a **little hole** in the **anode**, making a narrow electron beam. The electrons in the beam move at a **constant velocity** because there's **no field** beyond the anode — i.e., there's **no force**.

The *Electronvolt* is Defined Using *Accelerated Charges*

1) The **kinetic energy** that a particle with charge ***Q*** **gains** when it's **accelerated** through a p.d. of ***V*** volts is ***QV*** joules. That just comes from the definition of the **volt** (JC^{-1}).
2) If you replace ***Q*** in the equation with the charge of a **single electron**, **e**, you get: $\frac{1}{2}mv^2 = eV$
3) From this you can define a new **unit of energy** called the **electronvolt** (**eV**):

1 electronvolt is the **kinetic energy carried** by an **electron** after it has been **accelerated** through a **potential difference** of **1 volt**.

4) So, the **energy in eV** of an electron accelerated by a potential difference is:

energy gained by electron (eV) = accelerating voltage (V)

Conversion factor: $1\ eV = 1.6 \times 10^{-19}\ J$

See p.68 for more on using these units.

Charge/Mass Ratio of the Electron

Thomson Measured the Specific Charge of the Electron

AQA A only

1) The **specific charge** or **charge/mass ratio** of a charged particle is just its **charge** per unit **mass**.
2) There are a **few different ways** of measuring it, and you need to know about **one** of them. This isn't the method that Thomson used, but that's not important.

Check out Section 2 — Fields, if you're having trouble with the experiment.

Measuring the Charge/Mass Ratio of an Electron

1) Electrons are charged particles, so they can be deflected by an **electric** or a **magnetic field**. This method uses a magnetic field in a piece of apparatus called a **fine beam tube**.

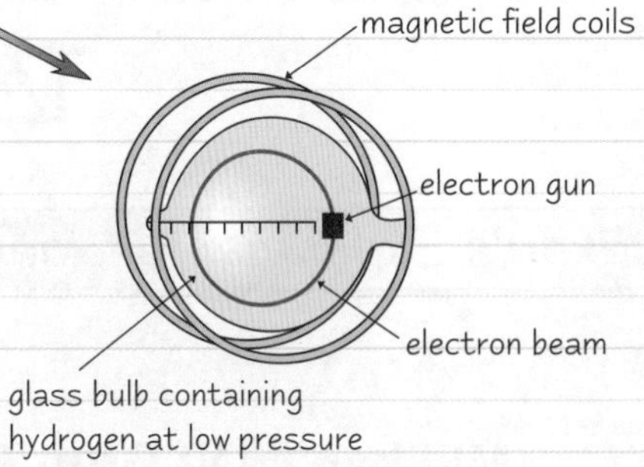

2) When the beam of electrons from the **electron gun** (see previous page) passes through the low-pressure gas, the hydrogen atoms along its path **absorb energy**. As the electrons in these **excited hydrogen atoms** fall back to the ground state, they **emit light** (see p. 70). The electron beam is seen as a **glowing trace** through the gas.
3) Two circular **magnetic field coils** either side generate a **uniform magnetic field** inside the tube.
4) The electron beam is initially fired at **right angles** to the **magnetic field**, so the beam curves round in a **circle**.
5) This means that the **magnetic force** on the electron (see p. 26) is acting as a **centripetal force** (see p. 9). So the radius of the circle is given by:

$$\frac{mv^2}{r} = Bev$$

where m is the mass of an electron, e is the charge on an electron, B is the magnetic field strength, v is the velocity of the electron and r is the radius of the circle.

6) From the previous page, you've got an equation that you can rearrange to give v in terms of the **accelerating potential** of the electron gun. If you substitute that expression for v into the equation above (and tidy it all up a bit) you get:

$$\frac{e}{m} = \frac{2V}{B^2r^2}$$

where m is the mass of an electron, e is the charge on an electron, B is the magnetic field strength, V is the accelerating potential and r is the radius of the circle.

You can **measure** all the quantities on the **right-hand side** of the equation using the **fine beam tube**, leaving you with the **specific charge, *e/m***. It turns out that ***e/m*** (1.76×10^{11} Ckg^{-1}) is about **1800 times greater** than the **specific charge of a hydrogen ion** or **proton** (9.58×10^{7} Ckg^{-1}). And the **mass** of a **proton** is about **1800 times greater** than the **mass** of an **electron** — **Thomson was right**, electrons and protons do have the **same size charge**.

Practice Questions

Q1 What is meant by thermionic emission?

Q2 Sketch a labelled diagram of an electron gun that could be used to accelerate electrons.

Q3 What was Thomson's main conclusion following his measurement of e/m for electrons?

Exam Questions

Q1 An electron of mass 9.1×10^{-31} kg and charge -1.6×10^{-19} C is accelerated through a potential difference of 1 kV.

(a) Write down its energy in eV. [1 mark]

(b) Calculate its energy in joules. [1 mark]

(c) Calculate its speed in ms^{-1} and express this as a percentage of the speed of light (3.0×10^{8} ms^{-1}). [3 marks]

Q2 Explain the main features of an experiment to determine the specific charge of the electron.
The quality of your written answer will be assessed in this question. [5 marks]

New Olympic event — the electronvault...

Electronvolts are really handy units — they crop up all over the rest of this book, particularly in nuclear and particle physics. It stops you having to mess around with a load of nasty powers of ten. Cathode ray tubes (CRTs) are pretty handy too — there might be one in your telly... unless it's one of those new-fangled flat-screen plasma thingummy-do-dahs...

Millikan's Oil-Drop Experiment

These pages are for AQA A Unit 5 Option D and OCR B Unit 4.

Thomson had already found the charge/mass ratio of the electron in 1897 — now it was down to Robert Millikan, experimenter extraordinaire, to find the absolute charge...

Millikan's Experiment used Stoke's Law

1) Before you start thinking about Millikan's experiment, you need a bit of **extra theory**.
2) When you drop an object into a fluid, like air, it experiences a **viscous drag** force. This force acts in the **opposite direction** to the velocity of the object, and is due to the **viscosity** of the fluid.
3) You can calculate this viscous force on a spherical object using **Stoke's law**:

$$F = 6\pi\eta rv$$

where η is the viscosity of the fluid, r is the radius of the object and v is the velocity of the object.

Millikan's Experiment — the Basic Set-Up

Millikan's Oil-Drop Experiment — Apparatus

Millikan's Set-Up

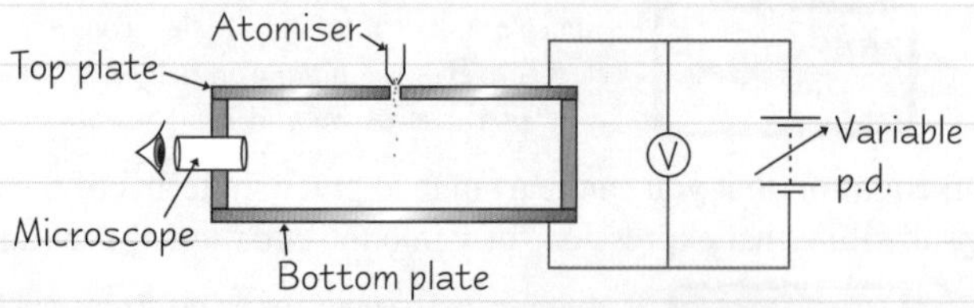

1) The **atomiser** created a **fine mist** of oil drops that were **charged** by **friction** as they left the atomiser (positively if they lost electrons, negatively if they gained electrons).
2) Some of the drops fell through a **hole** in the top plate and could be viewed through the **microscope**. (The eyepiece carried a **scale** to measure distances — and so **velocities** — accurately.)
3) When he was ready, Millikan could apply a **potential difference** between the two plates, producing a **field** that exerted a **force** on the charged drops. By **adjusting** the p.d., he could vary the strength of the field.

To give you a feel for the **size** of the apparatus, Millikan's plates were circular, with a diameter of about the width of this page. They were separated by about 1.5 cm.

Before the Field is Switched on, there's only Gravity and the Viscous Force

1) With the electric field turned off, the forces acting on each oil drop are:
   a) the **weight** of the drop — acting downwards
   b) the **viscous force** from the air — acting upwards

Millikan had to take account of things like upthrust as well, but you don't have to worry about that — keep it simple.

2) The drop will reach **terminal velocity** (i.e. it will stop accelerating) when these two forces are equal. So, from Stoke's law (see above):

$$mg = 6\pi\eta rv$$

3) Since the **mass** of the drop is the **volume** of the drop multiplied by the **density**, ρ, of the oil, this can be rewritten as:

$$\frac{4}{3}\pi r^3 \rho g = 6\pi\eta rv \Rightarrow r^2 = \frac{9\eta v}{2\rho g}$$

Millikan measured η and ρ in separate experiments, so he could now calculate r — ready to be used when he switched on the electric field...

Millikan's Oil-Drop Experiment

*Then he **Turned On** the **Electric Field**...*

1) The field introduced a **third major factor** — an **electric force** on the drop.
2) Millikan adjusted the applied p.d. until the drop was **stationary**. Since the **viscous force** is proportional to the **velocity** of the object, once the drop stopped moving, the viscous force **disappeared**.
3) Now the only two forces acting on the oil drop were:

   a) the **weight** of the drop — acting downwards
   b) the force due to the **uniform electric field** — acting upwards

4) The **electric force** is given by: $F = \frac{QV}{d}$ where Q is the charge on the oil drop, V is the p.d. between the plates and d is the distance between the plates. See p. 20–21

5) Since the drop is **stationary**, this electric force must be equal to the weight, so:

$$\frac{QV}{d} = \frac{4}{3}\pi r^3 \rho g$$

   The first part of the experiment gave a value for r, so the **only unknown** in this equation is Q.

6) So Millikan could find the **charge on the drop**, and repeated the experiment for hundreds of drops. The charge on any drop was always a **whole number multiple** of **-1.6×10^{-19} C**.

*These Results Suggested that **Charge** was **Quantised***

1) This result was **really significant**. Millikan concluded that charge can **never exist** in **smaller** quantities than 1.6×10^{-19} C. He assumed that this was the **charge** carried by an **electron**.
2) Later experiments confirmed that **both** these things are true.

Charge is "**quantised**". It exists in "packets" of size **1.6×10^{-19} C** — the **fundamental unit of charge**. This is the size of the charge carried by **one electron**.

Practice Questions

Q1 Write down the equation for Stoke's law, defining any variables.

Q2 List the forces that act on the oil drop in Millikan's experiment:
(a) with the drop drifting downwards at terminal velocity but with no applied electrical field,
(b) when the drop is stationary, with an electrical field applied.

Q3 Briefly explain the significance of Millikan's oil-drop experiment in the context of quantum physics.

Exam Question

Q1 An oil drop of mass 1.63×10^{-14} kg is held stationary in the space between two charged plates 3.00 cm apart. The potential difference between the plates is 5000 V. The density of the oil used is 880 kgm^{-3}.

(a) Describe the relative magnitude and direction of the forces acting on the oil drop. [2 marks]

(b) Calculate the charge on the oil drop using $g = 9.81$ Nkg^{-1}.
Give your answer in terms of e, the charge on an electron. [3 marks]

The electric field is switched off and the oil drop falls towards the bottom plate.

(c) Explain why the oil drop reaches terminal velocity as it falls. [3 marks]

(d) Calculate the terminal velocity of the oil drop using $\eta = 1.84 \times 10^{-5}$ kgm^{-1}s^{-1}. [3 marks]

So next time you've got a yen for 1.59×10^{-19} coulombs — tough...

This was a huge leap. Along with the photoelectric effect (see p. 130) this experiment marked the beginning of quantum physics. The world wasn't ruled by smooth curves any more — charge now jumped from one allowed step to the next...

Light — Newton vs Huygens

These pages are for AQA A Unit 5 Option D only.

Newton was quite a bright chap really, but even he could make mistakes — and this was his biggest one. The trouble with being Isaac Newton is that everyone just assumes you're right...

Newton had his Corpuscular Theory

1) In 1672, Newton published his **theory of colour**. In it he suggested that **light** was made up of **tiny particles** that he called '**corpuscles**'.
2) One of his major arguments was that light was known to travel in **straight lines**, yet waves were known to **bend** in the shadow of an **obstacle** (diffraction). Experiments weren't **accurate enough** then to detect the diffraction of light. Light was known to **reflect** and **refract**, but that was it.
3) His theory was based on the principles of his **laws of motion** — that all particles, including his 'corpuscles', will 'naturally' travel in **straight lines**.
4) Newton believed that **reflection** was due to a force that **pushed** the particles away from the surface — just like a ball bouncing back off a wall.
5) **Refraction** worked if the corpuscles travelled **faster** in a **denser** medium.

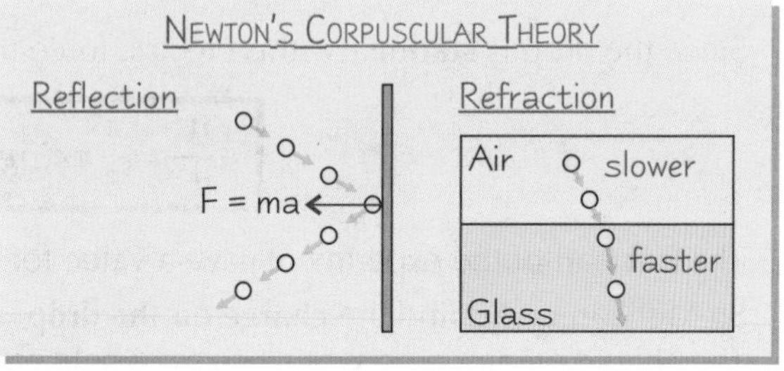

Huygens thought Light was a Wave

1) The idea that light might be a **wave** had existed for some time before it was formalised by Huygens in 1678.
2) At the time, nobody took much notice of him because his theory was **different** from Newton's.
3) Huygens developed a **general model** of the propagation of **waves** in what is now known as **Huygens' principle**:

HUYGENS' PRINCIPLE: Every point on a wavefront may be considered to be a **point source** of **secondary wavelets** that spread out in the forward direction at the speed of the wave. The **new wave front** is the surface that is **tangential** to all of these **secondary wavelets**.

The diagram below shows how this works:

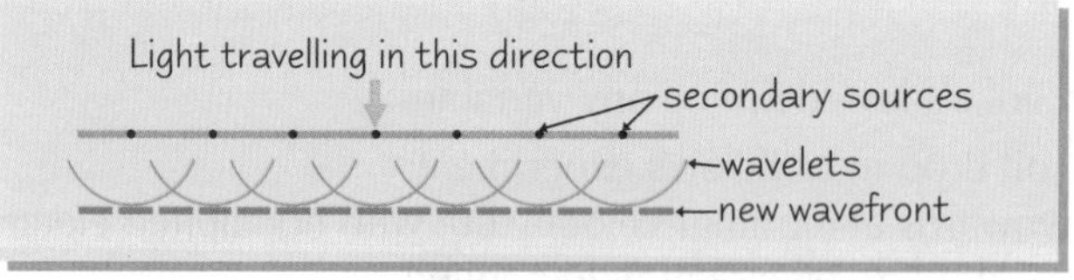

4) By applying his theory to **light**, he found that he could explain **reflection** and **refraction** easily.
   Huygens predicted that light should **slow down** when it entered a **denser medium**, rather than speed up.

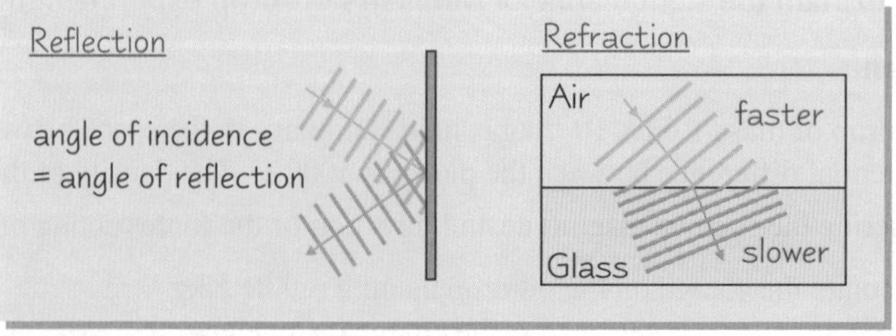

5) Huygens also predicted that light should **diffract** around tiny objects and that two coherent light sources should **interfere** with each other.

Up until the end of the 18th century, most scientists sided with **Newton**. He'd been right about so many things before, so it was generally assumed that he **must be right** about light being corpuscular. The debate raged for **over 100 years** until **Thomas Young** carried out experiments on the **interference** of light in Cambridge around **1800**...

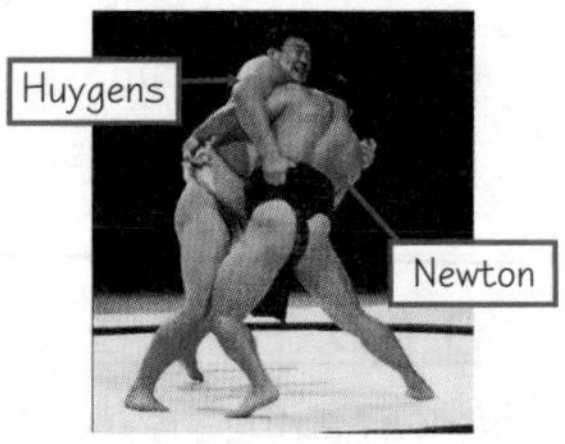

Light — Newton vs Huygens

Young Proved **Huygens Right** with his **Double-Slit Experiment**

1) **Diffraction** and **interference** are both uniquely **wave** properties. If it could be shown that **light** showed **interference** patterns, that would help decide once and for all between corpuscular theory and wave theory.
2) The problem with this was getting two **coherent** light sources, as **light** is emitted in **random bursts**.
3) Young solved this problem by using only **one point source of light** (a narrow slit with a filament lamp behind it). In front of this was a **screen** with **two narrow slits** in it. Light spreading out by **diffraction** from the slits was equivalent to **two coherent point sources**.
4) In the area on the screen where light from the two slits **overlapped**, bright and dark '**fringes**' were formed. This was **proof** that light could both **diffract** (through the narrow slits) and **interfere** (to form the interference pattern on the screen) — **Huygens** was right all along.

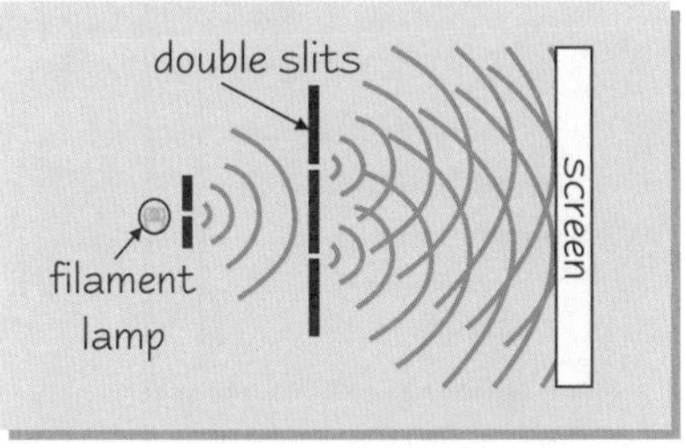

Observations and *Theories* Developed *Rapidly* during the *19th Century*

1) In 1808, Etienne-Louis Malus discovered that light was **polarised** by reflection. Physicists at the time thought that light spread like sound, as a longitudinal wave, so they struggled to explain polarisation.
2) In 1817, Young suggested that light was a **transverse wave** consisting of **vibrating electric** and **magnetic fields** at **right angles** to each other and the **direction of travel**. This explained why light could be **polarised**.
3) In the second half of the 19th century, James Clerk Maxwell showed theoretically that **all electromagnetic waves** should travel at the same speed in a vacuum, **c**.

> **James Clerk Maxwell** calculated the **speed of light** in a vacuum using:
>
> $$c = \frac{1}{\sqrt{\mu_0 \varepsilon_0}}$$
>
> where **c** is the speed of the wave in ms^{-1}, μ_0 ("mu-nought") is the permeability of free space (a constant — $4\pi \times 10^{-7}\ Hm^{-1}$) and ε_0 ("epsilon-nought") is the permittivity of free space (another constant — $8.85 \times 10^{-12}\ Fm^{-1}$).
>
> μ_0 relates to the **magnetic flux density** due to a current-carrying wire in free space, while ε_0 relates to the **electric field strength** due to a charged object in free space.

4) By that time, the **velocity of light** could be measured quite accurately, and it was found to be very close to Maxwell's value of **c**. This suggested that **light** is an **electromagnetic wave**. We now know that all electromagnetic waves, including light, travel in a **vacuum** at a **speed** of **2.998×10^8 ms^{-1}**.
5) In 1887, **Heinrich Hertz** produced and detected **radio waves** using electric sparks. He showed by **experiment** that they could be reflected, refracted, diffracted and polarised, and show interference. This helped confirm that radio waves, like light, are electromagnetic waves.
6) This was the accepted theory up until the very end of the 19th century, when the **photoelectric effect** was discovered. Then the particle theory had to be resurrected, and it was all up in the air again...

Practice Questions

Q1 What was the main argument that Newton used to support his corpuscular theory of light?

Q2 What part does diffraction play in a Young's double-slit experiment?

Q3 Sketch a diagram showing an experiment to demonstrate Young's fringes for white light in a laboratory.

Exam Questions

Q1 Describe Newton's corpuscular theory of light. [2 marks]

Q2 Give a brief history of the understanding of the nature of light in the 18th and 19th centuries. You should mention the various theories that have been proposed and the evidence that has been used to support them.
The quality of your written answer will be assessed in this question. [6 marks]

In the blue corner — the reigning champion... IsaaaAAAAC NEWton...

So, light's a wave, right? We've got that sorted — the double-slit experiment laid the whole argument to rest... or did it?

The Photoelectric Effect

This page is for AQA A Unit 5 Option D only — you did it at AS, though, so it should be familiar.

Shining Light on a Metal can Release Electrons

If you shine **light** of a **high enough frequency** onto the **surface of a metal**, it will **emit electrons**. For **most** metals, this **frequency** falls in the **UV** range.

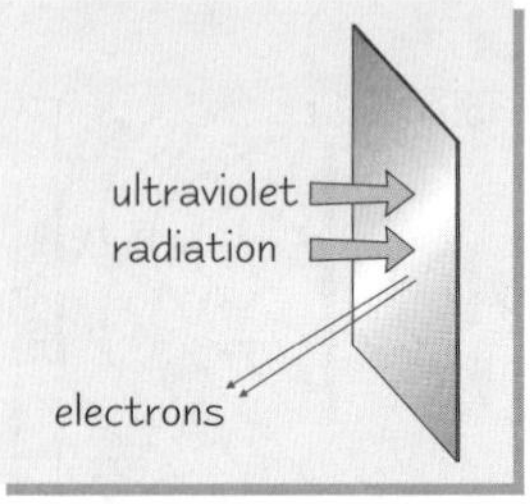

1) **Free electrons** on the **surface** of the metal **absorb energy** from the light, making them **vibrate** or move faster.
2) If an electron **absorbs enough** energy, the **bonds** holding it to the metal can be **broken** and the electron **released**.
3) This is called the **photoelectric effect** and the electrons emitted are called **photoelectrons**.

You don't need to know the details of any experiments on this — you just need to learn the three main conclusions:

Conclusion 1	For a given metal, **no photoelectrons are emitted** if the radiation has a frequency **below** a certain value — called the **threshold frequency**.
Conclusion 2	The photoelectrons are emitted with a variety of kinetic energies ranging from zero to some maximum value. This value of **maximum kinetic energy** increases with the **frequency** of the radiation, and is **unaffected** by the **intensity** of the radiation.
Conclusion 3	The **number** of photoelectrons emitted per second is **directly proportional** to the **intensity** of the radiation.

These are the two that had people puzzled. They can't be explained using wave theory.

The Photoelectric Effect Couldn't be Explained by Wave Theory

According to wave theory:

1) For a particular frequency of light, the **energy** carried is **proportional** to the **intensity** of the beam.
2) The energy carried by the light would be **spread evenly** over the wavefront.
3) **Each** free electron on the surface of the metal would gain a **bit of energy** from each incoming wave.
4) Gradually, each electron would gain **enough energy** to be able to leave the metal.

SO... If the light had a **lower frequency** (i.e. was carrying less energy) it would take **longer** for the electrons to gain enough energy — but it would happen eventually. There is **no explanation** for the **threshold frequency**.

The **higher the intensity** of the wave, the **more energy** it should transfer to each electron — so the kinetic energy should increase with **intensity**. There's **no explanation** for the **kinetic energy** depending only on the **frequency**.

Einstein came up with the Photon Model of Light

1) When Max Planck was investigating **black body radiation** (don't worry, you don't need to know about that just yet), he suggested that **EM waves** can **only** be **released** in **discrete packets**, or **quanta**.
2) The **energy carried** by one of these **wave-packets** had to be:

$$E = hf = \frac{hc}{\lambda}$$

where h = Planck's constant = 6.63×10^{-34} Js
and c = speed of light in a vacuum = 3.00×10^{8} ms^{-1}

3) **Einstein** went **further** by suggesting that **EM waves** (and the energy they carry) can only **exist** in discrete packets. He called these wave-packets **photons**.
4) He saw these photons of light as having a **one-on-one**, **particle-like** interaction with **an electron** in a **metal surface**. It would **transfer all** its **energy** to that **one**, **specific electron**.

The Photoelectric Effect

The **Photon Model** Explained the **Photoelectric Effect** Nicely

According to the photon model:
1) When light hits its surface, the metal is **bombarded** by photons.
2) If one of these photons **collides** with a free electron, the electron will gain energy equal to ***hf***.

Before an electron can **leave** the surface of the metal, it needs enough energy to **break the bonds holding it there**. This energy is called the **work function** (symbol ϕ) and its **value** depends on the **metal**.

It Explains the **Threshold Frequency...**

1) If the energy **gained** from the photon is **greater** than the **work function**, the electron can be **emitted**.
2) If it **isn't**, the electron will just **shake about a bit** or move faster, then release the energy as another photon or in collisions. The metal will heat up, but **no electrons** will be emitted.
3) Since for **electrons** to be released, $hf \geq \phi$, the **threshold frequency** must be:

$$f = \frac{\phi}{h}$$

... and the **Maximum Kinetic Energy**

1) The **energy transferred** to an electron is ***hf***.
2) The **kinetic energy** it will be carrying when it **leaves** the metal is ***hf* minus** any energy it's **lost** on the way out (there are loads of ways it can do that, which explains the **range** of energies).
3) The **minimum** amount of energy it can lose is the **work function**, so the **maximum kinetic energy** is given by the equation:

$$\frac{1}{2}mv_{max}^2 = hf - \phi$$

The **kinetic energy** of the electrons is **independent of the intensity**, because they can **only absorb one photon** at a time.

4) The maximum kinetic energy can be **measured** using the idea of **stopping potential**. The emitted electrons are made to lose their **energy** by **doing work against** an applied **potential difference**. The work done by the p.d. in **stopping** the **fastest electrons** is equal to the energy they were carrying:

$$\frac{1}{2}mv_{max}^2 = eV_s$$

where **e** = charge on the electron = 1.6×10^{-19} C,
V_s = stopping potential in V, and the maximum kinetic energy is measured in J.
The kinetic energy in eV is just equal to the stopping potential — see p. 124.

Practice Questions

Q1 What three main conclusions were drawn from detailed experimentation on the photoelectric effect?

Q2 What is meant by the work function energy of a metal?

Q3 How is the energy of a photon related to its frequency?

Exam Questions *Use Planck's constant = 6.63×10^{-34} Js, speed of light = 3.00×10^8 ms^{-1}, electron charge = 1.6×10^{-19} C.*

Q1 An isolated zinc plate with neutral charge is exposed to high-frequency ultraviolet light.
State and explain the effect of the ultraviolet light on the charge of the plate. [2 marks]

Q2 Light of wavelength 0.50 μm hits a metal surface and causes electrons to be released.
Their maximum kinetic energy is 2.0×10^{-19} J.
(a) Calculate the work function of the metal. [3 marks]
(b) Explain why a beam of light with a wavelength of 1.5 μm would not cause electrons to be emitted. [3 marks]

Q3 Potassium has a work function of 2.2 eV. A potassium anode is illuminated with light of wavelength 350 nm. What potential must be applied to stop the electrons leaving the anode? [4 marks]

And that's all there is to it — *sob*...

Confused? The best way to really get your head round this sort of thing is to try and explain it to someone else. Learn why the light theory can't explain the photoelectric effect, and how photon theory does — then tell someone else about it.

Wave-Particle Duality

***Theses pages are for** AQA A Unit 5 Option D **and** Edexcel Unit 4.*

Is it a wave? Is it a particle?

Interference and **Diffraction** show **Light** as a **Wave**

1) Light produces **interference** and **diffraction** patterns — **alternating bands** of **dark** and **light**.
2) These can **only** be explained using **waves interfering constructively** (when two waves overlap in phase) or **interfering destructively** (when two waves are out of phase).

The **Photoelectric Effect** Shows **Light** Behaving as a **Particle**

1) **Einstein** explained the results of **photoelectricity experiments** (see p. 130) by thinking of the **beam of light** as a series of **particle-like "photons"**.
2) If a **photon** of light is a **discrete** bundle of energy, then it can **interact** with an **electron** in a **one-to-one way**.
3) **All** the **energy** in the **photon** is **given** to one **electron**.

Neither the **wave theory** nor the **particle theory** describe what light actually **is**. They're just two different **models** that help to explain the way light behaves.

I'm not impressed — this is just speculation. What do you think Dad?

De Broglie came up with the **Wave-Particle Duality Theory**

1) Louis de Broglie made a **bold suggestion** in his **PhD thesis**:

> If "wave-like" **light** showed **particle properties** (photons), **"particles"** like **electrons** should be expected to show **wave-like properties**.

2) The **de Broglie equation** relates a **wave property** (**wavelength**, λ) to a **moving particle property** (**momentum**, mv). h = Planck's constant = 6.63×10^{-34} Js.

$$\lambda = \frac{h}{mv}$$

Most physicists at the time weren't very impressed — his ideas were just speculation.

3) The **de Broglie wave** of a particle can be interpreted as a **"probability wave"**. The **probability** of finding a particle at a point is **directly proportional** to the **square of the wave's amplitude**.
4) Later experiments **confirmed** the wave nature of electrons.

Electron Diffraction shows the **Wave Nature** of **Electrons**

1) De Broglie's suggestions prompted a lot of experiments to try to show that **electrons** can have **wave-like** properties. In **1927**, Davisson and Germer succeeded in **diffracting electrons**.
2) They saw **diffraction patterns** when **accelerated electrons** in a vacuum tube **interacted** with the **spaces** in a graphite **crystal**.
3) According to wave theory, the **spread** of the **lines** in the diffraction pattern **increases** if the **wavelength** of the wave **increases**.
4) In electron diffraction experiments, a **small accelerating voltage**, i.e. **slow** electrons, gives **widely spaced** rings.
5) **Increase** the **electron speed** and the diffraction pattern circles **squash together** towards the **middle**. This fits in with the **de Broglie** equation above — if the **velocity** is **higher**, the **wavelength** is **shorter** and the **spread** of the lines is **smaller**.

Electron diffraction patterns look like this.

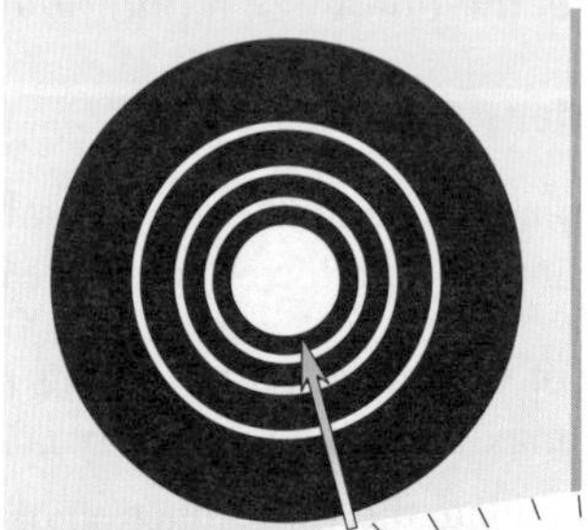

For AQA A astrophysics students, this circle is called the Airy disc (see p. 85).

> In general, λ for **electrons** accelerated in a **vacuum tube** is about the **same size** as λ for **electromagnetic waves** in the **X-ray** part of the spectrum.

6) **Just for AQA A**, the de Broglie wavelength of an electron (λ) is related to the **accelerating voltage** (V) by:

$$\lambda = \frac{h}{\sqrt{2meV}}$$

where e is the charge on the electron and m is its mass

Wave-Particle Duality

Particles Don't Show *Wave-Like Properties* All the Time

You **only** get **diffraction** if a particle interacts with an object of about the **same size** as its **de Broglie wavelength**.
A **tennis ball**, for example, with **mass 0.058 kg** and **speed 100 ms^{-1}** has a **de Broglie wavelength** of **10^{-34} m**.
That's **10^{19} times smaller** than the **nucleus** of an **atom**! There's nothing that small for it to interact with.

Example An electron of mass 9×10^{-31} kg is fired from an electron gun at $7 \times 10^6\ ms^{-1}$. What size object will the electron need to interact with in order to diffract?

Momentum of electron = $mv = 6.3 \times 10^{-24}$ kg ms^{-1}

$\lambda = h/mv = 6.63 \times 10^{-34} / 6.3 \times 10^{-24} = 1 \times 10^{-10}$ m

Only crystals with atom layer spacing around this size are likely to cause the diffraction of this electron.

You can also calculate the anode voltage needed to produce this wavelength using the formula at the bottom of the previous page: $\lambda = \frac{h}{\sqrt{2meV}} \Rightarrow V = \frac{h^2}{2me\lambda^2} = \mathbf{153\ V}$

A **shorter wavelength** gives **less diffraction**. This is important in **microscopes** where diffraction **blurs out details**.
The **tiny** wavelength of electrons means an **electron microscope** can resolve **finer detail** than a **light** microscope.

Electron Microscopes use *Electrons Instead of* Light

*AQA A **only***

In electron microscopes:

1) A **stream of electrons** is accelerated towards the sample using a **positive electric potential** — an **electron gun**.
2) To **resolve detail** around the size of an **atom**, the **electron wavelength** needs to be similar to the **diameter** of an **atom** (**0.1 nm**) — which (using the equation in the example above) means an **anode voltage** of **at least 150 V**.
3) The **stream of electrons** from the electron gun is confined into a thin **beam** using a **magnetic field**.
4) The beam is **focused** onto the sample and any interactions are transformed into an **image**. The sort of image you get depends on the **type of microscope** you're using:

A **transmission electron microscope** (**TEM**) works a bit like a **slide** projector, but uses electrons instead of light. A **very thin** specimen is used and the parts of the beam that pass through the specimen are projected onto a **screen** to form an image.

A **scanning tunnelling microscope** (**STM**) is a different kind of microscope that uses principles of **quantum mechanics**. A very fine **probe** is moved over the surface of the sample and a **voltage** is applied between the probe and the surface. Electrons "**tunnel**" from the probe to the surface, resulting in a weak **electrical current**. The smaller the **distance** between the probe and the surface, the **greater the current**. By scanning the probe over the surface and measuring the current, you produce an **image** of the **surface** of the sample.

Practice Questions

Q1 What name is normally given to "particles" of light?
Q2 What observation showed that electrons could behave as waves?
Q3 What is the advantage of an electron microscope over a light microscope?

Exam Questions

Use $h = 6.63 \times 10^{-34}$ Js, $e = 1.6 \times 10^{-19}$ C, $m_e = 9.1 \times 10^{-31}$ kg.

Q1 An electron is accelerated through a p.d. of 500 V.
(a) Calculate:
i) the velocity of the electron, ii) its de Broglie wavelength. [4 marks]
(b) In which region of the electromagnetic spectrum does this fall? [1 mark]

Q2 (a) Describe how a transmission electron microscope (TEM) uses a beam of electrons to produce an image. [3 marks]
(b) Show that an anode voltage of at least 150 V is needed for a TEM to resolve detail around the size of an atom (0.1 nm). [3 marks]

Wave-Particle duelity — pistols at dawn...

*Anyone doing AQA A will have seen a lot of this before at AS, but there are quite a few extra details this time round. You're getting into the weird bits of quantum physics now — it says that light isn't a wave, and it isn't a particle, it's **both**... at the **same time**. And if you think that's confusing, just wait till you get onto relativity — not that I want to put you off.*

The Speed of Light and Relativity

These pages are for AQA A Unit 5 Option D only. (If you're doing OCR B Unit 4, have a read too so the next two pages make more sense — you don't need to remember the details, though.)

First — a bit of a history lesson.

***Michelson** and **Morley** tried to find the **Absolute Speed** of the Earth*

1) During the 19th century, most physicists believed in the idea of **absolute motion**. They thought everything, including light, moved relative to a **fixed background** — something called the **ether**.
2) **Michelson** and **Morley** tried to measure the **absolute speed** of the **Earth** through the ether using a piece of apparatus called an **interferometer**.
3) They expected the motion of the Earth to affect the **speed of light** they measured in **certain directions**. According to Newton, the speed of light measured in a **lab** moving parallel to the light would be ($\boldsymbol{c} + \boldsymbol{v}$) or ($\boldsymbol{c} - \boldsymbol{v}$), where $\boldsymbol{v}$ is the speed of the lab. By measuring the speed of light **parallel** and **perpendicular** to the motion of the Earth, Michelson and Morley hoped to find $\boldsymbol{v}$, the absolute speed of the Earth.

*They used an **Interferometer** to Measure the Speed of the Earth*

The interferometer was basically **two mirrors** and a **partial reflector** (a beam-splitter). When you shine light at a partial reflector, some of the light is **transmitted** and the rest is **reflected**, making **two separate beams**.

The mirrors were at **right angles** to each other, and an **equal distance**, $\boldsymbol{L}$, from the beam-splitter.

The Michelson-Morley Interferometer

1) **Monochromatic light** is sent towards the **beam-splitter**.
2) The light is split into **two beams** travelling at **right angles** to each other.
3) The beams are reflected at **mirrors M1** and **M2**.
4) When the reflected beams meet back at the beam-splitter, they form an **interference pattern**.
5) This interference pattern is **recorded** by the observer.
6) Then the whole interferometer is **rotated** through **90°** and the experiment **repeated**.

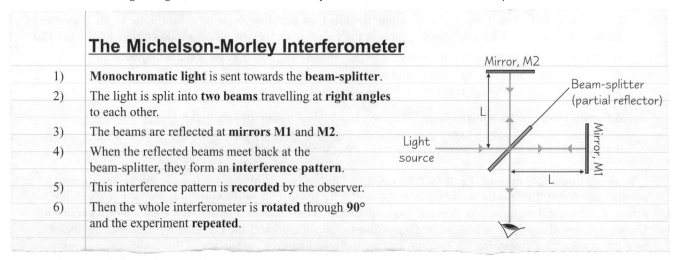

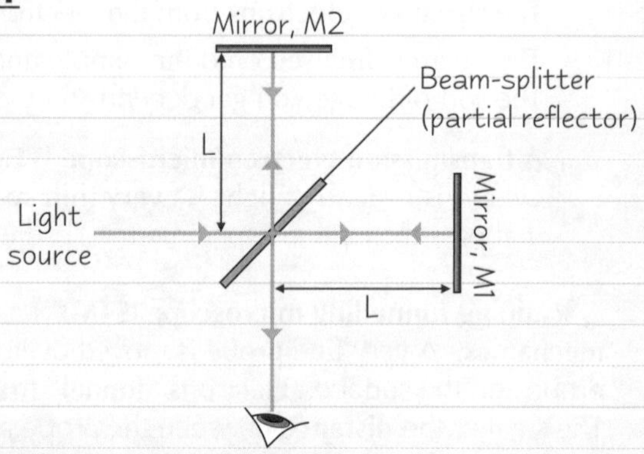

EXPECTED OUTCOME

According to Newton's laws, light moving **parallel** to the motion of the Earth should take **longer** to travel to the mirror and back than light travelling at **right angles** to the Earth's motion. So **rotating** the apparatus should have changed the **travel time** for the two beams.

This would cause a **tiny shift** in the **interference pattern**.

*They **Didn't** get the **Result** they were **Expecting***

They **repeated** the experiment **over** and **over** again — at different **times of day** and at different points in the **year**. Taking into account any **experimental errors**, there was **absolutely no shift** in the interference pattern.

The time taken by each beam to travel to each mirror was **unaffected** by rotating the apparatus.

So, Newton's laws **didn't work** in this situation.

Most scientists were really puzzled by this "null result". Eventually, the following **conclusions** were drawn:

a) It's **impossible** to detect **absolute motion** — the ether doesn't exist.
b) The **speed of light** has the **same value** for all observers.

The Speed of Light and Relativity

The **invariance** of the speed of light is one of the cornerstones of special relativity. The other is based on the concept of an **inertial frame of reference**.

*Anything Moving with a **Constant Velocity** is in an **Inertial Frame***

A reference frame is just a **space** that we decide to use to describe the **position of an object** — you can think of a reference frame as a **set of coordinates**.

> An **inertial reference frame** is one in which **Newton's 1st law** is obeyed. (Newton's 1st law says that objects won't accelerate unless they're acted on by an external force.)

1) Imagine sitting in a carriage of a train **waiting at a station**. You put a **marble** on the table. The marble **doesn't move**, since there aren't any horizontal **forces** acting on it. **Newton's 1st law** applies, so it's an **inertial frame**.
2) You'll get the **same result** if the carriage moves at a **steady speed** (as long as the track is **smooth, straight and level**) — another inertial frame.
3) As the train **accelerates** out of the station, the marble **moves** without any force being applied. Newton's 1st law **doesn't apply**. The accelerating carriage **isn't an inertial frame**.
4) **Rotating** or **accelerating** reference frames **aren't** inertial. In most cases, though, you can think of the **Earth** as an inertial frame — it's near enough.

A stationary train carriage is an inertial frame

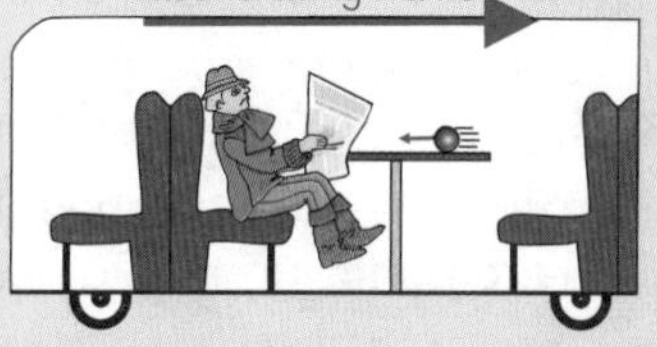

An accelerating train carriage is NOT an inertial frame

*Einstein's **Postulates** of **Special Relativity***

Einstein's theory of **special relativity** only works in **inertial frames** and is based on **two postulates** (assumptions):

> 1) **Physical laws have the same form in all inertial frames.**
> 2) **The speed of light in free space is invariant.**

1) The first postulate says that if we do **any physics experiment** in any inertial frame we'll always get the **same result**. That means it's **impossible** to use the result of **any experiment** to work out if you're in a **stationary reference frame** or one moving at a **constant velocity**.
2) The second postulate says that the **speed of light** (in a vacuum) always has the **same value**. It isn't affected by the **movement** of the **person measuring it** or by the movement of the **light source**.

Practice Questions

Q1 Draw a labelled diagram showing the apparatus used by Michelson and Morley to determine the absolute speed of the Earth. Include the light source, mirrors, beam-splitter and the position of the observer.

Q2 State the postulates of Einstein's theory of special relativity.

Q3 Explain why a carriage on a rotating Ferris wheel is not an inertial frame.

Exam Questions

Q1 In the Michelson-Morley interferometer experiment, interference fringes were observed.
When the apparatus was rotated through 90 degrees the expected result was not observed.

(a) What was the expected result? [1 mark]

(b) What conclusions were eventually drawn from these observations? [2 marks]

Q2 (a) Using a suitable example, explain what is meant by an inertial reference frame. [2 marks]

(b) Explain what is meant by the invariance of the speed of light. [2 marks]

The speed of light is always the same — whatever your reference frame...

Michelson and Morley showed that Newton's laws didn't always work. This was a huge deal. Newton's laws of motion had been treated like gospel by the physics community since the 17th century. Then along came Herr Einstein...

Special Relativity

These pages are for AQA A Unit 5 Option D and OCR B Unit 4 (just the concepts — you don't need the equations)..

Special relativity ONLY WORKS IN INERTIAL FRAMES — it doesn't work in an accelerating frame.

A Moving Clock Runs Slow

1) Time runs at **different speeds** for two observers **moving relative** to each other.
2) A **stationary** observer measures the interval between two events as t_0, the **proper time**. (Since there's no such thing as absolute motion, a "stationary" observer means someone that's stationary relative to the reference frame the events are happening in.) An observer moving at a **constant velocity**, v, will measure a **longer** interval, t, between the two events. t is given by the equation:

$$t = \frac{t_0}{\sqrt{1-\frac{v^2}{c^2}}}$$

where $\sqrt{1-\frac{v^2}{c^2}}$ is called the relativity factor and c is the speed of light.

3) This is called **time dilation**.

A THOUGHT EXPERIMENT TO ILLUSTRATE TIME DILATION

Anne is on a high-speed train travelling at 0.9c. She switches on a torch for exactly 2 seconds.
Claire is standing on the platform and sees the same event, but records a longer time.
It appears to Claire that Anne's clock is running slow.

In this experiment, **Anne** is the **stationary observer**, so she measures the **proper time**, t_0.
Claire is **moving** at 0.9**c relative to the events**, and so measures a time t given by:

$$t = \frac{t_0}{\sqrt{1-\frac{v^2}{c^2}}} = \frac{2}{\sqrt{1-\frac{(0.9c)^2}{c^2}}} = \frac{2}{\sqrt{1-0.9^2}} = \mathbf{4.59\ s}$$

To the **external observer** (e.g. Claire) **moving clocks** run **slowly**.

It's really important that you get the "stationary observer" right.

There's Proof of Time Dilation from Muon Decay

1) **Muons** are **particles** created in the **upper atmosphere** that move towards the ground at speeds close to **c**.
2) In the laboratory (**at rest**) they have a **half-life** of less than **2 μs**. From this half-life, you would expect most muons to **decay** between the top of the atmosphere and the Earth's surface, but that **doesn't happen**.

Experiment to Measure Muon Decay

1) Measure the speed, v, of the muons (this is about **0.99*c***).
2) Place a detector (MR1) at high altitude and measure the muon count rate.
3) Use another detector (MR2) to measure the count rate at ground level.
4) Compare the two figures.

Here are some typical results:
MR1 = 500 per minute
MR2 = 325 per minute
Distance between detectors (***d***) = 2000 m
Time as measured by an observer = ***d/v*** = 6.73 μs
Half-life of muons at rest = 1.53 μs

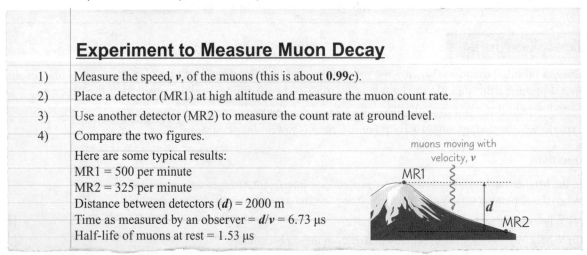

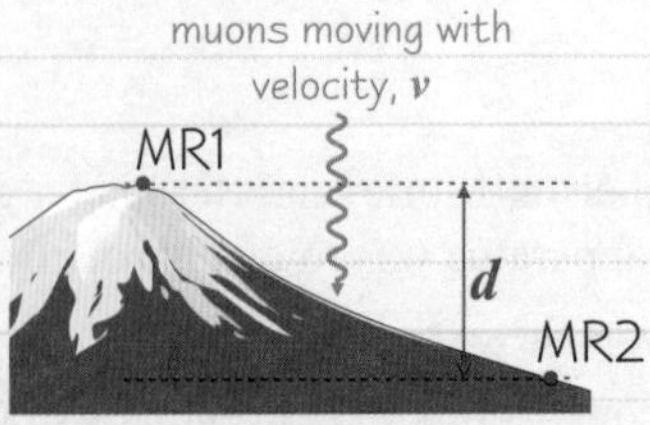

3) We can do some calculations using the data above. In the reference frame of the **observer** the muons seemed to have travelled for **4.4 half-lives** between the two detectors. You would expect the count rate at the **second detector** to be only about **25 counts per minute**.
4) However, in a **muon's reference frame**, travelling at 0.99**c**, the time taken for the journey is just t_0 **= 0.94 μs**. From the point of view of the muons, the time elapsed is **less** than their **half-life**. From the point of view of the **observer**, it appears that the half-life of the muons has been **extended**.

Special Relativity

A Moving Rod Looks Shorter

1) A **rod** moving in the **same direction** as its **length** looks **shorter** to an external observer.
2) A **stationary** observer measures the length of an object as l_0. An observer moving at a **constant velocity**, v, will measure a **shorter** length, l. l is given by the equation:

$$l = l_0\sqrt{1-\frac{v^2}{c^2}}$$

This is called **length contraction**.

A THOUGHT EXPERIMENT TO ILLUSTRATE LENGTH CONTRACTION

*Anne (still in the train moving at 0.9**c**) measures the length of her carriage as 3 m. Claire, on the platform, measures the length of the carriage as it moves past her.*

Claire measures a length: $l = l_0\sqrt{1-\frac{v^2}{c^2}} = 3\sqrt{1-\frac{(0.9c)^2}{c^2}} = 3\sqrt{1-0.9^2} = \mathbf{1.3\ m}$

The Mass of an Object Increases with Speed

1) The **faster** an object **moves**, the **more massive** it gets.
2) An object with rest mass m_0 moving at a **velocity** v has a **relativistic mass** m given by the equation:

$$m = \frac{m_0}{\sqrt{1-\frac{v^2}{c^2}}}$$

So increasing an object's kinetic energy increases its mass — but it's only noticeable near the speed of light.

3) As the relative speed of an object approaches **c**, the mass approaches **infinity**. So, in practice, no massive object can move at a speed **greater than** or **equal to** the speed of light.

Mass and Energy are Equivalent

1) Einstein extended his idea of **relativistic mass** to write down the most famous equation in physics: $E = mc^2$
2) This equation says that **mass** can be **converted** into **energy** and vice versa. Or, alternatively, **any energy** you supply to an object **increases** its **mass** — it's just that the increase is usually **too small** to measure.
3) The **total energy** of a relativistic object is given by the equation: ⟹

$$E = \frac{m_0c^2}{\sqrt{1-\frac{v^2}{c^2}}}$$

This is just substituting the relativistic mass into $E = mc^2$.

Practice Questions

Q1 State the equations for time dilation and length contraction, carefully defining each symbol.

Q2 Using the results from the muon experiment (page 136), show that the time elapsed in the reference frame of the muon is 0.94 μs.

Q3 A particle accelerated to near the speed of light gains a very large quantity of energy. Describe how the following quantities change as the particle gains more and more energy: a) the mass; b) the speed.

Exam Questions

Q1 A subatomic particle has a half-life of 20 ns when at rest. If a beam of these particles is moving at 0.995c relative to an observer, calculate the half-life of these particles in the frame of reference of the observer. [3 marks]

Q2 Describe a thought experiment to illustrate time dilation. [4 marks]

Q3 For a proton ($m_0 = 1.67 \times 10^{-27}$ kg) travelling at 2.8×10^8 ms^{-1} calculate:

(a) the relativistic mass, [1 mark]

(b) the total energy. [1 mark]

Have you ever noticed how time dilates when you're revising physics...

*In a moving frame, time stretches out, lengths get shorter and masses get bigger. One of the trickiest bits is remembering which observer's which — t_0, m_0 and l_0 are the values you'd measure if the object was **at rest**.*

Exponentials and Natural Logs

Mwah ha ha ha... you've hacked your way through the rest of the book and think you've finally got to the end of A2 Physics, but no, there's this tasty titbit of exam fun to go. You can get asked to look at and work out values from log graphs all over the shop, from astrophysics to electric field strength. And it's easy when you know how...

Many Relationships in Physics are **Exponential**

A fair few of the relationships you need to know about in A2 Physics are **exponential** — where the **rate of change** of a quantity is **proportional** to the **amount** of the quantity left. Here are just a few you should have met before (if they don't ring a bell, go have a quick read about them)...

Charge on a capacitor — the decay of charge on a capacitor is proportional to the amount of charge left on the capacitor: $Q = Q_o e^{(-t/RC)}$ (see p. 38)

Radioactive decay — the rate of decay is proportional to the **number of nuclei left** to decay in a sample: $N = N_o e^{(-\lambda t)}$ (see p. 49)

The **activity** of a radioactive sample behaves in the same way: $A = A_o e^{(-\lambda t)}$ (see p. 49)

You can **Plot** Exponential Relations Using the **Natural Log, ln**

When it came to logs, Geoff always took time to smell the flowers...

1) Say you've got two variables, x and y, which are related to each other by the formula $y = ke^{-ax}$ (where k and a are constants).
2) The inverse of e is the natural logarithm, **ln**.
3) By definition, $\ln(e^x) = x$. So far so good... now you need some **log rules**:

$\ln(ab) = \ln a + \ln b$ $\qquad \ln\left(\frac{a}{b}\right) = \ln a - \ln b$ $\qquad \ln a^b = b \ln a$

If you're doing OCR A or OCR B you get given the log rules on your formula sheet.

4) So, if you take the natural log of the exponential function you get:
$\ln y = \ln(ke^{-ax}) = \ln k + \ln(e^{-ax}) \Longrightarrow$ $\boxed{\ln y = \ln k - ax}$
5) Then all you need to do is plot ($\ln y$) against x, and Eric's your aunty:

You get a **straight-line** graph with (**ln** k) as the y**-intercept**, and $-a$ as the **gradient**.

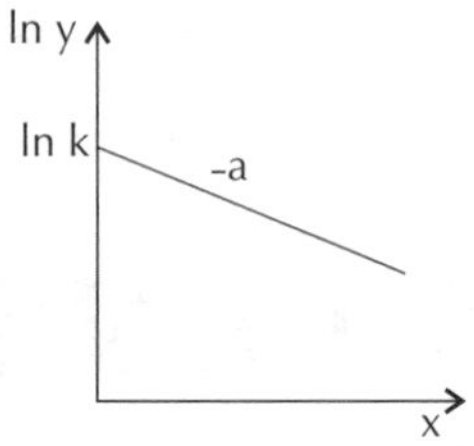

You Might be Asked to find the **Gradient** of a Log Graph...

This log business isn't too bad when you get your head around which bit of the log graph means what. On the plus side, they won't ask you to plot a graph like this (yipee) — they'll just want you to find the **gradient** or the **y-intercept**.

Example — finding the radioactive half-life of material X

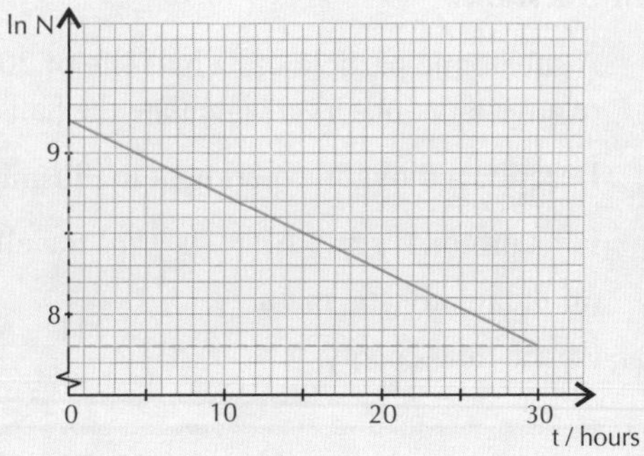

The graph shows the radioactive decay of substance X.
(a) Find the initial number of atoms, N_o, in the sample.

You know that the number of radioactive atoms in a sample, N, is related to the initial number of atoms by the equation $N = N_o e^{-\lambda t}$.

So, $(\ln N) = (\ln N_o) - \lambda t$ and $\ln N_o$ is the y-intercept of the graph $= 9.2$, $N_o = e^{9.2} \approx$ **9900 atoms**.

(b) Find the decay constant λ of substance X.

$-\lambda$ is the gradient of the graph, so: $\lambda = \frac{\Delta \ln N}{\Delta t} = \frac{9.2 - 7.8}{30 \times 60 \times 60} = \frac{1.4}{108\,000} = 1.3 \times 10^{-5}\ s^{-1}$(2s.f.)

Log Graphs and Long Answer Questions

You can Plot **Any Power Law** as a **Log-Log Graph**

You can use logs to plot a straight-line graph of **any power law** — it doesn't have to be an exponential.
Take the relationship between the energy stored in a spring, E, and the spring's extension, x:

$$E = kx^n$$

Take the log (base 10) of both sides to get:

$$\log E = \log k + n \log x$$

So **log k** will be the **y**-intercept and **n** the gradient of the graph.

Example

The graph shows how the intensity of radiation from the Sun, I, varies with its distance, d.
I is related to d by the power law $I = kd^n$. Find n.

$\log I = \log (kd^n) = \log k + \log d^n$
$= \log k + n \log d$.

so n is the **gradient** of the graph.
Reading from the graph:

$$n = \frac{\Delta \log I}{\Delta \log d} = \frac{15.4 - 5.4}{5 - 10} = \frac{10}{-5} = -2$$

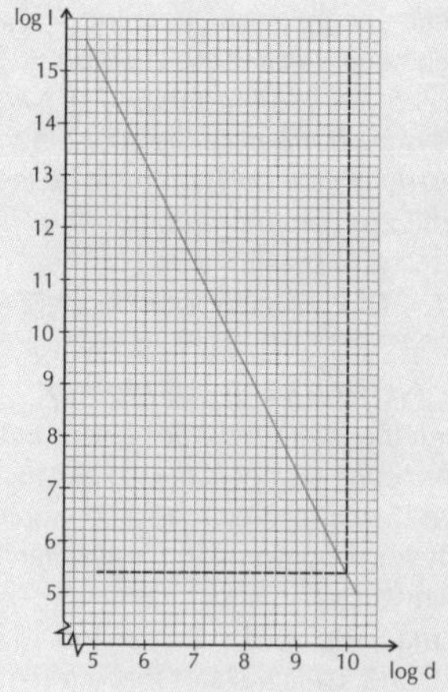

And that's the End of Logs... Now **Explain Yourself...**

In A2, they often give a couple of marks for 'the quality of written communication' when you're writing a slightly long answer (and not just pumping numbers into an equation). You can pick up a couple of easy marks just by making sure that you do the things in the fetching blue box.

1) **Explain** your ideas or argument **clearly** as this is usually what you'll get a mark for. And make sure you **answer the question** being asked — it's dead easy to go off on a tangent. Like my mate Phil always says... have I ever told you about Phil? Well he...
2) Write in **whole sentences**.
3) Use **correct spelling**, **grammar** and **punctuation**.
4) Also check how many marks the question is worth.
If it's only a two-marker, they don't want you to spend half an hour writing an essay about it.

Example

A large group of people walk across a footbridge. When the frequency of the group's footsteps is 1 Hz, the bridge noticeably oscillates and 'wobbles'.
Fully describe the phenomenon causing the bridge to wobble.
Suggest what engineers could to do in order to solve this problem.
The quality of your written answer will be assessed in this question. *[6 marks]*

Good Answer

The pedestrians provide a driving force on the bridge causing it to oscillate. At around 1 Hz, the driving frequency from the pedestrians is roughly equal to the natural frequency of the bridge, causing it to resonate. The amplitude of the bridge's oscillations when resonating at 1 Hz will be greater than at any other driving frequency. The oscillations at this frequency are large enough to be noticed by pedestrians.

Engineers could fix this problem by critically damping the bridge to stop any oscillations as quickly as possible.

They could also adjust the natural frequency of the bridge so that it was not so close to a known walking frequency of large groups of people.

Bad Answer

resonance
driving frequency of group = nat. freq.
damping

There's nothing wrong with the physics in the bad answer, but you'd miss out on some nice easy marks just for not bothering to link your thoughts together properly or put your answer into proper sentences.

Lumberjacks are great musicians — they have a natural logarithm...

Well, that's it folks. Crack open the chocolate bar of victory and know you've earnt it. Only the tiny detail of the actual exam to go... ahem. Make sure you know which bit means what on a log graph and you'll pick up some nice easy marks. Other than that, stay calm, be as clear as you can and good luck — I've got my fingers, toes and eyes crossed for you.

Answers

Section One — Forces and Oscillations

Page 3 — Momentum and Impulse

1) a) total momentum before collision = total momentum after [1 mark]
$(0.6 \times 5) + 0 = (0.6 \times -2.4) + 2\mathbf{v}$
$3 + 1.44 = 2\mathbf{v}$ [1 mark for working] $\Rightarrow \mathbf{v} = 2.22\ \text{ms}^{-1}$ [1 mark]

b) Kinetic energy before collision = $\frac{1}{2} \times 0.6 \times 5^2 + \frac{1}{2} \times 2 \times 0^2 = 7.5$ J
Kinetic energy after the collision = $\frac{1}{2} \times 0.6 \times 2.4^2 + \frac{1}{2} \times 2 \times 2.22^2$
$= 1.728 + 4.9284 = 6.6564$ J [1 mark]. The kinetic energy of the two balls is greater before the collision than after (i.e. it's not conserved) [1 mark], so the collision must be inelastic [1 mark].

2) momentum before = momentum after [1 mark]
$\Rightarrow (0.7 \times 0.3) + 0 = 1.1\mathbf{v}$
$0.21 = 1.1\mathbf{v}$ [1 mark for working] $\Rightarrow \mathbf{v} = 0.19\ \text{ms}^{-1}$ [1 mark]

Page 5 — Newton's Laws of Motion

1) a) When the parachutist first jumps out of the plane, the only vertical force acting on her is due to gravity, so there is a resultant downward force [1 mark]. Newton's 2nd law states that, the acceleration of a body is proportional to the resultant force, so she will accelerate downwards [1 mark].

b) $\mathbf{F} = \mathbf{ma} = \mathbf{mg} = 78 \times 9.81 = 765.18$ N [1 mark]

c) Newton's 1st law states that a force is needed to change the velocity of an object [1 mark] — the parachutist's velocity is not changing, so the resultant force acting on her must be zero [1 mark].

2) Force perpendicular to river flow = 500 – 100 = 400 N [1 mark]
Force parallel to river flow = 300 N

Resultant force = $\sqrt{400^2 + 300^2} = 500$ N [1 mark]

$\mathbf{a} = \mathbf{F/m}$ [1 mark] $= 500/250 = 2\ \text{ms}^{-2}$ [1 mark]

Page 7 — Work and Energy

1)

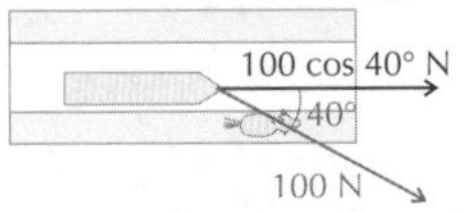

Force in direction of travel = 100 cos 40° = 76.6 N [1 mark]
$\mathbf{W} = \mathbf{Fs} = 76.6 \times 1500 = 114\ 900$ J [1 mark]

2) a) Use $\mathbf{W} = \mathbf{Fs}$ [1 mark] $= 20 \times 9.81 \times 3 = 588.6$ J [1 mark]

b) Use $\mathbf{P} = \mathbf{Fv}$ [1 mark] $= 20 \times 9.81 \times 0.25 = 49.05$ W [1 mark]

Page 9 — Circular Motion

1) a) $\omega = \frac{\theta}{t}$ [1 mark] so $\omega = \frac{2\pi}{3.2 \times 10^7} = 2.0 \times 10^{-7}\ \text{rad s}^{-1}$ [1 mark]

b) $\mathbf{v} = \mathbf{r}\omega$ [1 mark] $= 1.5 \times 10^{11} \times 2.0 \times 10^{-7} = 30\ \text{kms}^{-1}$ [1 mark]

c) $\mathbf{F} = \mathbf{m}\omega^2\mathbf{r}$ [1 mark] $= 6.0 \times 10^{24} \times (2.0 \times 10^{-7})^2 \times 1.5 \times 10^{11}$
$= 3.6 \times 10^{22}$ N [1 mark]

The answers to b) and c) use the rounded value of ω calculated in part a) — if you didn't round, your answers will be slightly different.

d) The gravitational force between the Sun and the Earth [1 mark]

2) a) Gravity pulling down on the water at the top of the swing gives a centripetal acceleration of 9.81 ms^{-2} [1 mark].
If the circular motion of the water needs a centripetal acceleration of less than 9.81 ms^{-2}, gravity will pull it in too tight a circle. The water will fall out of the bucket.

Since $\mathbf{a} = \omega^2\mathbf{r}$, $\omega^2 = \frac{\mathbf{a}}{\mathbf{r}} = \frac{9.81}{1}$, so $\omega = 3.1\ \text{rad s}^{-1}$ [1 mark]

$\omega = 2\pi\mathbf{f}$, so $\mathbf{f} = \frac{\omega}{2\pi} = 0.5\ \text{rev s}^{-1}$ [1 mark]

b) Centripetal force = $\mathbf{m}\omega^2\mathbf{r} = 10 \times 5^2 \times 1 = 250$ N [1 mark].
This force is provided by both the tension in the rope, $\mathbf{T}$, and gravity:
$\mathbf{T} + (10 \times 9.81) = 250$. So $\mathbf{T} = 250 - (10 \times 9.81) = 152$ N [1 mark].

Page 11 — Simple Harmonic Motion

1) a) Simple harmonic motion is an oscillation in which an object always accelerates towards a fixed point [1 mark] with an acceleration directly proportional to its displacement from that point [1 mark]. [The SHM equation would get you the marks if you defined all the variables.]

b) The acceleration of a falling bouncy ball is due to gravity. This acceleration is constant, so the motion is not SHM. [1 mark].

2) a) Maximum velocity = $(2\pi\mathbf{f})\mathbf{A} = 2\pi \times 1.5 \times 0.05 = 0.47\ \text{ms}^{-1}$ [1 mark].

b) Stopclock started when object released, so $\mathbf{x} = \mathbf{A}\cos(2\pi\mathbf{f}t)$ [1 mark].
$\mathbf{x} = 0.05 \times \cos(2\pi \times 1.5 \times 0.1) = 0.05 \times \cos(0.94) = 0.029$ m [1 mark].

c) $\mathbf{x} = \mathbf{A}\cos(2\pi\mathbf{f}t) \Rightarrow 0.01 = 0.05 \times \cos(2\pi \times 1.5\mathbf{t})$.
So $0.2 = \cos(3\pi\mathbf{t}) \Rightarrow \cos^{-1}(0.2) = 3\pi\mathbf{t}$. $3\pi\mathbf{t} = 1.37 \Rightarrow \mathbf{t} = 0.15$ s.
[1 mark for working, 1 mark for correct answer]

Page 13 — Simple Harmonic Oscillators

1) a) Extension of spring = 0.20 – 0.10 = 0.10 m [1 mark]. Hooke's Law gives $\mathbf{k} = \frac{\text{force}}{\text{extension}}$, so $\mathbf{k} = \frac{0.10 \times 9.8}{0.10} = 9.8\ \text{Nm}^{-1}$ [1 mark].

b) $\mathbf{T} = 2\pi\sqrt{\frac{\mathbf{m}}{\mathbf{k}}} \Rightarrow \mathbf{T} = 2\pi \times \sqrt{\frac{0.10}{9.8}} = 2\pi \times \sqrt{0.01} = 0.63$ s [1 mark].

c) $\mathbf{m} \propto \mathbf{T}^2$ so if $\mathbf{T}$ is doubled, $\mathbf{T}^2$ is quadrupled and $\mathbf{m}$ is quadrupled [1 mark]. So mass needed = 4 × 0.10 = 0.40 kg [1 mark].

2) $5\mathbf{T}_{\text{short pendulum}} = 3\mathbf{T}_{\text{long pendulum}}$, and $\mathbf{T} = 2\pi\sqrt{\frac{\mathbf{l}}{\mathbf{g}}}$ [1 mark].

Let length of long pendulum = $\mathbf{l}$. So $5\left(2\pi\sqrt{\frac{0.20}{\mathbf{g}}}\right) = 3\left(2\pi\sqrt{\frac{\mathbf{l}}{\mathbf{g}}}\right)$ [1 mark].

Dividing by 2π gives $5 \times \sqrt{\frac{0.20}{\mathbf{g}}} = 3 \times \sqrt{\frac{\mathbf{l}}{\mathbf{g}}}$. Squaring and simplifying gives $5 = 9\mathbf{l}$ so length of long pendulum = 5/9 = 0.56 m [1 mark].

Page 15 — Free and Forced Vibrations

1) a) When a system is forced to vibrate at a frequency that's close to, or the same as its natural frequency [1 mark] and oscillates with a much larger than usual amplitude [1 mark].

b) See graph below. [1 mark] for showing a peak at the natural frequency, [1 mark] for a sharp peak.

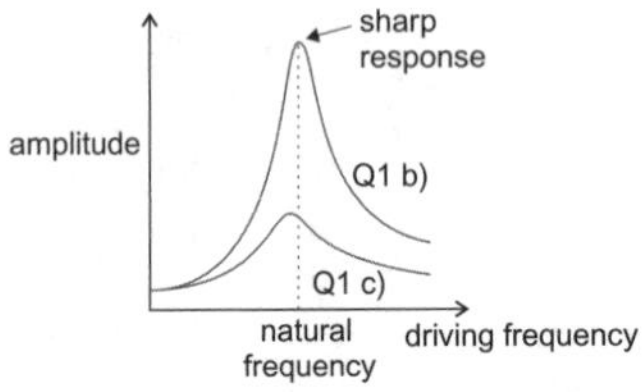

c) See graph. [1 mark] for a smaller peak at the natural frequency [the peak will actually be slightly to the left of the natural frequency due to the damping, but you'll get the mark if the peak is at the same frequency in the diagram].

2) a) A system is critically damped if it returns to rest in the shortest time possible [1 mark] when it's displaced from equilibrium and released.

b) e.g. suspension in a car [1 mark].

Section Two — Fields

Page 17 — Gravitational Fields

1) $\mathbf{g} = \frac{\mathbf{GM}}{\mathbf{r}^2} \Rightarrow \mathbf{M} = \frac{\mathbf{gr}^2}{\mathbf{G}} = \frac{9.81 \times (6400 \times 1000)^2}{6.67 \times 10^{-11}}$ [1 mark]
$= 6.02 \times 10^{24}$ kg [1 mark]

2) a) $\mathbf{g} = \frac{\mathbf{GM}}{\mathbf{r}^2} = \frac{6.67 \times 10^{-11} \times 7.35 \times 10^{22}}{(1740 \times 1000)^2} = 1.62\ \text{Nkg}^{-1}$ [1 mark]

b) $\mathbf{E} = -\frac{\mathbf{GMm}}{\mathbf{r}} = -\frac{6.67 \times 10^{-11} \times 7.35 \times 10^{22} \times 25}{(1740 + 10) \times 1000}$ [1 mark]
$= -7.00 \times 10^7$ J [1 mark]

Page 19 — Motion of Masses in Gravitational Fields

1) a) $\mathbf{T} = \sqrt{\frac{4\pi^2\mathbf{r}^3}{\mathbf{GM}}} = \sqrt{\frac{4\pi^2 \times [(6400 + 200) \times 1000]^3}{6.67 \times 10^{-11} \times 5.98 \times 10^{24}}}$ [1 mark]
= 5334 seconds OR 1.48 hours [1 mark]

b) $\mathbf{v} = \sqrt{\frac{\mathbf{GM}}{\mathbf{r}}} = \sqrt{\frac{6.67 \times 10^{-11} \times 5.98 \times 10^{24}}{(6400 + 200) \times 1000}}$ [1 mark]
$= 7774\ \text{ms}^{-1} = 7.77\ \text{kms}^{-1}$

2) Period = 24 hours = 24 × 60 × 60 = 86 400 s [1 mark]

$\mathbf{T} = \sqrt{\frac{4\pi^2\mathbf{r}^3}{\mathbf{GM}}} \Rightarrow \mathbf{r} = \sqrt[3]{\frac{\mathbf{T}^2\mathbf{GM}}{4\pi^2}} = \sqrt[3]{\frac{86400^2 \times 6.67 \times 10^{-11} \times 5.98 \times 10^{24}}{4\pi^2}}$

$\mathbf{r} = 4.23 \times 10^7\ \text{m} = 4.23 \times 10^4$ km [1 mark]
Height above Earth $= 4.23 \times 10^4 - 6.4 \times 10^3 = 35\ 900$ km [1 mark]

Answers

3) Over 50 000 years, the Sun will have only lost a tiny fraction of its mass (9.5×10^{21} kg overall) [1 mark], which will not have caused any significant change in the Earth's orbit [1 mark].

Page 21 — Electric Fields

1)

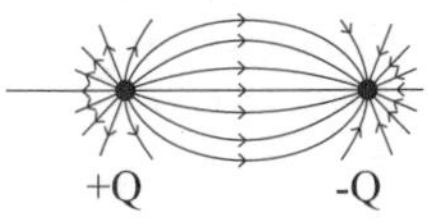

Recognisable pattern around the charges (not just in between) [1 mark], lines equally spaced around the charges and joined to the charges, and general symmetry of the diagram [1 mark], arrows along field lines between the charges with arrows pointing away from the positive and towards the negative charge [1 mark].

2) $$E = \frac{Q}{4\pi\varepsilon_0 r^2}$$

$$E = \frac{1.6 \times 10^{-19}}{4\pi \times 8.85 \times 10^{-12} \times \left(1.75 \times 10^{-10}\right)^2}$$

$= 4.698 \times 10^{10}$ [1 mark] Vm^{-1} or NC^{-1} [1 mark]

3) a) $E = V/d = 1500/(4.5 \times 10^{-3}) = 3.3 \times 10^5$ [1 mark] Vm^{-1} [1 mark]
The field is perpendicular to the plates. [1 mark]

b) $d = 2 \times (4.5 \times 10^{-3}) = 9.0 \times 10^{-3}$ m [1 mark]
$E = V/d \Rightarrow V = Ed = [1500/(4.5 \times 10^{-3})] \times 9 \times 10^{-3} = 3000$ V [1 mark]

Page 23 — Gravitational and Electric Fields

1) $$F_g = -\frac{Gm_1m_2}{r^2} = \frac{6.67 \times 10^{-11} \times (9.11 \times 10^{-31})^2}{(8 \times 10^{-10})^2} = -8.65 \times 10^{-53} N$$

$$F_e = \frac{1}{4\pi\varepsilon_0}\frac{Q_1Q_2}{r^2} = \frac{1}{4\pi\varepsilon_0}\frac{(1.60 \times 10^{-19})^2}{(8 \times 10^{-10})^2} = 3.60 \times 10^{-10} N \text{ [1 mark]}$$

The electric force on each electron is much larger than the gravitational force, by a factor of over 10^{40} [1 mark]. The gravitational force is attractive, while the electric force is repulsive [1 mark].

2) a) Oil drop is stationary, so $mg = F_e = Vq/d$ [1 mark]
$\Rightarrow q = mgd/V = (1.5 \times 10^{-14} \times 9.81 \times 0.03)/5000$ [1 mark]
$= 8.8 \times 10^{-19}$ C [1 mark]

b) The drop would accelerate towards the positive lower plate [1 mark].

3) a) The beam of electrons curves downwards, so the field must act upwards [1 mark] because electrons are negatively charged so experience a force in the opposite direction to the field [1 mark]. The beam of electrons follow a smooth curve, so the field must be uniform [1 mark].

b) The electrons experience a constant downward force whilst they are between the plates [1 mark], which makes them accelerate downwards at a constant rate [1 mark].
However, since there is no horizontal force, the electrons continue to move at a constant horizontal velocity [1 mark]. The combination of constant horizontal velocity and constant vertical acceleration results in a curved (parabolic) path [1 mark].

Page 25 — Magnetic Fields

1) a) $F = BIl = 2 \times 10^{-5} \times 3 \times 0.04$ [1 mark] $= 2.4 \times 10^{-6}$ N [1 mark]

b) $F = BIl \sin\theta = 2.4 \times 10^{-6} \times \sin 30° = 2.4 \times 10^{-6} \times 0.5$ [1 mark]
$= 1.2 \times 10^{-6}$ N [1 mark]

Page 27 — Charged Particles in Magnetic Fields

1) a) $F = Bqv = 0.77 \times 1.6 \times 10^{-19} \times 5 \times 10^6$ [1 mark]
$= 6.16 \times 10^{-13}$ N [1 mark]

b) The force acting on the electron is always at right angles to its velocity, and the speed of the electron is constant. This is the condition for circular motion. [1 mark]

2) Electromagnetic force = centripetal force [1 mark]
so, $Bqv = mv^2/r$ [1 mark]

$$\text{so, } r = \frac{mv}{Bq} = \frac{9.11 \times 10^{-31} \times 2.3 \times 10^7}{0.6 \times 10^{-3} \times 1.6 \times 10^{-19}} = 0.218 \text{ m [1 mark]}$$

3) $r = \frac{mv}{Bq}$ [1 mark], which rearranges to give $B = \frac{mv}{rq}$.
v, r and q are all constant, so $\frac{B}{m} = \textbf{constant}$ [1 mark]
Find the constant when $B = 0.20$ T, $m = 35$: $0.20 \div 35 = 5.7 \times 10^{-3}$.
Now use this value to find B when $m = 37$:
$B = 37 \times 5.7 \times 10^{-3} = 0.21$ T [1 mark]

Page 29 — Electromagnetic Induction

1) a) $\phi = BA$ [1 mark] $= 2 \times 10^{-3} \times 0.23 = 4.6 \times 10^{-4}$ Wb [1 mark]

b) $\Phi = BAN$ [1 mark] $= 2 \times 10^{-3} \times 0.23 \times 150 = 0.069$ Wb [1 mark]

c) $$V = \frac{\Delta\Phi}{\Delta t} = \frac{(B_{start} - B_{end})AN}{\Delta t}$$
$$= \frac{(2 \times 10^{-3} - 1.5 \times 10^{-3})(0.23 \times 150)}{2.5} = 6.9 \times 10^{-3} \text{ V}$$
[3 marks available, one for each stage of the workings]

2) a) $\Phi = BAN$ [1 mark] $= 0.9 \times 0.01 \times 500 = 4.5$ Wb [1 mark]

b) Find the flux linkage after the movement:
$\Phi = BAN\cos\theta$ [1 mark]
$= 500 \times 0.9 \times 0.01 \times \cos 90° = 0$ Wb [1 mark]

$$V = \frac{\Delta\Phi}{\Delta t} \text{ [1 mark]}$$
$$= \frac{4.5 - 0}{0.5} = 9 \text{ V [1 mark]}$$

Page 31 — Electromagnetic Induction

1) a) $V = Blv$ [1 mark] $= 60 \times 10^{-6} \times 30 \times 100 = 0.18$ V [1 mark]

b)

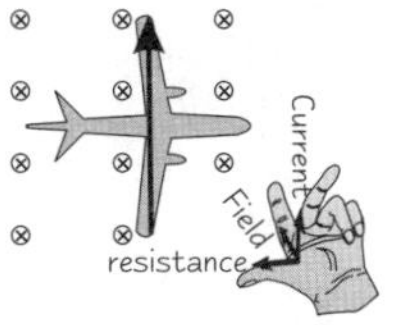

[1 mark]

2)

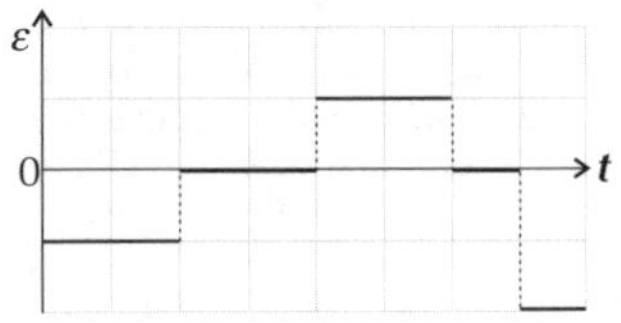

Step graph [1 mark], with the first and third steps negative and second step positive [1 mark] and the last step twice the height of the others [1 mark].

Page 33 — Transformers

1) a) $\frac{V_p}{V_s} = \frac{N_p}{N_s}$ [1 mark] so, $N_s = \frac{45 \times 150}{9} = 750$ turns [1 mark]

b) $\frac{V_p}{V_s} = \frac{I_s}{I_p}$ [1 mark] so, $I_s = \frac{V_pI_p}{V_s} = \frac{9 \times 1.5}{45} = 0.3$ A [1 mark]

c) efficiency $= \frac{V_sI_s}{V_pI_p}$ [1 mark] $= \frac{10.8}{9 \times 1.5} = 0.8$ (i.e. 80%) [1 mark]

2) AC current flowing in the primary coil creates a changing magnetic flux/field in the core of the transformer [1 mark]. This induces an e.m.f. and current in the core [1 mark], which creates a magnetic flux/field in the core that opposes the original change of flux [1 mark]. [1 mark for a clear sequence of ideas.]

Section Three — Capacitance

Page 36 — Capacitors

1) a) Capacitors are used to control a camera's flash by providing a short pulse of high current. [1 mark]

b) Capacitors are suitable because they can deliver a short pulse of high current [1 mark], which results in a brief flash of bright light when needed [1 mark].

2) Capacitance $= \frac{Q}{V}$ = gradient of line $= \frac{660\ \mu C}{3\ V} = 220\ \mu F$.
[1 mark for 'gradient', 1 mark for correct answer.]
Charge stored $= Q$ = area $= 15 \times 10^{-6} \times 66 = 990\ \mu C$.
[1 mark for 'area', 1 mark for correct answer.]

Answers

3) a) $E = \frac{1}{2}CV^2$ *[1 mark]* $= \frac{1}{2} \times 0.5 \times 12^2 = 36$ *J [1 mark]*

b) $Q = CV$ *[1 mark]* $= 0.5 \times 12 = 6$ *C [1 mark]*

4) *The voltage across all the components in a parallel circuit is the same as the source voltage, whereas in a series circuit the source voltage is shared between the components [1 mark]. This means that the two capacitors in parallel will each have a higher voltage across them than the two in series [1 mark]. Charge stored is proportional to voltage, so the capacitors in parallel will store more charge than those in series [1 mark]. [1 mark for a clear sequence of ideas.]*

Page 39 — Charging and Discharging

1) a) *The charge falls to 37% after* **RC** *seconds [1 mark], so* $t = 1000 \times 2.5 \times 10^{-4} = 0.25$ *seconds [1 mark]*

b) $Q = Q_0 e^{-\frac{t}{RC}}$ *[1 mark], so after 0.7 seconds:* $Q = Q_0 e^{-\frac{0.7}{0.25}} = Q_0 \times 0.06$ *[1 mark]. There is 6% of the initial charge left on the capacitor after 0.7 seconds [1 mark].*

c) i) *The total charge stored will double [1 mark].*
ii) *None [1 mark].* iii) *None [1 mark].*

2)

Time (s)	Charge (C)	dQ/dt (Cs^{-1})	ΔQ (C)	New charge (C)
0	5.0×10^{-2}	-2.5×10^{-2}	-1.25×10^{-2}	3.75×10^{-2}
0.5	3.75×10^{-2}	-1.88×10^{-2}	-0.94×10^{-2}	2.81×10^{-2}
1.0	2.81×10^{-2}	-1.41×10^{-2}	-0.70×10^{-2}	2.11×10^{-2}
1.5	2.11×10^{-2}	-1.05×10^{-2}	-0.53×10^{-2}	1.58×10^{-2}
2.0	1.58×10^{-2}			

[1 mark for each correct stage of iteration, to a total of 5 marks. Otherwise 1 mark for an attempt at an iterative method]

Section Four — Nuclear and Particle Physics

Page 41 — Scattering to Determine Structure

1) a) *The majority of alpha particles are not scattered because the nucleus is a very small part of the whole atom and so the probability of an alpha particle getting near it is small [1 mark]. Most alpha particles pass undeflected through the empty space around the nucleus [1 mark].*

b) *Alpha particles and atomic nuclei are both positively charged [1 mark]. If an alpha particle travels close to a nucleus, there will be a significant electrostatic force of repulsion between them [1 mark]. This force deflects the alpha particle from its original path. [1 mark]*

2) a) *All particles have wave-like properties, with an associated wavelength [1 mark]. If the wavelength of a beam of particles is similar to the atomic spacing of the material it's passing through, the beam produces a diffraction pattern. [1 mark]*

b) *Electrons are not affected by the strong nuclear force. [1 mark]*

c) *Maximum diffraction occurs when the nucleus is the same size as the wavelength of the electrons [1 mark]. Larger nuclei cause less diffraction for the same electron energy [1 mark].*

Page 43 — Nuclear Radius and Density

1) a) *Rearrange* $r = r_0 A^{1/3}$ *in terms of* r_0 *[1 mark], then substitute for* **r** *and* **A***:*

$$r_0 = \frac{r}{A^{1/3}} = \frac{3.2 \times 10^{-13}}{12^{1/3}} = 1.40 \times 10^{-15} \text{ m} \quad [1 \text{ mark}]$$

b) *For radium,* $A = 226$*:* $r = r_0 A^{1/3} = 1.4 \times 10^{-15} \times 226^{1/3} = 8.53 \times 10^{-15}$ m *[1 mark]*

c) *Volume* $= \frac{4}{3}\pi r^3 = \frac{4}{3}\pi(8.53 \times 10^{-15})^3 = 2.6 \times 10^{-42}$ m³ *[1 mark]*

So density (ρ) $= \frac{m}{v} = \frac{3.75 \times 10^{-25}}{2.6 \times 10^{-42}} = 1.44 \times 10^{17}$ kgm^{-3} *[1 mark]*

2) *The mass density of a gold nucleus is much larger than the mass density of a gold atom [1 mark]. This implies that the majority of a gold atom's mass is in the nucleus [1 mark]. The nucleus is small compared to the size of the atom [1 mark]. There must be a lot of nearly empty space inside each atom [1 mark].*

Page 45 — The Strong Nuclear Force

1) a) $$F = \frac{1}{4\pi\varepsilon_0}\frac{Q_1Q_2}{r^2} = \frac{1}{4\pi(8.85 \times 10^{-12})}\frac{(1.6 \times 10^{-19})(1.6 \times 10^{-19})}{(9 \times 10^{-15})^2} = 2.8N$$

[1 mark for working, 1 mark for correct answer]

b) *The electrostatic force will increase [1 mark].*

c) *There is no electrostatic force between a proton and a neutron [1 mark] because a neutron has no charge [1 mark].*

2) a) *The strong interaction must be repulsive at very small nucleon separations to prevent the nucleus being crushed to a point [1 mark].*

b) *Beyond 10 fm, the strong interaction is smaller than the electrostatic force [1 mark]. This means the protons in the nucleus would be forced apart. So a nucleus bigger than this would be unstable. [1 mark]*

Page 47 — Radioactive Emissions

1) *Place different materials between the source and detector and measure the amount of radiation getting through [1 mark]:*

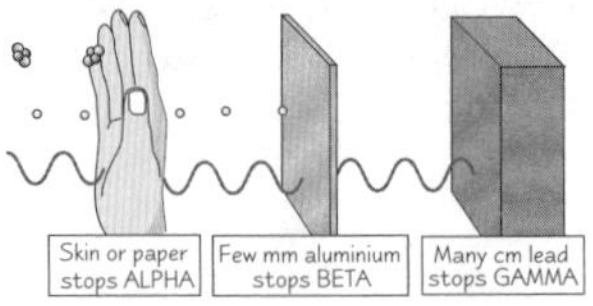

[1 mark for each material stopping correct radiation]

2) $I \propto \text{count rate} \propto \frac{1}{x^2}$ *[1 mark]*

The G-M tube is 4 times the original distance from the source.

$\frac{1}{4^2} = \frac{1}{16}$*, so the count rate at 40 cm will be 1/16th that at 10 cm [1 mark]. The count rate at 40 cm will be* $\frac{240}{16} = 15$ counts s^{-1} *[1 mark].*

Page 49 — Exponential Law of Decay

1) *Any one of: You can't say which atom/nucleus in a sample will be the next one to decay. / You can only estimate the fraction of nuclei that will decay or the probability an atom/nucleus will decay in a given time. / You cannot say exactly how many atoms will decay in a given time. [1 mark]*

2) a) *Activity,* **A** *= measured – background = 750 – 50 = 700 Bq [1 mark]*
$A = \lambda N \Rightarrow 700 = 50\,000\,\lambda$ *[1 mark] So* $\lambda = 0.014$ s^{-1} *[1 mark]*

b) $T_{\frac{1}{2}} = \frac{\ln 2}{\lambda} = \frac{0.693}{0.014} = 49.5$ seconds

[1 mark for the half-life equation, 1 mark for the correct half-life]

c) $N = N_0 e^{-\lambda t} = 50\,000 \times e^{-0.014 \times 300} = 750$
[2 marks available — 1 mark for the decay equation, 1 mark for the number of atoms remaining after 300 seconds]

Page 51 — Modelling Decay

1) a) $t_{\frac{1}{2}} = \ln 2 \times RC = \frac{\ln 2}{\lambda}$ *[1 mark], so* $RC = \frac{1}{\lambda}$ *[1 mark]*

b) $RC = 500 \times 10^{-6} \times 144 \times 10^3 = 72$ *[1 mark]*
$\lambda = 1 \div 72 = 0.0139$ s^{-1} *[1 mark]*

c) $t_{\frac{1}{2}} = \frac{\ln 2}{\lambda}$ *[1 mark]* $= 0.693 \div 0.0139 = 50$ s *[1 mark]*

2)

Time (s)	0	20	40	60
Activity (Bq)	60.0	52.6	46.1	40.4
ln(activity)	4.09	3.96	3.83	3.70

[2 marks]

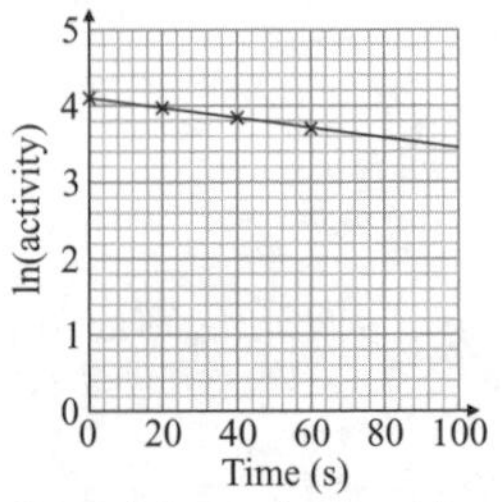

[1 mark for each axis with correct units and sensible scale]
[1 mark for plotting points correctly]
Gradient = $-\lambda = -0.4 \div 60 = -0.00667$*, so* $\lambda = 0.00667$ *[1 mark]*

$t_{\frac{1}{2}} = \frac{\ln 2}{\lambda}$ *[1 mark]* $= 0.693 \div 0.00667 \approx 104$ s *[1 mark]*

Answers

Page 53 — Nuclear Decay

1) a) $^{226}_{88}\mathbf{Ra} \rightarrow {}^{222}_{86}\mathbf{Rn} + {}^{4}_{2}\alpha$ [3 marks available — 1 mark for alpha particle, 1 mark each for proton and nucleon number of radon]

b) $^{40}_{19}\mathbf{K} \rightarrow {}^{40}_{20}\mathbf{Ca} + {}^{0}_{-1}\beta$ [3 marks available — 1 mark for beta particle, 1 mark each for proton and nucleon number of calcium]

2) Mass defect = $(6.695 \times 10^{-27}) - (6.645 \times 10^{-27}) = 5.0 \times 10^{-29}$ kg [1 mark]. Using the equation $\mathbf{E} = \mathbf{mc}^2$ [1 mark], $\mathbf{E} = (5.0 \times 10^{-29}) \times (3 \times 10^8)^2 = 4.5 \times 10^{-12}$ J [1 mark]

Page 55 — Binding Energy

1) a) There are 6 protons and 8 neutrons, so the mass of individual parts $= (6 \times 1.007276) + (8 \times 1.008665) = 14.112976$ u [1 mark]
Mass of $^{14}_{6}\mathbf{C}$ nucleus = 13.999948 u
so, mass defect = 14.112976 – 13.999948 = 0.113028 u [1 mark]
Converting this into kg gives mass defect = 1.88×10^{-28} kg [1 mark]

b) $\mathbf{E} = \mathbf{mc}^2 = (1.88 \times 10^{-28}) \times (3 \times 10^8)^2 = 1.69 \times 10^{-11}$ J [1 mark]
1 MeV = 1.6×10^{-13} J, so energy = $\frac{1.69 \times 10^{-11}}{1.6 \times 10^{-13}} = 106$ MeV [1 mark]

2) a) Fusion [1 mark]

b) The increase in binding energy per nucleon is about 0.86 MeV [1 mark]. There are 2 nucleons in ^{2}H, so the increase in binding energy is about 1.72 MeV — so about 1.7 MeV is released (ignoring the positron) [1 mark].

Page 57 — Nuclear Fission and Fusion

1) a) Nuclear fission can be induced by neutrons and produces more neutrons during the process [1 mark]. This means that each fission reaction induces more fission reactions, resulting in a ongoing chain of reactions [1 mark].

b) For example, control rods limit the rate of fission by absorbing neutrons [1 mark]. The number of neutrons absorbed by the rods is controlled by varying the amount they are inserted into the reactor [1 mark].
A suitable material for the control rods is boron [1 mark].

c) In an emergency shut-down, the control rods are released into the reactor [1 mark]. The control rods absorb the neutrons, and stop the reaction as quickly as possible [1 mark].

2) Advantages (two of e.g.): the nuclear reactor itself doesn't produce any waste gases that could be harmful to the environment, e.g. sulfur dioxide (leading to acid rain) or carbon dioxide [1 mark]. It can be used to supply a continuous supply of electricity, unlike some renewable sources [1 mark].
Disadvantages (two of e.g.): problems with the reactor getting out of control [1 mark], risks of radiation from radioactive waste [1 mark], the emissions released in the case of an accident [1 mark], the long half-life of nuclear waste [1 mark].

3) a) mass defect = mass before – mass after [1 mark] = (2.013553 + 3.015501) – (4.001505 + 1.008665) = 0.018884 u [1 mark]

b) 0.018884 × 931 = 17.6 MeV [1 mark]

Page 59 — Classification of Particles

1) Proton, electron and electron antineutrino [1 mark]. The electron and the electron antineutrino are leptons [1 mark]. Leptons are not affected by the strong interaction, so the decay can't be due to the strong interaction [1 mark].

2) Mesons are hadrons but the muon is a lepton [1 mark]. The muon is a fundamental particle but mesons are not [1 mark]. Mesons feel the strong interaction but the muon does not [1 mark].

Page 61 — Antiparticles

1) $e^+ + e^- \rightarrow \gamma + \gamma$ [1 mark]. This is called annihilation [1 mark].

2) The protons, neutrons and electrons which make up the iron atoms would need to annihilate with their antiparticles [1 mark]. No antiparticles are available in the iron block [1 mark].

3) Baryon number is not conserved / The creation of a particle of matter requires the creation of its antiparticle — in this case no antineutron has been produced [1 mark].

4) Energy before = energy after.
Total energy before annihilation for each particle = $\mathbf{E}_{rest} + \mathbf{E}_{kinetic}$
$\mathbf{E}_{rest} = \mathbf{m}_e\mathbf{c}^2 = 9.11 \times 10^{-31} \times (3.0 \times 10^8)^2 = 8.2 \times 10^{-14}$ J = 0.5 MeV [1 mark] $\mathbf{E}_{tot}$ = 2 × (300 MeV + 0.5 MeV) = 601 MeV [1 mark]
Total energy of the two photons = 601 MeV
So the energy of 1 photon = 601 ÷ 2 = 300.5 MeV [1 mark]

Page 64 — Quarks

1) **uud** [1 mark]

2) $\pi^- = d\bar{u}$ [1 mark]
Charge of down quark = –1/3 unit. Charge of anti-up quark = –2/3 unit. Total charge = –1 unit [1 mark]

3) The weak interaction converts a down quark into an up quark plus an electron and an electron antineutrino. [1 mark]
The neutron (udd) becomes a proton (uud). [1 mark]

4) The baryon number changes from 2 to 1 so baryon number is not conserved [1 mark]. The strangeness changes from 0 to 1 so strangeness is not conserved [1 mark].

Page 67 — Detecting Particles

1) Charged particles follow curved tracks in a magnetic field [1 mark]. +ve and –ve particle tracks curve in opposite directions [1 mark]. You can identify the direction of curvature for negative particles by looking for knock-on electrons OR applying Fleming's left-hand rule. [1 mark]

2) Antineutrinos are neutral and so will not leave tracks in many standard detectors. Beta particles are charged and so will ionise particles and leave a track, and so are more easily detected. [1 mark]

3) The proton and the positive pion give tracks but the neutron and the neutral pion do not. [1 mark]

4)

[1 mark for two tracks going in opposite directions, 1 mark for not showing a track for the photon, 1 mark for tracks spiralling inwards.]

5) $\mathbf{p} = \mathbf{rBQ}$ [1 mark] $= 3.2 \times 1.8 \times 10^{-6} \times 1.6 \times 10^{-19} = 9.2 \times 10^{-25}$ kgms^{-1} [1 mark]

Page 69 — Particle Accelerators

1) The alternating electric field accelerates the particles from one side of the cyclotron to the other increasing their energy [1 mark]. The magnetic field keeps the particles moving in a circular path [1 mark].

2) $\mathbf{E}_{rest} = \mathbf{m}_p\mathbf{c}^2 = 1.7 \times 10^{-27} \times (3.0 \times 10^8)^2 = 1.53 \times 10^{-10}$ J [1 mark]
$1.53 \times 10^{-10} \div 1.6 \times 10^{-19} = 9.6 \times 10^8$ eV [1 mark]
$\mathbf{E}_{tot} = 500 \times 10^9$ eV
So $\gamma = \mathbf{E}_{tot} \div \mathbf{E}_{rest}$ [1 mark] $= 500 \times 10^9 \div 9.6 \times 10^8 = 520 \approx 500$ [1 mark]

Page 71 — Electron Energy Levels

1) a) $\mathbf{E} = \mathbf{hf} = 6.6 \times 10^{-34} \times 4.57 \times 10^{14}$ [1 mark] $= 3.0 \times 10^{-19}$ J [1 mark]

b)

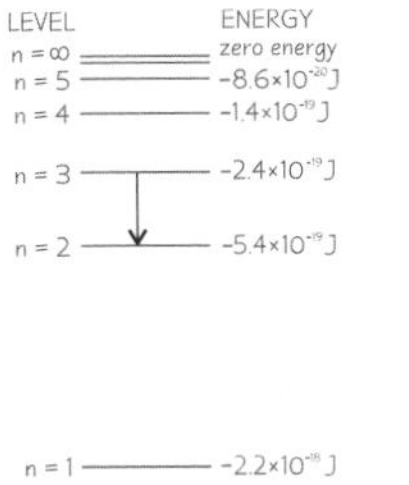

[1 mark]

The difference between these energy levels is 3.0×10^{-19} J, so the electron must have fallen between these energy levels.

2) a) 3.8×10^{-5} eV $= 3.8 \times 10^{-5} \times 1.6 \times 10^{-19} = 6.1 \times 10^{-24}$ J
$\Delta\mathbf{E} = \mathbf{hf} \Rightarrow \mathbf{f} = \Delta\mathbf{E}/\mathbf{h} = 6.1 \times 10^{-24} / 6.6 \times 10^{-34}$ [1 mark] $= 9.2 \times 10^9$ Hz [1 mark]

b) 9.2×10^9 oscillations occur every second [1 mark].

Section Five — Thermal Physics

Page 73 — Ideal Gases

1) a) i) Number of moles = $\frac{\text{mass of gas}}{\text{molar mass}} = \frac{0.014}{0.028} = 0.5$ [1 mark]

ii) Number of molecules = number of moles × Avogadro's constant $= 0.5 \times 6.02 \times 10^{23} = 3.01 \times 10^{23}$ [1 mark]

b) $\mathbf{pV} = \mathbf{nRT}$, so $\mathbf{p} = \frac{\mathbf{nRT}}{\mathbf{V}}$ [1 mark] $= \frac{0.5 \times 8.31 \times 300}{0.01} = 125\,000$ Pa [1 mark]

c) The pressure would also halve [1 mark] because it is proportional to the number of molecules — pV = NkT [1 mark].

2) At ground level, $\frac{\mathbf{pV}}{\mathbf{T}} = \frac{1 \times 10^5 \times 10}{293} = 3410$ JK^{-1} [1 mark]
$\mathbf{pV/T}$ is constant, so higher up $\mathbf{pV/T} = 3410$ JK^{-1} [1 mark]
Higher up, $\mathbf{p} = \frac{3410 \times \mathbf{T}}{\mathbf{V}} = \frac{3410 \times 260}{25} = 35\,500$ Pa [1 mark]

Answers

Page 75 — The Pressure of an Ideal Gas

1) a) $pV = \frac{1}{3}Nm\overline{c^2}$ [1 mark] Rearrange the equation:

$$\overline{c^2} = \frac{3pV}{Nm} = \frac{3\times1\times10^5\times7\times10^{-5}}{2\times10^{22}\times6.6\times10^{-27}} = 159\ 091\ (ms^{-1})^2 \text{ [1 mark]}$$

b) r.m.s. speed = $\sqrt{\overline{c^2}} = \sqrt{159\ 091} = 399\ ms^{-1}$ [1 mark]

c) pV is proportional to T, so doubling T will double pV. [1 mark]

r.m.s. speed = $\sqrt{\overline{c^2}} = \sqrt{\frac{3pV}{Nm}}$, so doubling pV will increase the r.m.s. speed by a factor of $\sqrt{2}$. r.m.s. speed = $399 \times \sqrt{2} = 564\ ms^{-1}$ [1 mark]

Page 77 — Internal Energy and Temperature

1) a) Molecule mass = $\frac{\text{mass of 1 mole}}{N_A} = \frac{2.8\times10^{-2}}{6.02\times10^{23}} = 4.65\times10^{-26}$ kg [1 mark]

b) $\frac{1}{2}m\overline{c^2} = \frac{3kT}{2}$ Rearranging gives: $\overline{c^2} = \frac{3kT}{m}$ [1 mark]

$$\overline{c^2} = \frac{3\times1.38\times10^{-23}\times300}{4.65\times10^{-26}} = 2.67\times10^5\ m^2s^{-2} \text{ [1 mark]}$$

Typical speed = r.m.s. speed = $\sqrt{2.67\times10^5} = 517\ ms^{-1}$ [1 mark]

c) Gas molecules move at different speeds because they have different amounts of energy [1 mark]. The molecules have different amounts of energy because they are constantly colliding and transferring energy between themselves [1 mark].

2) a) Time = distance ÷ speed = 8.0 m ÷ 400 = 0.02 s [1 mark]

b) Although the particles are moving at an average of 400 ms^{-1}, they are frequently colliding with other particles. [1 mark]
This means their motion in any one direction is limited and so they only slowly move from one end of the room to the other. [1 mark]

c) At 30 °C the average speed of the particles would be slightly faster [1 mark] since the absolute temperature would have risen from 293 K to 303 K and the temperature determines the average speed [1 mark]. This means the speed of diffusion would also be faster [1 mark].

Page 79 — Specific Heat Capacity & Specific Latent Heat

1) Electrical energy: $\Delta E = VI\Delta t = 12 \times 7.5 \times 180 = 16200$ J [1 mark]
The temperature rise is 12.7 – 4.5 = 8.2 °C

$$c = \frac{\Delta E}{m\Delta\theta} \text{ [1 mark]} = \frac{16200}{2\times8.2} = 988\ J\ kg^{-1}\,°C^{-1} \text{ [1 mark]}$$

You need the right unit for the third mark — J kg^{-1} K^{-1} would be right too.

2) a) A molecule's energy is the sum of its potential and kinetic energy [1 mark]. The water is at 373 K so the molecules have the same kinetic energy [1 mark]. This means that one must have more potential energy than the other — i.e. one is liquid and the other is gas [1 mark].

b) Total amount of energy needed to boil all the water:
$\Delta E = ml = 2.26\times10^6\times0.5 = 1.13\times10^6$ J [1 mark]
3 kW means you get 3000 J in a second,
so time in seconds = $1.13\times10^6 / 3000$ [1 mark] = 377 s [1 mark]

Page 81 — The Boltzmann Factor

1) a) $kT = 1.38\times10^{-23}\times300 \approx 4\times10^{-21}$ J [1 mark]

b) For two bonds, $\varepsilon = 2\times3.2\times10^{-20} = 6.4\times10^{-20}$ J [1 mark]

c) $\frac{\varepsilon}{kT} = \frac{6.4\times10^{-20}}{4\times10^{-21}} \approx 16$ [1 mark]

d) With an ε/kT ratio of about 16, processes can take place using random thermal energy [1 mark]. Although the average energy of a water particle is much less than it needs to escape [1 mark], some particles will have enough energy to break their bonds and escape, meaning that the tank must be topped up to replace the water lost by evaporation [1 mark].

Section Six — Astrophysics and Cosmology

Page 83 — The Solar System & Astronomical Distances

1) a) [1 mark each for 5 sensible points], e.g., planets are generally much bigger than comets. Planets are made out of rock and gas but comets are largely made of frozen substances like ice. Planets have almost circular orbits but comets have highly elliptical orbits. Comets have tails when they're close to the Sun. Comets can take millions of years to orbit the Sun; planets have much shorter periods.

b) A comet has a tail because the energy from the Sun has started to melt it to produce a vapour trail [1 mark]. It always points away from the Sun as it is being 'blown' by the solar wind [1 mark].

2) a) A light-year is the distance travelled by a photon of light through a vacuum in one year [1 mark].

b) Seconds in a year = 365.25 × 24 × 60 × 60 = 3.16×10^7 s [1 mark].
Distance = **c** × time = $3.0\times10^8\times3.16\times10^7 = 9.5\times10^{15}$ m [1 mark].

c) To see something, light must reach us. Light travels at a finite speed, so it takes time for that to happen [1 mark]. The further out we see, the further back in time we're looking. The Universe is ~14 billion years old so we can't see further than ~14 billion light years. [1 mark].

Page 86 — Optical Telescopes

1) a)

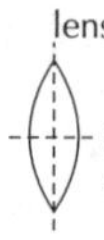

The principal focus is where rays parallel to the principal axis converge [1 mark]. The focal length is the distance between the lens axis and the principal focus [1 mark].

b) $\frac{1}{u}+\frac{1}{v}=\frac{1}{f}$ [1 mark]. So $\frac{1}{0.2}+\frac{1}{v}=\frac{1}{0.15}$ [1 mark].

$\frac{1}{v}=\frac{1}{0.15}-\frac{1}{0.2}=\frac{5}{3} \Rightarrow v = 0.6m$ [1 mark].

c) Using lens equation: $\frac{1}{v}=\frac{1}{0.15}-\frac{1}{0.10}=-\frac{10}{3} \Rightarrow v = -0.3m$ [1 mark]

The sign of **v** is negative, indicating that the image is a virtual image on the same side of the lens as the object [1 mark].

2) a) Separation of lenses needs to be $f_o + f_e$ = 5.0 + 0.10 = 5.1 m [1 mark].

b) The angular magnification is the angle subtended by the image at the eye divided by the angle subtended by the object at the unaided eye [1 mark]. $M = f_o/f_e$ = 5.0 / 0.10 = 50 [1 mark].

3) a) When light strikes a pixel on a CCD, electrons [1 mark] are liberated from the silicon and are stored in a potential well [1 mark]. Once the exposure has been taken, electrons are shunted along the potential wells [1 mark] and emerge in sequence at the output, where they can be measured.

b) CCDs have a quantum efficiency greater than 70% [1 mark] whereas photographic emulsion only has a 4% efficiency. So fewer photons are needed for an image and fainter objects can be detected [1 mark]. The output is in electronic form and can be processed digitally by computers, making it easier for the images to be enhanced [1 mark].

Page 89 — Non-Optical Telescopes

1) The collecting power of the telescope is proportional to the area of the objective dish or mirror [1 mark]. Radio telescopes tend to have larger dishes than UV telescopes, so radio telescopes tend to have greater collecting powers [1 mark]. Resolving power depends on the wavelength of the radiation and the diameter of the dish [1 mark]. Since UV radiation has a much, much smaller wavelength than radio, UV telescopes have a greater resolving power. [1 mark]

2) a) The telescope emits infrared radiation, which masks the infrared it is trying to detect [1 mark]. The colder the telescope, the less infrared it emits [1 mark].

b) They are set up at high altitude in dry places [1 mark].

3) a) On high altitude aeroplanes / weather balloons [1 mark], to get above the level of the atmosphere that absorbs the radiation [1 mark].

b) A UV telescope uses a single parabolic mirror, whereas an X-ray telescope uses a series of nested 'grazing' mirrors [1 mark]. This is because UV reflects in the same way as visible light [1 mark] but X-rays can only be reflected at very shallow angles / would be absorbed by a parabolic mirror [1 mark].

4) a) power ∝ diameter^2 [1 mark].

b) $\frac{\text{power of Arecibo}}{\text{power of Lovell}} = \frac{300^2}{76^2}$ [1 mark]. Ratio = 15.6:1 [1 mark].

Page 91 — Luminosity and Magnitude

1) The absolute magnitude is the apparent magnitude [1 mark] that the object would have if it were 10 parsecs [1 mark] away from Earth.

2) Distance to Sun in parsecs = $1/(2\times10^5) = 5\times10^{-6}$ pc [1 mark].
$m - M = 5\ lg\ (d/10)$ [1 mark] $\Rightarrow -27 - M = 5\ lg\ (5\times10^{-6}/10)$ [1 mark]
$\Rightarrow -27 - M = 5\ lg\ (5\times10^{-7}) \Rightarrow -27 - M = -31.5 \Rightarrow M = 4.5$ [1 mark].

3) a) Sirius is the brighter of the two [1 mark].

Answers

b) $m - M = 5 \lg (d/10)$ *[1 mark]* $\Rightarrow -0.72 - (-5.5) = 5 \lg (d/10)$ *[1 mark]*
$\Rightarrow 4.78 = 5 \lg (d/10) \Rightarrow \lg (d/10) = 0.956 \Rightarrow d/10 = 10^{0.956}$
So $d = 90$ pc *[1 mark]*.

Page 93 — Stars as Black Bodies

1) a) According to Wein's displacement law $\lambda_{max} \times T = 0.0029$, so for this star $\lambda_{max} = 0.0029 \div 4000 = 7.25 \times 10^{-7}$ m *[1 mark]*. Curve Y peaks at ~0.7 μm (= 7×10^{-7} m), so could represent the star *[1 mark]*.

b) $L = \sigma A T^4$, so $3.9 \times 10^{26} = 5.67 \times 10^{-8} \times A \times 4000^4$ *[1 mark]*, which gives $A = 2.7 \times 10^{19}$ m^2 *[1 mark]*.

2) $\lambda_{max} \times T = 0.0029$ *[1 mark]*. So $T = 0.0029/(436 \times 10^{-9}) \approx 6650$ K *[1 mark]*.
$L = \sigma A T^4$ *[1 mark]*. So $2.3 \times 10^{27} = 5.67 \times 10^{-8} \times A \times 6650^4$, which gives $A = 2.1 \times 10^{19}$ m^2 *[1 mark]*.

Page 95 — Spectral Classes and the H-R Diagram

1) a) To get strong Balmer lines, the majority of the electrons need to be at the $n = 2$ level *[1 mark]*. At low temperatures, few electrons have enough energy to be at the $n = 2$ level *[1 mark]*. At very high temperatures, most electrons will be at $n = 3$ or above, leading to weak Balmer lines *[1 mark]*.

b) Spectral classes B *[1 mark]* and A *[1 mark]*

c) Stars in spectral class F are white in colour *[1 mark]*, have a temperature of 6000 – 7500 K *[1 mark]* and show prominent absorption lines from metal ions *[1 mark]*.

2) Molecules are only present in the lowest temperature stars *[1 mark]*. At higher temperatures molecules are broken up into individual atoms *[1 mark]*.

3)

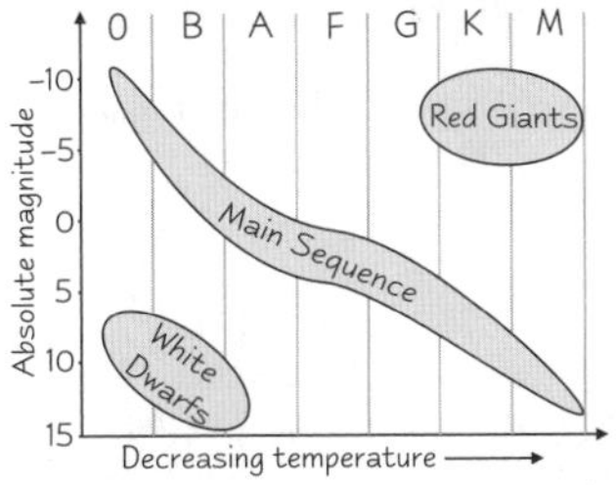

[5 marks maximum, 1 mark each for correctly labelled axes, 1 mark each for 'Main Sequence', 'White Dwarfs' and 'Red Giants'.]

Page 97 — Stellar Evolution

1) High mass stars spend much less time on the main sequence than low mass stars *[1 mark]*. As a red giant, low mass stars only fuse hydrogen and/or helium, but the highest mass stars can fuse nuclei up to iron *[1 mark]*. Lower mass stars eject their atmospheres to become white dwarfs *[1 mark]*, but high mass stars explode in supernovae *[1 mark]* to leave neutron stars *[1 mark]* or black holes *[1 mark]*.

2) a) The Schwarzschild radius is the distance *[1 mark]* from the centre of a black hole to where the escape velocity is the speed of light *[1 mark]*.

b) $R_s = \frac{2GM}{c^2} = \frac{2 \times 6.67 \times 10^{-11} \times 6 \times 10^{30}}{(3 \times 10^8)^2}$ *[1 mark]* ≈ 8.9 km *[1 mark]*

Page 99 — The Doppler Effect and Redshift

1) a) Object A is moving towards us *[1 mark]*.

b) Object B is part of a binary star system (or is being orbited by a planet) *[1 mark]* with a period of two weeks *[1 mark]*.

c) Find the velocity of object C using $\frac{\Delta\lambda}{\lambda} = \frac{v}{c}$, so $v = c\frac{\Delta\lambda}{\lambda}$. *[1 mark]*

$$v = 3.0 \times 10^8 \times \frac{(667.83 \times 10^{-9} - 656.28 \times 10^{-9})}{656.28 \times 10^{-9}} = 5.28 \times 10^6\,ms^{-1}$$

So object C is moving away from us *[1 mark]* at 5.28×10^6 ms^{-1} *[1 mark]*.

2) a) Their spectrum shows an enormous redshift *[1 mark]*.

b) Intensity is proportional to 1/distance^2 *[1 mark]*. So, e.g. if a quasar is 500 000 times further away than, but just as bright as, a star in the Milky Way it must be 500 000^2 times brighter than the star *[1 mark]*.

c) A supermassive black hole *[1 mark]* surrounded by a doughnut-shaped mass of whirling gas *[1 mark]*.

Page 101 — The Big Bang Model of the Universe

1) a) $v = H_0 d$ *[1 mark]* where v is recessional velocity (in kms^{-1}), d is distance (in Mpc) and H_0 is Hubble's constant in (kms^{-1}Mpc^{-1}). *[1 mark]*

b) Hubble's law suggests that the Universe originated with the Big Bang *[1 mark]* and has been expanding ever since. *[1 mark]*

c)i) $H_0 = v \div d = 50$ kms$^{-1} \div 1$ Mpc^{-1}.
50 kms^{-1} = 50×10^3 ms^{-1} and 1 Mpc^{-1} = 3.09×10^{22} m
So, $H_0 = 50 \times 10^3$ ms$^{-1} \div 3.09 \times 10^{22}$ m $= 1.62 \times 10^{-18}$ s^{-1}
[1 mark for the correct value, 1 mark for the correct unit]

ii) $t = 1/H_0$ *[1 mark]* $= 1/1.62 \times 10^{-18} = 6.18 \times 10^{17}$ s $\approx$ 20 billion years *[1 mark]*. The observable Universe has a radius of 20 billion light years. *[1 mark]*

2) a) $z \approx v/c$ *[1 mark]* so $v \approx 0.37 \times 3.0 \times 10^8 \approx 1.1 \times 10^8$ ms^{-1} *[1 mark]*

b) $d = v/H_0 \approx 1.1 \times 10^8 / 2.4 \times 10^{-18} = 4.6 \times 10^{25}$ m *[1 mark]*
$= 4.6 \times 10^{25} / 9.5 \times 10^{15}$ ly = 4.9 billion ly *[1 mark]*

c) $z = v/c$ is only valid if $v << c$ — it isn't in this case *[1 mark]*.

3) The cosmic background radiation is microwave radiation *[1 mark]* showing a perfect black body spectrum *[1 mark]* of a temperature of about 3 K *[1 mark]*. It is very nearly isotropic and homogeneous *[1 mark]*. It suggests that the ancient Universe was very hot, producing lots of electromagnetic radiation *[1 mark]* and that its expansion has stretched the radiation into the microwave region *[1 mark]*.
[1 mark for clearly linking the evidence to the explanation.]

Page 103 — Evolution of the Universe

1) a) The curvature of the Universe depends on its average density *[1 mark]*. Current estimates for the density of the Universe are close to the critical density required for the Universe to be flat *[1 mark]*.

b) A flat Universe can be modelled by a 2-dimensional plane where parallel lines never meet and the angles in a triangle add up to 180° *[1 mark]*. In a flat Universe, gravity is just strong enough to stop the expansion at $t = \infty$ *[1 mark]*, which means that the Universe will expand for ever, but more and more slowly with time *[1 mark]*.

2) a) Find H_0 in SI units: H_0 = 100 kms^{-1}Mpc^{-1}
So, $H_0 = 100 \times 10^3 \div 3.09 \times 10^{22} = 3.236 \times 10^{-18}$ s^{-1} *[1 mark]*

Average density: $\rho_0 = \frac{3H_0^2}{8\pi G}$ *[1 mark]*

$G = 6.67 \times 10^{-11}$ Nm^{2}kg^{-2} *[1 mark]*

$$\rho_0 = \frac{3 \times (3.236 \times 10^{-18})^2}{8 \times \pi \times 6.67 \times 10^{-11}} = 1.87 \times 10^{-26}\ kgm^{-3}$$ *[1 mark]*

b) The average density of the Universe is 1.87×10^{-26} kgm^{-3}, so on average, each m^3 of the Universe has a mass of 1.87×10^{-26} kg *[1 mark]*. This is equivalent to $1.87 \times 10^{-26} \div 1.7 \times 10^{-27}$ = 11 hydrogen atoms. So there would be 11 hydrogen atoms in every m^3 if the entire mass of the Universe was hydrogen *[1 mark]*.

3) A slight excess of matter was produced over antimatter *[1 mark]*. The matter and antimatter annihilated into photons *[1 mark]*. The remaining matter was in the form of quarks and leptons *[1 mark]*. As the Universe expanded and cooled the quarks combined to form particles like protons and neutrons *[1 mark]*. Some of the protons fused together to form helium *[1 mark]*. After about 300 000 years the Universe was cool enough for electrons to combine with the protons and helium nuclei to form atoms *[1 mark]*. The Universe became transparent since the photons could no longer interact with any free charges *[1 mark]*. There were fluctuations in the density of the Universe *[1 mark]* that allowed gravity to clump matter together, condensing matter into stars and galaxies *[1 mark]*.
[1 mark for a clear, logical progression of ideas in the answer.]

Section Seven — Medical Physics

Page 105 — Physics of the Eye

1) a) The distance will be the focal length of the lens *[1 mark]*
$v = f = 1/\text{power} = 1/60 = 0.017$ m *[1 mark]*

b) $1/u + 1/v = 1/f$, $u = 0.3$ m, $v = 1/60$ m *[1 mark]*.
$1/f = 63.3$ D *[1 mark]*. So the extra power needed = 3.3 D *[1 mark]*.

2) a) Light enters the eye through the cornea, which focuses the light *[1 mark]*. It then passes through the aqueous humour, then through the iris, which controls the amount of light entering the eye *[1 mark]*, to reach the lens. The lens acts as a fine focus *[1 mark]* so that light travels through the vitreous humour and is focused on the retina *[1 mark]*.

Answers

b) Spatial resolution is greatest at the yellow spot on the retina where the photoreceptors are most densely packed [1 mark]. Away from the yellow spot, spatial resolution decreases with receptor density, and because of an increase in the number of receptors per nerve cell [1 mark].

Page 107 — Defects of Vision

1) Focal length of diverging lens needs to be –4 m [1 mark].
Power = $1/\mathbf{f} = -0.25$ D [1 mark for value, 1 mark for negative sign]

2) Lens equation $1/\mathbf{u} + 1/\mathbf{v} = 1/\mathbf{f}$ [1 mark]. When $\mathbf{u} = 0.25$ m, $\mathbf{v} = -2$ m
$\Rightarrow 1/\mathbf{f} = 1/0.25 - 1/2 = 3.5$. Power = +3.5 D [1 mark for value, 1 mark for sign]

3) a) Cylindrical lenses [1 mark].

b)

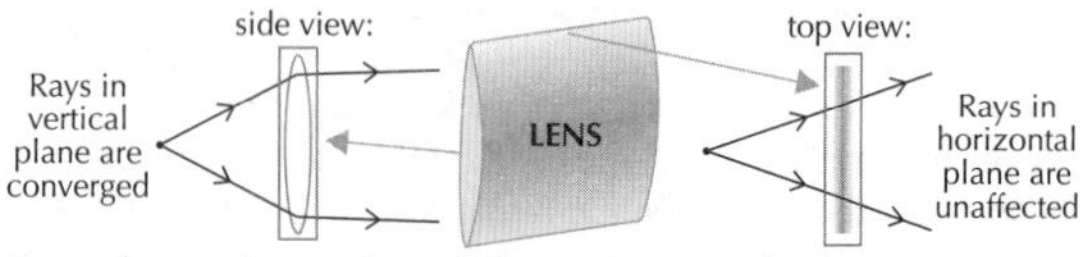

[2 marks maximum, 1 mark for each correctly drawn axis]

Page 109 — Physics of the Ear

1) a) The pinna concentrates the sound energy entering the ear into the auditory canal, increasing its intensity [1 mark].

b) Sound energy entering the ear causes the tympanic membrane (eardrum) to vibrate [1 mark]. The vibrations are transmitted through the middle ear by the malleus, incus and stapes in turn [1 mark]. The stapes is connected to the oval window, so causes it to vibrate [1 mark].

c) The amplitude of a sound is proportional to the square root of its intensity, and the intensity is inversely proportional to the area [1 mark]. This means that the amplitude is inversely proportional to the square root of the area [1 mark], so if the area is decreased by a factor of 14, the amplitude is increased by a factor of $\sqrt{14} \approx 3.74$ [1 mark].

d) Pressure waves in the cochlea cause the basilar membrane to vibrate [1 mark], which causes hair cells on the membrane to trigger electrical impulses [1 mark].

e) Different regions of the basilar membrane have different natural frequencies [1 mark]. When the frequency of a sound wave matches the natural frequency of a part of the membrane, that part resonates, causing the hair cells in that area to trigger impulses, so different frequencies trigger different nerve cells [1 mark].

Page 111 — Intensity and Loudness

1) a) 1×10^{-12} Wm^{-2} [1 mark]

b) $\mathbf{IL} = 10\log\left(\frac{\mathbf{I}}{\mathbf{I}_0}\right)$ [1 mark] $= 10\log\left(\frac{0.94}{1\times10^{-12}}\right) = 119.7$ dB [1 mark]

c) The ear is most sensitive at about 3000 Hz, so the siren will sound as loud as possible [1 mark].

2) The patient has suffered hearing loss at all frequencies, but the loss is worst at high frequencies [1 mark]. If the patient's hearing had been damaged by excessive noise, you would expect to see a peak at a particular frequency [1 mark]. This isn't present, so the patient's hearing loss is more likely to be age-related [1 mark].

Page 113 — Physics of the Heart

1) a) Dead skin cells and hairs are removed [1 mark]. Conductive gel is used to give a good electrical contact [1 mark].

b) The P wave corresponds to the depolarisation and contraction of the atria [1 mark]. The QRS wave corresponds to the depolarisation and contraction of the ventricles [1 mark] and the repolarisation and relaxation of the atria [1 mark].

2) a) A membrane is initially polarised so that the outside is positively charged and the inside is negatively charged [1 mark]. When the membrane is stimulated, it becomes permeable to sodium ions [1 mark]. The ions move through the membrane and into the cell, depolarising the system [1 mark] and then polarising it the other way. In repolarisation, the membrane becomes impermeable to sodium, but very permeable to potassium ions [1 mark]. The potassium ions move through the membrane to reverse the polarisation, and the Na-K pump moves sodium ions out of the cell to restore equilibrium [1 mark]. [1 mark for quality of written communication.]

b) The sinoatrial node produces ~70 electrical pulses a minute [1 mark]. These make the atria contract [1 mark]. They then pass to the atrioventricular node, which delays the pulses [1 mark] then passes them to the ventricles to make them contract shortly after [1 mark].

Page 115 — X-Ray Imaging

1)

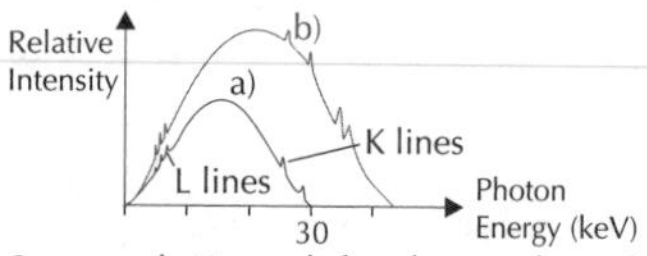

a) See graph [1 mark for shape of graph, 1 mark for 30 keV maximum energy and 1 mark for correct labelling of line spectrum]

b) Find the energy of each electron using $\mathbf{E} = \mathbf{QV}$:
$\mathbf{E} = 1.6 \times 10^{-19} \times 30 \times 10^{3} = 4.8 \times 10^{-15}$ J [1 mark]
Kinetic energy = $\frac{1}{2}\mathbf{mv}^2 = 4.8 \times 10^{-15}$ [1 mark]
So, $\mathbf{v}^2 = (2 \times 4.8 \times 10^{-15}) \div (9.11 \times 10^{-31}) = 1.054 \times 10^{16}$ [1 mark]
$\mathbf{v} = 1.03 \times 10^{8}$ ms^{-1} [1 mark]

2) a) Half-value thickness is the thickness of material required to reduce the intensity of an X-ray beam to half its original value [1 mark].

b) $\mu = \frac{\ln 2}{x_{\frac{1}{2}}} = \frac{\ln 2}{3} = 0.23\text{mm}^{-1}$ [1 mark], $\mathbf{I} = \mathbf{I}_0 \mathbf{e}^{-\mu x} \Rightarrow \frac{\mathbf{I}}{\mathbf{I}_0} = \mathbf{e}^{-\mu x}$ [1 mark].
So, $0.01 = \mathbf{e}^{-0.23x} \Rightarrow \ln(0.01) = -0.23\mathbf{x}$ [1 mark], $\mathbf{x} = 20$mm [1 mark].

Page 117 — Ultrasound Imaging

1) a) $\alpha = \left(\frac{\mathbf{Z}_{tissue} - \mathbf{Z}_{air}}{\mathbf{Z}_{tissue} + \mathbf{Z}_{air}}\right)^2 = \left(\frac{1630 - 0.430}{1630 + 0.430}\right)^2$ [1 mark], $\alpha = 0.999$ [1 mark]

b) From part a), 0.1% enters the body when no gel is used [1 mark].
$\alpha = \left(\frac{\mathbf{Z}_{tissue} - \mathbf{Z}_{gel}}{\mathbf{Z}_{tissue} + \mathbf{Z}_{gel}}\right)^2 = \left(\frac{1630 - 1500}{1630 + 1500}\right)^2 = 0.002$ [1 mark], so 99.8% of the ultrasound is transmitted [1 mark]. Ratio is ~1000 [1 mark].

2) a) $\mathbf{Z} = \rho\mathbf{v}$ [1 mark], $\mathbf{v} = (1.63 \times 10^{6})/(1.09 \times 10^{3}) = 1495$ ms^{-1}
= 1.50 kms^{-1} [1 mark].

b) A pulse from the far side of the head travels an extra 2**d** cm, where **d** is the diameter of the head [1 mark].
Time taken to travel this distance = 2.4 × 50 = 120 μs [1 mark].
Distance = speed × time, so 2**d** = 1500 × 120 × 10^{-6}
= 0.18 m [1 mark]. So **d** = 9 cm [1 mark].

Page 119 — Endoscopy

1) a) $\sin \boldsymbol{\theta}_c = \mathbf{n}_2/\mathbf{n}_1 = 1.30/1.35$ [1 mark], $\boldsymbol{\theta} = 74.4°$ [1 mark].

b) When the angle of incidence is greater than or equal to the critical angle, the beam of light will undergo total internal reflection [1 mark]. If the angle of incidence falls below the critical angle, then some light will be lost [1 mark].

2) A coherent fibre-optic bundle consists of a large number of very thin fibres [1 mark], arranged in the same way at either end of the bundle [1 mark]. Lots of thin fibres are used to increase the resolution of the image [1 mark]. The relative positions of the fibres have to remain constant or the image would be jumbled up [1 mark].

Page 121 — Magnetic Resonance Imaging

1) a)

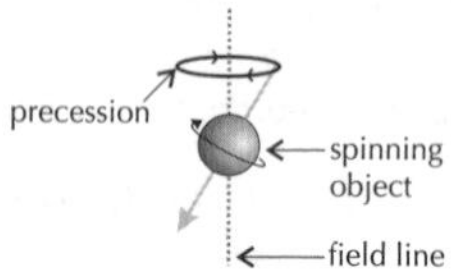

The axis of rotation of a spinning object [1 mark] describes a circular path around the field line [1 mark].

b) The Larmor frequency is the frequency at which the protons, or other particles, in a magnetic field precess [1 mark]. In an MRI scanner it is typically 10^{3}–10^{9} Hz [1 mark].

2) The patient lies in the centre of a large magnet, which produces a magnetic field [1 mark]. The magnetic field aligns hydrogen nuclei in the patient's body [1 mark]. Radio frequency coils are used to transmit radio waves, which cause the aligned protons to absorb energy [1 mark]. When the radio waves stop the protons emit the stored energy as radio waves, which are recorded by the scanner [1 mark]. A computer analyses the received radio waves to produce an image of the patient's body [1 mark]. [1 mark for quality of written communication.]

3) Advantages, e.g. no known side effects / doesn't use ionising radiation / an image can be made for any slice in any orientation of the body / images of soft tissues are higher quality than using other techniques (e.g. CT, X-ray) / contrast can be weighted to investigate different situations.

Answers

Disadvantages, e.g. other techniques give better quality images of bony structures / people can suffer claustrophobia inside the scanner / MRI cannot be used on people with pacemakers/some metal implants / MRI scanners are very expensive.
[1 mark for each advantage explained, to a maximum of 3 marks.
1 mark for each disadvantage explained, to a maximum of 3 marks.
6 marks are available in total.]

Page 123 — Medical Uses of Nuclear Radiation

1) The patient is injected with a medical tracer consisting of a gamma source/positron-emitter bound to a substance used by the body [1 mark]. After a period of time, the radiation in the patient's body is recorded using a gamma camera/PET scanner [1 mark]. A computer uses this information to form an image, which might show a tumour as an area of high metabolic activity [1 mark].

2) a) The ionising energy of the particles released in 1000 s will be: $1000 \times 3 \times 10^{10} \times 8 \times 10^{-13} = 24$ J [1 mark]
Absorbed dose = ionising energy ÷ mass = 24 ÷ 70 = 0.34 Gy [1 mark]
b) The effective dose of this absorbed dose is: $H = 0.343 \times 20 = 6.9$ Sv [1 mark]

Section Eight — Turning Points in Physics

Page 125 — Charge/Mass Ratio of the Electron

1) a) 1000 eV [1 mark]
b) $1000 \text{ eV} \times 1.6 \times 10^{-19}$ J/eV $= 1.6 \times 10^{-16}$ J [1 mark]
c) Kinetic energy = $\frac{1}{2}\mathbf{mv}^2 = 1.6 \times 10^{-16}$ J [1 mark]
$\mathbf{v}^2 = (2 \times 1.6 \times 10^{-16}) \div (9.1 \times 10^{-31}) = 3.5 \times 10^{14} \Rightarrow \mathbf{v} = 1.9 \times 10^7$ ms^{-1} [1 mark]. Divide by 3.0×10^8: 6.3% of the speed of light [1 mark]

2) [Your answer will depend on which experiment you describe, e.g.] Electrons are accelerated using an electron gun [1 mark]. A magnetic field [1 mark] exerts a centripetal force [1 mark] on the electrons, making them trace a circular path. By measuring the radius of this path and equating the magnetic and centripetal forces [1 mark] you can calculate e/m. [1 mark for quality of written communication]

Page 127 — Millikan's Oil-Drop Experiment

1) a) The forces acting on the drop are its weight, acting downwards [1 mark] and the equally sized force due to the electric field, acting upwards [1 mark].
b) Weight = electric force, so $\mathbf{mg} = \frac{\mathbf{QV}}{\mathbf{d}}$, and $\mathbf{Q} = \frac{\mathbf{mgd}}{\mathbf{V}}$ [1 mark].

$$\mathbf{Q} = \frac{1.63 \times 10^{-14} \times 9.81 \times 3.00 \times 10^{-2}}{5000} = 9.59 \times 10^{-19}\text{C} \quad [1 \text{ mark}]$$

Divide by the electron charge: $9.59 \times 10^{-19} \div 1.6 \times 10^{-19} = 6$
$\Rightarrow \mathbf{Q} = 6\mathbf{e}$ [1 mark]
c) The forces on the oil drop as it falls are its weight and the viscous force from the air [1 mark]. As the oil drop accelerates, the viscous force increases until it equals the oil drop's weight [1 mark]. At this point, there is no resultant force on the oil drop, so it stops accelerating, but continues to fall at terminal velocity [1 mark].
d) At terminal velocity, $\mathbf{mg} = 6\pi\eta\mathbf{rv}$. Rearranging, $\mathbf{v} = \frac{\mathbf{mg}}{6\pi\eta\mathbf{r}}$ [1 mark]
Find the radius of the oil drop, using mass = volume × density:

$$\mathbf{m} = \frac{4}{3}\pi\mathbf{r}^3\rho. \text{ So, } \mathbf{r}^3 = \frac{3\mathbf{m}}{4\pi\rho} = \frac{3 \times 1.63 \times 10^{-14}}{4 \times \pi \times 880} = 4.42 \times 10^{-18}$$

and $r = 1.64 \times 10^{-6}$ m [1 mark].

$$\text{So, } \mathbf{v} = \frac{1.63 \times 10^{-14} \times 9.81}{6 \times \pi \times 1.84 \times 10^{-5} \times 1.64 \times 10^{-6}} = 2.81 \times 10^{-4}\text{ms}^{-1} \text{ [1 mark]}$$

Page 129 — Light — Newton vs Huygens

1) Light consists of particles [1 mark]. The theory was based on Newton's laws of motion with the straight-line motion of light as evidence [1 mark].

2) Most scientists in the 18th century supported Newton's corpuscular theory [1 mark]. He said that light was made up of particles that obey his laws of motion [1 mark]. In Huygens' wave theory, light is a wave [1 mark]. This is supported by the diffraction and interference seen in Young's double-slit experiment [1 mark]. In the second half of the 19th century, Maxwell described light as an electromagnetic wave [1 mark] consisting of oscillating electric and magnetic fields. [1 mark for quality of written communication.]

Page 131 — The Photoelectric Effect

1) Electrons in the metal absorb energy from the UV light and leave the surface [1 mark], causing the plate to become positively charged [1 mark].

2) a) $\phi = \mathbf{hf} - (\frac{1}{2}\mathbf{mv}^2)_{max} = \mathbf{hc}/\boldsymbol{\lambda} - (\frac{1}{2}\mathbf{mv}^2)_{max}$ [1 mark]
$= [(6.63 \times 10^{-34} \times 3.00 \times 10^8)/(0.5 \times 10^{-6})] - 2.0 \times 10^{-19}$ J [1 mark]
$= 1.98 \times 10^{-19}$ J [1 mark]
b) Electrons will only be emitted if the energy they gain from photons in the beam of light is greater than the work function energy [1 mark]. The energy supplied by the beam of light is:
$\mathbf{E} = \mathbf{hc}/\lambda = (6.63 \times 10^{-34} \times 3.00 \times 10^8)/(1.5 \times 10^{-6}) = 1.33 \times 10^{-19}$ J [1 mark], which is less than the work function calculated in (a) ($1.33 \times 10^{-19} < 1.98 \times 10^{-19}$), so will not supply enough energy for electrons to be released [1 mark].

3) $\phi = 2.2 \text{ eV} = 2.2 \times 1.6 \times 10^{-19} \text{ J} = 3.52 \times 10^{-19}$ J
$(\frac{1}{2}\mathbf{mv}^2)_{max} = \mathbf{hf} - \phi = (\mathbf{hc}/\boldsymbol{\lambda}) - \phi$ [1 mark]
$= [6.63 \times 10^{-34} \times (3.00 \times 10^8/350 \times 10^{-9})] - 3.52 \times 10^{-19}$
$= 2.16 \times 10^{-19}$ J [1 mark]
Stopping potential, $\mathbf{V_s} = (\frac{1}{2}\mathbf{mv}^2)_{max}/\mathbf{e}$ [1 mark]
$\Rightarrow \mathbf{V_s} = 2.16 \times 10^{-19}/1.6 \times 10^{-19} = 1.35$ V [1 mark]

Page 133 — Wave-Particle Duality

1) a) i) Velocity is given by $\frac{1}{2}\mathbf{mv}^2 = \mathbf{eV}$ [1 mark]
$\Rightarrow \mathbf{v}^2 = 2\mathbf{eV}/\mathbf{m} \Rightarrow \mathbf{v} = 1.3 \times 10^7$ ms^{-1} [1 mark]
ii) de Broglie $\boldsymbol{\lambda} = \mathbf{h}/\mathbf{mv}$ [1 mark] $\Rightarrow \boldsymbol{\lambda} = 5.5 \times 10^{-11}$ m [1 mark]
b) This is in the X-ray region of the EM spectrum [1 mark].

2) a) A stream of electrons is accelerated towards the sample using an electron gun [1 mark]. The beam of electrons is focused onto the sample using a magnetic field [1 mark]. The parts of the beam that pass through the sample are projected onto a screen to form an image of the sample [1 mark].
b) To resolve detail around the size of an atom, the electron wavelength needs to be around 0.1 nm [1 mark]. The relationship between anode voltage and electron wavelength is given by $\boldsymbol{\lambda} = \frac{\mathbf{h}}{\sqrt{2\mathbf{meV}}}$,
which rearranges to give $\mathbf{V} = \frac{\mathbf{h}^2}{2\mathbf{me}\boldsymbol{\lambda}^2}$ [1 mark].
Substituting $\mathbf{m} = 9.1 \times 10^{-31}$ kg, $\mathbf{e} = 1.6 \times 10^{-19}$ C, $\boldsymbol{\lambda} = 0.1 \times 10^{-9}$ m

$$\text{gives: } \mathbf{V} = \frac{(6.63 \times 10^{-34})^2}{2 \times 9.1 \times 10^{-31} \times 1.6 \times 10^{-19} \times (0.1 \times 10^{-9})^2} = 151\text{ V},$$

showing that the minimum anode voltage ≈ 150 V [1 mark].

Page 135 — The Speed of Light and Relativity

1) a) The interference pattern would move/be shifted [1 mark].
b) The speed of light has the same value for all observers [1 mark]. It is impossible to detect absolute motion [1 mark].

2) a) An inertial reference frame is one in which Newton's 1st law is obeyed [1 mark], e.g. a train carriage moving at constant speed along a straight track (or any other relevant example) [1 mark].
b) The speed of light is unaffected by the motion of the observer [1 mark] or the motion of the light source [1 mark].

Page 137 — Special Relativity

1) $\mathbf{t} = \frac{\mathbf{t_0}}{\sqrt{1 - \frac{\mathbf{v}^2}{\mathbf{c}^2}}}$ [1 mark] and $\mathbf{t_0} = 20 \times 10^{-9}$ s [1 mark]

$$\mathbf{t} = \frac{20 \times 10^{-9}}{\sqrt{1 - \frac{(0.995\mathbf{c})^2}{\mathbf{c}^2}}} = 200 \text{ ns or } 2 \times 10^{-7} \text{ s [1 mark]}$$

2) Your description must include:
A diagram or statement showing relative motion [1 mark].
An event of a specified duration in one reference frame [1 mark].
Measurement of the time interval by a moving observer [1 mark].
Time interval for "external" observer greater than time interval for the "stationary" observer or equivalent [1 mark].

3) a) $\mathbf{m} = \mathbf{m_0} \div \sqrt{1 - \frac{\mathbf{v}^2}{\mathbf{c}^2}} = 1.67 \times 10^{-27} \div \sqrt{1 - \frac{2.8^2}{3.0^2}} = 4.65 \times 10^{-27}$ kg [1 mark]
b) $\mathbf{E} = \mathbf{mc}^2 = 4.65 \times 10^{-27} \times (3 \times 10^8)^2 = 4.2 \times 10^{-10}$ J [1 mark]

Index

Index

Index